FORESTRY COMMISSION
BULLETIN No. 14

FORESTRY PRACTICE

A Summary of Methods of Establishing,
Maintaining and Harvesting Forest Crops
with Advice on Planning and other
Management Considerations for Owners,
Agents and Foresters

Edited by
O. N. Blatchford, B.Sc.
Forestry Commission

LONDON: HER MAJESTY'S STATIONERY OFFICE

BOD HUNTER

ISBN 0 11 710150 8

FOREWORD

This latest edition of *Forestry Practice* sets out to give a comprehensive account of silvicultural practice and forest management in Britain. Since the first edition, the Forestry Commission has produced a large number of Bulletins, Booklets, Forest Records and Leaflets covering very fully a wide variety of forestry matters. Reference is made to these where appropriate so that the reader may supplement the information and guidance given here. Titles given in the bibliography at the end of each chapter are normally available through a library and those currently in print are listed in the Forestry Commission Catalogue of Publications obtainable from the Publications Officer, Forest Research Station, Alice Holt Lodge, Wrecclesham, Farnham, Surrey. Research and Development Papers mainly unpriced may be obtained only from that address.

ACKNOWLEDGMENTS

The cover picture and all the photographs are from the Forestry Commission's photographic collection. Fair drawings of diagrams were made, where appropriate, by J. Williams, the Commission's Graphics Officer.

CONTENTS

Chapter 1

SEED SUPPLY AND COLLECTION

Chapter 2

NURSERY PRACTICE

Chapter 3

ESTABLISHMENT AND MAINTENANCE OF PLANTATIONS

Chapter 4

DISEASES AND INSECT PESTS

Chapter 5

WILDLIFE MANAGEMENT

Chapter 6

FIRE PROTECTION

Chapter 7

THE FOREST AND RECREATION

Chapter 8

PLANNING, ORGANISING AND CONTROLLING PRODUCTION

Chapter 9

HARVESTING

Chapter 10

MARKETING AND UTILISATION

Chapter 11

ROADS

Chapter 14

ADVICE TO WOODLAND OWNERS

Chapter 15

MANAGEMENT AND ADMINISTRATION OF A WOODLAND ESTATE

Chapter 16

SAFETY IN FORESTRY: A LEGAL SUMMARY

APPENDIX

Chapter 1

SEED SUPPLY AND COLLECTION

Two interacting factors affect the growth of plants: their genetic constitution and the environment in which they grow. To raise high quality plantations, the forester requires well-filled healthy seeds capable of producing plants which have an ability to grow well on the chosen forest sites when given sound sylvicultural treatment. To produce high quality wood for the market intended, it is essential that trees have good stem-form and crown-habit (straight unforked circular stems with regularly spaced small-sized branches coupled with good natural pruning, horizontal branching and freedom from spiral grain or fluting), and good health with resistance to diseases and insects. The forester can go a long way towards meeting these requirements by carefully selecting his seed sources.

Seed cost is a minute proportion of the total sum needed for establishing a plantation, and is commonly less than 0·1 per cent of the total cost. Thus the use of seed from sources which give even small increases in growth-rate, or improved timber quality, is a good investment for the future.

SEED SOURCES

Seed Stands

The genetic quality of a seed is dependent upon both the mother tree and the source of the pollen. For this reason, home-collected seed should normally be taken from the very best stands in the region where it is intended to plant. The stands should be well separated from low quality stands of the same species, or from related species, where cross-pollination may occur. The stands should be uniformly good and any trees of poor form, or suffering from diseases or some other weakness, should not be used as seed parents. In addition, the stands should be over two hectares in size, since small plantations may have been derived from a common mother—a situation which leads to poor quality seed and the risk of inbreeding depression in the planting stock.

Some young conifer stands of particularly good quality are selected and managed purely for seed production. Early and heavy thinnings are aimed at retaining as much live-crown, and therefore as much potential seed-bearing surface area, as possible on the remaining trees; only the best trees are kept. In broadleaved seed stands, weeding and cleaning are often necessary to reduce competition from weed species which flourish in the more than usually open conditions, and in order to facilitate seed collection—particularly where these are harvested from the stand floor. Since 1973 the Forest Reproductive Material Regulations, which arise from our membership of the

European Community, have required the Forestry Commission to maintain a National Register of seed stands, seed orchards and poplar stool beds which have been inspected and found to meet minimum quality standards. The National Register covers 13 species and one genus all common in European forestry, they are:—

European silver fir, European larch, Japanese larch, Norway spruce, Sitka spruce, Austrian and Corsican pine, Scots pine, Weymouth pine, Douglas fir, beech, Sessile oak, Pedunculate oak, Red oak and poplar.

As far as seed originating from sources in Great Britain is concerned, only that coming from stands or orchards included in the National Register may be marketed in the United Kingdom and other EEC countries. Seed of the listed species and cuttings of poplar intended for export to non-EEC countries are not covered by the Forest Reproductive Material Regulations, nor, of course, is seed of other species. An owner wishing to have a plantation of one of the listed species or a poplar stool bed considered for inclusion in the National Register should contact his nearest Conservator of Forests. An inspection fee will be charged whether or not the stands meet the criteria prescribed by law.

For species not covered by the EEC regulations, seed from recommended sources is obviously to be preferred to seed from 'unknown' sources. There are desirable and less-desirable origins and higher prices can be expected for those in the first category.

If locally produced seed is unavailable, or where even the best stands are of inferior quality, it may be possible to purchase seed from a source growing on a broadly similar site elsewhere in Britain. Seed may be purchased from seed merchants or from the Forestry Commission Seeds Officer at Alice Holt Lodge, Wrecclesham, Farnham, Surrey. As an alternative, plants raised from seed may be purchased from commercial forest nurseries and this will normally be cheaper than buying seed and raising transplants on a small scale. (See Chapter 2).

When only seed imported from abroad is available, it is most important to obtain material from origins known to grow well in the region in which it is to be planted. Seed from unsuitable sources must obviously be avoided. Within the EEC, the parent sources of imported seed of the listed species must have been approved by a recognised authority within the country of origin.

Some suggested suitable sources of seed are listed in Leaflet 60, *Selection of Conifer Seed for British*

1

TABLE 1

SEED PRODUCTION OF TREES IN BRITAIN

English Name	Age of First Good Seed Crop (Years)	Age of Maximum Production (Years)	Average Interval† Between Good Seed Crops	Recommended Time of Seed collection‡			Notes	Average Number of Cones per hectolitre	Average Yield in grams of Clean Seed per litre of Cones	Notes on Seed Collection
				Earliest	Normal	Latest				
BROADLEAVED										
Ash*	25–30	40–60	3–5	Aug.(1)	Oct.(2)	Nov.	(1) For immediate sowing (2) For stratification for 16–18 months			
Beech**	50–60	80–200	5–10	Sept.	Oct.	Nov.	Flowers sometimes damaged by late frosts			
Birch*	15	20–30	1–2	Aug.	Aug./ Sept.	Sept.	Good seed producers in Britain. Some seed most years.			
Chestnut, Horse**	20	30	1–2	Sept.	Oct.	Nov.	A warm late summer is required to ripen nuts. Collect biggest nuts only.			
Chestnut, Sweet**	30–40	50	1–4	May	June	June				
Oak,** Sessile and Pedunculate	40–50 / 25–30	80–120 / 40–60	3–5 / 2–3	Sept. / Sept.	Oct. / Sept./ Oct.	Nov. / Oct.	Some seed most years.			
Sycamore	30–40	40	1–2							
Wych elm**	40			May	June	June				
CONIFERS										
Scots pine	15–20	60–100	2–3	Nov.	Jan.	Feb.	Some seed borne every year. Most seed produced in SE & E England	5,500	6	Some seed retained in cones until early spring.
Corsican pine	25–30	60–90	3–5	Nov.	Dec.	Jan.		2,800	9	
Lodgepole pine	15–20	30–40	2–3	Mid-Aug.	Late Aug./ early Sept.	Late Sept.		4,500	4	
European larch	15–20	40–60	3–5	Nov.	Feb./ Mch.	April	Flowers often damaged by frost	10,000	10	As for Scots pine
Japanese and Hybrid larch*	15–20	40–60	3–5	Sept.	Sept.	Nov.	Flowers often damaged by frost.	9,500	14	Also during November in Scotland in some years. Collect before European.
Douglas fir	30–35	50–60	4–6	Sept.	Sept.	Oct.		3,000	5	Collect when cones a light golden brown or yellow colour.
Norway spruce	30–35	50–60	3–5	Oct.	Oct.	Nov.	Rarely seeds heavily.	1,000	13	As for Scots pine.
Sitka spruce	30–35	40–50	3–5	Sept.	Sept./ Oct.	Dec.		3,600	9	
Grand fir	40–45	—	3–5	Aug.	Aug./ Sept.	Sept.	A poor seed producer.	700	26	Collect immediately the scales loosen and the cone softens, otherwise seed will be lost.
Noble fir	30–35	40–60	2–4	Aug.	Aug./ Sept.	Sept.		2,200	22	
Western hemlock	30–35	40–60	3	Aug.	Sept.	Sept.		58,000	13	Collect as soon as cones change colour from bright green to yellow and the tips of the seed wings are visible and a light brown colour.
Western red cedar	20–25	40–60	2–3	Aug.	Sept.	Sept.	A good producer	190,000	14	
Lawson cypress	20–25	40–60	2–3	Aug.	Sept.	Sept.	A good seed producer	107,000	44	

Notes: † The figures refer to the intervals between good seed years. In Scots pine, for example, 2–3 years of relatively poor production will generally follow a good seed year. ‡ *Sept./Oct.* means at the end of *September* or beginning of *October*. * Collect by climbing or special felling. ** Collect fallen seed from the ground.

Forestry and Bulletin 43, *Nursery Practice*, (the Forest Seed Association referred to in Bulletin 43 no longer exists, and more detailed advice on the suitability of certain seed origins can be obtained from the Chief Research Officer, Forestry Commission, Northern Research Station, Roslin, Midlothian EH25 9SY).

Seed Orchards

Detailed accounts of the establishment and maintenance of seed orchards are given in Bulletin 54, *Seed Orchards*. The Forestry Commission, and some private estate owners, have established clonal or seedling seed orchards of some species. These are plantations of grafted plants or selected seedling progenies derived from highly selected parents, and which are well isolated to minimise contaminant pollination from other sources. They are sited and especially managed to produce frequent, abundant, easily collected seed. Seed from orchards is preferred to that which is collected from a registered stand.

COLLECTION OF SEED

Heavy seed crops often follow a year with a prolonged hot, dry, early summer and collection costs are reduced in heavy crop years. It is a common practice to collect several years' supply of seed for those species, the seed of which can be satisfactorily stored for long periods.

Large seeds such as acorns, beechnuts and chestnuts, are collected from the ground, and to facilitate this the ground must be cleared of all vegetation and debris beforehand. Ripe cones are collected by climbing or, in mature seed stands, from felled trees to provide a mixture of genetically diverse material (See Plate 1). When trees are climbed the men must be fully trained for the task and provided with approved and tested safety equipment, details of which are given in Forest Record 39, *Collection of Cones from Standing Trees*. Some of the equipment listed in Forest Record 39 has been outdated by improved, lighter equipment, and may not be readily available. Any climbing equipment covered by British Standards Specification should be suitable. Table I summarises most of the important information on seed production for the more widely used forest species.

STORAGE OF FRUIT AND SEEDS

Collections should only be made in dry weather since moist cones and fruit frequently heat up or go mouldy during temporary storage. Bags of fruit or cones must be kept well ventilated. The bags, which **must** be porous and not impervious, should be stored where they are protected from the rain, and any damp cones should be spread out on the floor of a well-ventilated shed and turned until dry.

Conifers

The ease of extracting seeds from cones varies according to species. Cones of Silver firs break up soon after collection. Western hemlock, Western red cedar and Lawson cypress cones can be opened by spreading them in shallow boxes or trays in a cool well-ventilated building. Cones of most other species are normally dried in a special kiln in which the temperature of the air-stream is progressively raised as drying proceeds. After drying, the seeds are separated by shaking through coarse sieves or by rotating them in a wire-mesh drum, and are then collected in a tray. Seeds with detachable wings are de-winged by gentle rubbing between cloth sheets or in a machine especially designed for the purpose. Wings, cone scales, empty seed and other impurities are separated from the seed by winnowing. The seed is then ready for testing for germination percentage and moisture content, and storage. Seed can be satisfactorily stored in this condition until the following spring, provided it is kept cool in sealed containers. However, seed to be stored beyond six months should be dried in warm dry air (radiant heat should not be used) until the moisture content is between six and eight per cent (eight and ten per cent for true firs). The dried seed is placed in air-tight containers and stored in a cold store. The longevity of seed can be extended by storing it at $-5°C$, but for normal purposes seed of all species can be safely stored at $+2°C$ for 3–5 years, provided the moisture content is suitably adjusted.

Broadleaved Species

Hardwood fruit and seeds vary in size and shape, ranging from those in husks, like chestnut or beech, or berries like gean, to those which are dry and may or may not be winged. In general, seed should be separated from its husk if dry, or from its soft coat if a berry. Broadleaf seed like birch with small wings has to be sown with the wings remaining on the seed coat, while seed like sycamore can have the wings broken off. Pulpy fruits should first be macerated by squashing or gentle mashing and mixing with water; pulp and skins can usually be separated from the seed by washing through sieves to remove unwanted heavy material and by flotation in water to remove unwanted light material.

REGULATIONS GOVERNING THE PURCHASE, LABELLING AND SALE OF SEED

Under the Forest Reproduction Material Regulations, seed of the 13 species listed on page 1 may not be marketed within the EEC unless it has been derived from sources approved and registered by the Forestry Commission in Great Britain, or by the relevant authority in another member state of the EEC or Northern Ireland. (There are exceptions for seed or cones authorised by the Forestry Commissioners in writing to be used in tests or for scientific purposes.)

Furthermore, seed produced in Great Britain can only be marketed if it has been tested at the Official Testing Station at Alice Holt Lodge, Wrecclesham, Farnham, Surrey and found to be of the required standard. Seed, whether it originates from Great Britain or from another member state of the EEC, may only be marketed if it has been tested, either in Britain or abroad, during the same seed testing year as that in which it is marketed. There are minimum weights for samples of batches for analysis.

Each lot of seed, fruit or cones should be clearly labelled at all stages from collection to sowing. This is mandatory under the Forest Reproductive Material Regulations for the 13 EEC species. All cones, fruits and seeds should be kept in separate lots clearly distinguished from each other by species, variety, clone (if any), region of provenance, origin and year of ripening. The provenance and altitude must also be given for material of the 13 EEC species which, although not derived from officially approved sources, has been specially authorised for marketing.

Persons marketing forest tree seed of the 13 EEC species are required to furnish the buyer with a Supplier's Certificate in respect of any seed sold. The Supplier's Certificate must contain details of the seed and, in the case of Tested Reproductive Material (from sources tested by experiment and proved to have improved value for use) must be on blue coloured paper, and Selected Reproductive Material (from the selected material not falling into the Tested category) must be on green coloured paper.

Under the Forest Reproductive Material Regulations any one collecting seed of the 13 EEC species for marketing may only do so from stands which have been approved and registered by the Forestry Commission, whose officers will need to be satisfied that seed being collected is from the specified registered sources. The Regulations require seed collectors to inform the Forestry Commission of the times and places of the collection.

An explanatory booklet *The Marketing of Forest Tree Seed and Plants within the European Economic Community* is available from the Forestry Commission and gives a fuller outline of the Regulations.

BIBLIOGRAPHY: SEED
Forestry Commission Publications

BULLETINS

No. 43   *Nursery practice. 1972.*
No. 54   *Seed orchards. 1975.*

LEAFLETS

No. 28   *Collection and storage of acorns and beech mast. 1962.*
No. 33   *Collection and storage of ash, sycamore and maple seed. 1960.*
No. 60   *Selection of conifer seed for use in British forestry. 1974.*

FOREST RECORD

No. 39   *Collection of cones from standing trees. 1965.*

RESEARCH AND DEVELOPMENT PAPERS

No. 76   *Bibliography on international provenance experiments begun in 1938. 1976.*
No. 98   *International Norway spruce experiment at The Bin, Huntly Forest, Aberdeenshire: Results up to twenty-five years. 1973.*
No. 99   *Inventory provenance test with Norway spruce in Britain: First results. 1973.*
No. 103 *Survey of losses of first-year conifer seeds and seedlings in Forestry Commission nurseries 1972. 1973.*
No. 105 *Summary report on the IUFRO 1938 provenance experiments with Norway spruce, Picea Abies. 1974.*
No. 114 Pinus Contorta *provenance studies. 1976.*

EXPLANATORY BOOKLET

The marketing of forest tree seed and plants within the European Economic Community.

LEGISLATION

The Forest Reproductive Material Regulations 1973 (SI 1973 No. 944), as amended by SI 1973 No. 1108 and SI 1974 No. 877 (under the Plant Varieties and Seeds Act 1964).

Chapter 2

NURSERY PRACTICE

The raising of young trees in nurseries is the first stage in planting a forest and the Forestry Commission has had a long experience of this work backed by years of research. The subject is fully covered in Bulletin 43, *Nursery Practice*, and anyone concerned with the management of forest nurseries is advised to consult this publication. The following paragraphs therefore have been kept brief and references given in Bulletin 43 are not repeated here.

OBJECTIVES

The principle objective of the forest nursery is to produce good quality plants as cheaply as possible. In this context 'good quality' can be taken as meaning a sturdy plant, with a well-balanced root and shoot, and with a well-developed fibrous root system.

METHOD

Plants of the required standard are raised by a two-stage process. Seed, given the appropriate pre-sowing treatment (chilling where dormant etc.), is sown quite densely in prepared seedbeds, designed to ensure maximum germination of the seed, and good growth of the seedlings in their first growing season. The seedlings are then lifted and transplanted into lines where they have enough space to grow into well shaped plants fit to go into the forest at the end of a further growing season, referred to as '1 + 1 transplants'. This is the basis of the process but there are modifications which are given later. The less favoured nurseries or the slower growing species may not produce usable plants in two years, and longer periods may have to be allowed in seedbeds and lines.

NURSERY SOILS

Nursery Soils

Both seedlings and transplants of conifers, and most broadleaved species (there are exceptions, e.g. ash and poplar), grow best in acid soils. Acidity is measured on a pH scale in which 1 is extreme of acid, and 10 extreme of alkaline conditions. Soils in the range pH 4·5 to 5·5 are the most suitable for forest nurseries—pH levels under 4·5 are too acid and those above 5·5 are too alkaline. Soil texture is also important because the nursery process involves soil cultivations in winter and early spring. At these seasons, soils with a clay plus silt content over 15 per cent are often too wet to cultivate, a factor which delays the nursery operation so that valuable growing time is lost. Although the clay or silt fraction in soil is valuable for its water and nutrient retaining characteristics, the factor of 'workability' is more important in the nursery and the nutrient retention problem is overcome by the addition of fertilisers. The best nursery soils therefore are the sandy loams or even sands which have the additional merit that they tend to be sufficiently acid.

Seedbeds

Successful seedling production depends on a number of factors probably the two most important (provided good quality seed is available) being correct preparation of the seedbed and time of sowing. A properly prepared seedbed with a good tilth, well consolidated, is essential. If sowing is delayed beyond the optimum date (normally March in the south and April in the north) the time available for growth in the summer will be reduced and may result in seedlings too small to transplant. Sowing density is also important, and depends on the species being sown and the viability of the seed. Seed which has a high proportion of viable seeds has to be sown at lower density to give adequate growing space to the seedlings, with the aim of producing 600 usable seedlings per square metre.

Transplants

Correct spacing is important to allow plants to develop to the required size, but the success and cost of this operation is very dependent on the workability of the soil. Light sandy soils are both easy to work and quicker to dry out in the spring. The lining out process can be carried out by hand (see Plate 2) but is usually partly or wholly mechanised. Partial mechanisation involves the use of special ploughs which place the soil against the tree roots, at the same time cutting the face for the next line of trees. Full mechanisation depends on machines that place the seedlings in position and firm soil round their roots, but even these still require the seedlings to be fed into the planting mechanism by hand.

Mechanisation requires greater space to turn the machines at the end of beds, and hence long lines to obtain maximum output. This is one reason why the maximum benefit of mechanisation will only be obtained in larger nurseries.

If purchased seedlings are to be transplanted in the nursery, supplies should be ordered well in advance against samples which should be used to check the stocks actually supplied. Purchased seedlings will almost inevitably bring in weeds, and pathogens.

Plant Nutrition

Successful nursery production depends very much on correct fertiliser application for both seedbeds and transplant lines. Suitable fertiliser regimes for both seedbeds and transplant lines have been developed from many years' research, and experience has shown how local knowledge, soil analysis and foliage analysis (of the crops) can be used to modify the general recommendations to suit a particular nursery. Most nutritional regimes are based on the use of both organic and inorganic fertilisers, although the inorganic material supplies the major part of the crop's nutritional requirement. Organic fertilisers are used mainly because there are indications that they help to maintain soil organic matter levels, thus preventing deterioration in moisture holding capacity and workability. Results of experiments suggest that inorganic fertilisers alone will give satisfactory results over long periods of time, and whilst soil organic matter levels have fallen, there has been little evidence of a fall in productivity. However, some soils, particularly heavier soils, have tended to become markedly more difficult to cultivate after continuous inorganic fertiliser application.

In practice, organic fertilisers are applied mainly to areas which will carry transplants in the following season. The use of organics in seedbeds is not recommended because initially they often make the soil fluffy and difficult to consolidate. Experiments have shown that the incorporation of hopwaste, for instance, slightly reduces the number of seedlings germinating in a seedbed.

The importance of not introducing weed seeds limits the sources of bulk organic materials. Hopwaste is the most commonly used organic manure for this reason. Composts from town waste and sewage are not suitable because they are variable and may contain base metal contaminants which can accumulate in the soils and may reach levels that are harmful to young trees.

Weed Control

Uncontrolled weeds will result in substantially reduced growth of seedlings and to a lesser extent of transplants, and as weeds quickly produce fertile seeds the aim is to keep a weed-free nursery. The attack on weeds depends on the type and life cycle of the individual weed species, but clearly a nursery free of weeds from the start is a great advantage. The inadvertent introduction of weed seeds in composts, organic fertilisers, imported seedlings and even tractor tyres or men's feet should be guarded against. Acid soils have a further advantage in that they have a smaller weed flora than the less acid or alkaline soils.

Modern herbicides give the nurseryman a much more effective armoury against weeds than was available previously by hand and cultivation techniques. The use of vaporising oil as a pre-emergence spray in seedbeds is a well established technique and more recently, paraquat has come into use for the same purpose. Provided four weeks have elapsed after the tree seedlings have emerged white

spirit can be used as a post emergence spray, though some conifers are only moderately resistant. The most widely used herbicide for weed control in transplant lines is simazine. With all herbicides, careful adherence to dosage rates and timing is essential. There is no universal answer to the wide range of weed species in the different phases of nursery work, and the nurseryman has to apply the appropriate technique for each set of circumstances. The subject is treated in full in Chapter 10 of Bulletin 43.

OTHER PLANT PRODUCTION TECHNIQUES

There are a number of alternative techniques to the main nursery method of seedbed and transplant lines outlined above. They are:

Undercutting

Instead of transplanting seedlings, their roots can be severed in the seedbed by drawing a sharpened steel blade through the bed at the appropriate depth. The effect of this is to cut the main root and stimulate the formation of a branched and fibrous root system. Seed has to be sown at a lower density to give greater growing space, and this involves keeping down weeds in a larger area of seedbeds. However, undercutting in nurseries that are weed free can produce good plants at acceptable cost.

Vegetative Propagation

Few forest trees can be grown easily from cuttings, the exceptions being poplar, willow, London plane and elm, and amongst the conifers, Lawson cypress, Western red cedar and Leyland cypress. The technique is particularly valuable when seed is not readily available, as in the case of particular clones and cultivars. Difficult subjects can be raised under glass in either a heated frame or glasshouse.

Small Containers

Recent development work has centred round the raising of seedlings in small plastic tubes, or Paperpots, in heated greenhouses of glass or polythene. This system has the advantage that seedlings can be raised in 8 to 25 weeks, and can be safely planted in the forest outside the normal planting season because their roots are protected and remain undisturbed in the container. Plants can be raised at short notice to match unforeseen availability of land. However, the seedlings are inevitably smaller than orthodox transplants and less robust. Costs are no less than for ordinary transplants, so future use will depend on such factors as the need to plant in late spring and during the summer in order to complete large planting programmes, the necessity for additional weeding in the forest, the incidence of beating up and the possibilities of machine planting. The use of containerised plants is showing promise in different parts of the country. In Scotland, tubed seedlings of Sitka spruce and Lodgepole pine are being used on extensive areas of peat and in East Anglia it is hoped that the use of Corsican pine in Paperpots will give better survival rates for this difficult species.

NURSERY PROTECTION

Seedling losses due to birds are commonplace, and it is now becoming usual practice to net seedbeds immediately after sowing, for about 12 weeks, to prevent birds from taking seed and small seedlings. Nurseries are normally surrounded by stock and rabbit-proof fences, as occasional incursions from such animals can cause enormous losses. In some areas it is also necessary to fence out deer.

Forest nurserymen are fortunate in not having to combat fungi, insects or climatic damage as a matter of routine. Damage can occur on occasions, though, and the nurseryman needs to be able to diagnose the problem from the symptoms and take appropriate remedial steps. These are fully covered in Chapter 4, p. 39 and 44.

SITE SELECTION

It will be clear from the above that the selection of a suitable nursery site is the foundation of the successful nursery. Summing up, the requirements are:
—a sand or sandy loam soil of acidity between pH 4·5 and 5·5
—a gently sloping, free draining site that avoids frost hollows
—preferably a heathland or woodland area free from weeds
—availability of labour, supervision and management
—water on site, buildings for storage and mechanical equipment.

TRENDS IN NURSERY MANAGEMENT

During the last twenty years the trend in the Forestry Commission has been to reduce the number of nurseries, and concentrate production in a few large ones where the skilled labour and management, specialised equipment and favourable site conditions can be brought to bear on a large output, and so result in lower production costs. A centralised nursery policy does present management problems in distributing plants to the various forests at the right time, but these are generally offset by the lower production cost and improved handling and storage techniques which have followed from the use of polythene bags and cold stores.

BIBLIOGRAPHY: NURSERY PRACTICE

Forestry Commission Publications

BULLETINS

No. 37 *Experiments on nutrition problems in forest nurseries.* 1965. Vols I and II.
No. 43 *Nursery practice.* 1972.
No. 53 *Production and use of tubed seedlings.* 1975.

LEAFLETS

No. 50 *Grey mould in forest nurseries.* 1969.
No. 61 *Tubed seedlings.* 1975.

FOREST RECORDS

No. 60 *Progeny-testing in Britain with special reference to nursery practice.* 1967.
No. 67 *Effect of fertiliser and density pretreatment on spruce seedling survival and growth.* 1968.
No. 74 *Development of glasshouse techniques for early progeny test procedures in forest tree breeding.* 1971.
No. 88 *Cold storage of forest plants.* 1973.

RESEARCH AND DEVELOPMENT PAPERS

No. 46 *A review of research and development in forest nursery techniques in Great Britain (1949–1966).* 1967.
No. 85 *A plan for the improvement of Sitka spruce by selection and breeding.* 1972.
No. 87 *Production and use of ball-rooted planting stock in Sweden and Finland.* 1972.
No. 103 *Survey of losses of first-year conifer seeds and seedlings in Forestry Commission nurseries 1972.* 1973.
No. 109 *Fertiliser effects on the growth and composition of Sitka and Norway spruce nursery transplants and on the composition of a podzol profile after 15 years cropping.* 1974.
No. 111 *Low-pressure sodium (SOX) tube lights as a source of supplementary lighting for the improved growth of Sitka spruce seedlings.* 1976.

Chapter 3

ESTABLISHMENT AND MAINTENANCE OF PLANTATIONS

CARE FOR THE LANDSCAPE

Forests and woodlands provide an important visual contrast to an increasingly urbanised Britain. As public interest in the visual quality of landscape is likely to continue to grow, it is important for foresters, while pursuing their main objective—usually that of timber production, to conserve and, where possible, enhance the beauty of all forest and woodland landscapes.

The careful application of landscape design principles and techniques to all forestry activities will be one of the important ways in which a reasonable balance between the efficient management of an activity and good visual amenity can be obtained.

These principles and techniques are explained in detail in FC Booklet No. 44 'The Landscape of Forests and Woods' by Dame Sylvia Crowe, an eminent Landscape Architect who was Landscape Consultant to the Forestry Commission from 1963–1976.

SELECTION OF TREE SPECIES FOR PLANTING

The choice of species to be planted on a site is made by arriving at the best possible compromise between the desired object(s) of management and the site factors that obtain. Many species will survive on a broad range of site types. A few site types have such extreme characteristics that the number of species that will grow on them is severely limited. Unfortunately, these 'extreme' sites are in fact represented by a large area of land that becomes available for planting trees in the United Kingdom.

First, it is proposed to discuss the various objects of management that may apply, whilst remembering that more than one can arise in any planting. It is then proposed to consider the site factors in rather more detail, to indicate the range of tolerance shown by species and their reaction to extremes of site type.

Ways of approaching the choice of species on any land that is to be planted or replanted will be suggested, together with some comments on ground preparation, existing vegetation and side effects relating to fungi, insects, labour and other factors.

Objects of Management

Frequently, more than one object of management will apply on any site, although one will probably be major, usually timber production. Others included with timber production, and exceptionally without, are amenity and shelter.

AMENITY

Amenity may come into consideration under a variety of heads. Visual amenity suggests a variety of species both coniferous and broadleaved, together with the marriage between local countryside and the woodland. Recreation may simply mean that the woodland must be usable for walking and other compatible activities for a great part of its life (long rotations and some admixture of broadleaves), but it may also include sporting which can mean the careful design of the woods to provide the type of shooting and game feeding required. Equally it can mean conservation and the maintenance of a system already in existence (replacement of broadleaves by similar species or conifers by conifers). These subsidiary objectives of management do not allow of maximum volume production.

SHELTER

Shelter is often required in farming areas for the protection of buildings, arable crops or animals. The type of shelter required in each case may be very different and hence the choice of species will differ. Thus some arable crops benefit from a permeable screen of trees which simply reduces the impact of the wind, whilst animals require a more solid barrier to aid them during hard weather. In the latter case, a mixture of species may be desirable in order to maintain some wind resistance throughout the height of the crop. It may be desirable to bring stock into the shelterbelt at some stage, and room at ground level has to be left for this. The forester's control over the choice of species enables him to ensure ground-to-tree-top connection together with some open spaces within the shelterbelt.

Site Factors

Geology and soils, climate both general and local, together with the elevation, aspect and exposure and the vegetation already existing on the site, are the most readily apparent site factors. Others of equal importance may be less obvious but equally limiting on species choice. Thus the existence of air pollution may rule out conifers or reduce the possible species to Austrian, Corsican and Lodgepole pines and larches, the main crop being broadleaved (beech, sycamore etc.). The presence of insect, animal or fungal pests may again limit the number of species that can be used with confidence. Thus an attempt to replant an old broadleaf area with conifers may be thwarted by the existence of a large infection of the old site by Honey fungus. Sites that are not too acid and have been cultivated for agricultural crops in the past are a frequent source of *Fomes annosus* infection, and the choice of species should consider this factor.

PLANT INDICATORS

Vegetation growing on the site is a useful guide to the species that may be planted, and this is dealt with in more detail in Table 2. The forester must be especially careful if the area has been used for a purpose other than forestry in the recent past. For example, moorland used for sheep grazing will almost certainly have been burned over periodically, with resultant changes in vegetation. As soon as the area is fenced, drained or ploughed and grazing is stopped, a rapid return of the old vegetation can be expected. Drier conditions will tend to produce more heather, with attendant problems for species such as spruce. On grassy sites, the increase in vegetation will encourage voles, and these can rapidly grow to plague proportions and become a very real problem by girdling broadleaf and many coniferous species.

Generally speaking, the larger the variety of plants present in the vegetation the more suitable the site is to support a wide variety of tree species. Some individual plant species have been used as indicators in the past, but the whole plant community on an area gives a much better guide, together with a careful look at soil profiles, the exposed soils on drain sides, exposure and drainage. Bracken has often been used as an indicator of fertility in the past, but is in fact more likely to indicate good local drainage on the area. The absence or poor performance of bracken may equally well be caused by the tendency of the area to suffer from frosts. Such plant indicators as the Twayblade orchid for chalk really only confirm what should be obvious from the examination of the surrounding countryside. Sometimes the dominant plant species or plant associations are of value in choosing species in extreme conditions. Thus in wet peat areas, the poorest sites are normally indicated by deer grass and crossleaved

heaths, and in such places possibly only one species, Lodgepole pine, will prove successful.

PREVIOUS OR ADJOINING CROPS

Knowledge of the performance of species that have grown on the site before, or are growing in adjoining plantations, can be invaluable. Existing plantations are well worth visiting and examining in detail. Examination of the vegetation and soil in them is important, as well as a close look at the trees. Records may show the seed origin of the trees which relates to their performance. Consideration must be given to all the site factors of the existing crop, compared with those that are present on the proposed planting area. When the tree crop has existed on an area for some time it affects the soil profile by root action and leaf fall, and maintains a much drier situation underneath it than on adjoining land. Hence conditions on the proposed planting area, if it is a new planting, can seem to be very different from those existing in the established plantation, but they can easily be the result of the action of the trees themselves.

TABLES

In general, choice of species must be based on the ecological nature of the sites to be planted. This in turn can be adjusted as far as is possible to meet the desired objects of management. Table 2 gives details of the plant associations and site conditions that are favourable to most groups of species. Tables 3 and 4 deal separately with coniferous and broadleaf species that are most normally considered for planting, together with the conditions that justify their choice. Tables 5 and 6 give notes on species that are less regularly employed. These Tables also give notes about the timber uses of different species, and the range of volume yield that they may be expected to give.

TABLE 2

PLANT INDICATORS

Plant Associations	Site Conditions indicated	Tree Species indicated	Remarks
Grass/herb	Moist and fertile soils. Often on lower slopes of hills and in valleys. If rushes are present, there may be a shallow layer of peat.	Beech, if soil is dry and calcareous. Generally broadleaf soils. Ash, sycamore, Wych elm. Douglas fir, European larch and Norway and Sitka spruce.	Wood sanicle, wild garlic and Dog's mercury are sometimes present and often indicate suitable conditions for ash.
Fern/grass	Steep, moist slopes.	Japanese and European larches, Douglas fir, Norway and Sitka spruce, Broadleaves, if fertile soils; oak, beech, Sweet chestnut.	

T ABLE 2 *(continued)*

PLANT INDICATORS

Plant Associations	Site Conditions indicated	Tree Species indicated	Remarks
Bracken	Slopes with fairly deep well-drained soil. Frequent on former woodland.	European larch, Japanese larch, Douglas fir, Sitka spruce.	Bracken grows on a wide range of sites, and should be treated with reserve as an indicator. Deep bracken litter can be a difficult planting medium.
Grass/heath	Dry slopes and knolls.	Scots pine, European larch and Japanese larch; Sessile oak, if really fertile. Corsican pine in south.	The grasses are usually fine; typical grasses are *Deschampsia flexuosa*, *Festuca* spp. and *Agrostis* spp. Bell heather (*Erica cinerea*) is sometimes present.
Rush/grass	Heavy clay soils.	Scots pine, Norway and Sitka spruce, Lawson cypress. Corsican pine in South.	Mosses are usually present.
Purple moor grass (*Molinia caerulea*)	Usually heavy clay soils often with a layer of shallow peat. Drainage is usually poor.	Norway and Sitka spruce, but avoid the latter in frosty hollows.	The Purple moor grass is often found pure over large areas.
Heather or ling (*Calluna vulgaris*)	Usually a leached and compacted soil of low fertility in an area of fairly low rainfall.	Scots pine, Japanese larch and Lodgepole pine. On more fertile heathland, Sitka spruce with herbicide treatment. Corsican pine on southern heaths.	Typical of the 'grouse moor' in the North. Ling or heather is usually an indicator of unsuitable conditions for establishing spruces, but the destruction of the ling may render the ground suitable, provided the tree crop is soon established and so checks the ling's return.
Heather or ling mixed with Purple moor grass	Usually in the wetter regions of the west and north. The soil may vary but peat is always present and may be deep.	Scots pine and Lodgepole pine, if mainly heather. If mainly grass, Sitka spruce may be used in mixture with either Scots or Lodgepole pine.	Unsuitable for Norway spruce. On the poorest sites, there may be Crossleaved heath (*Erica tetralix*) and Deer grass (*Trichophorum caespitous*); on these sites only Lodgepole pine should be planted.
Matgrass/bilberry (*Nardus stricta Vaccinum myrtilis*)	Common in Pennines. Free draining, often rocky.	Scots, Corsican and Lodgepole pine, Japanese and hybrid larch.	Spruces may check and should be restricted to high rainfall sites.
Cotton grass (*Eriophorum* spp.)	Usually wet deep peat.	Lodgepole pine. Sitka spruce only when Cotton grass is mixed with other herbs.	Crops will need fertilisers at planting and subsequent top dressing.
Deer grass/ling or Crossleaved heath	Lowest fertility deep peat bogs.	Lodgepole pine is the only reliable sp. Hybrid larch may be used for amenity.	Crops will need fertilisers at planting and subsequent top dressing.

Tabular Notes on Individual Species
    The main characteristics of the best known species are summarised in Tables 3 to 6 which follow. The uses of timbers are further discussed in Chapter 10.
    *The figures quoted for the yield of various species are the range found in Britain, followed by the average in brackets. The annual rate of growth, averaged over the previous life of the crop, rises with age to a peak value, and then declines. This peak value is the yield, or 'maximum mean annual increment', and it is given in cubic metres per hectare per annum.

TABLE 3

NOTES ON INDIVIDUAL SPECIES: MOST COMMONLY USED CONIFERS

Species and Native Country	Conditions Justifying Selection	Unsuitable conditions	Notes on Timber	General Remarks and Yield (m³/hectare/annum)*
Scots pine *Pinus sylvestris* (L.) British Isles and Northern Europe	An adaptable tree which succeeds over a wide range of conditions. The easiest tree to plant on dry heather sites. Thrives on light or sandy soils and at low or moderate elevations. Very frost hardy. A strong light demander. Does well in low rainfall areas. A useful nurse species.	Avoid soft ground and sites exposed to sea wind. Not easy to establish on moorland country under high rainfall. Unsuitable for chalk or limestone soils except as a nurse for beech. Not a tree for high elevations, except in north-east Scotland, where it thrives up to 1,500 ft in glens.	A general purpose timber with good strength properties. It works, nails, and finishes well. Takes preservatives readily so is easily treated for outdoor use. Its wide range of uses include fencing, joinery, building, flooring, box and packing case manufacturer, pitwood, fibre-board, wood-wool and chipboard manufacture, pulp-wood, railway sleepers and telegraph poles. The 'redwood' of the imported timber trade.	Although growth is rather slow and volume production is not high compared with more exacting species, generally it is a 'safe' tree to plant. 4—14 (8)
Corsican pine *Pinus nigra* var. *maritima* (Ait) Melville Corsica	Low elevations, particularly sandy areas near the sea. Light sandy soils and also heavy clays in the midlands and south and east England; low rainfall areas. More successful on chalky soils than Scots pine. Tolerates smoke better than other conifers.	Avoid high elevations. Not suitable for the northern and western uplands of Britain.	The timber resembles that of Scots pine, but is somewhat coarser in texture, has a higher proportion of sapwood, and has slightly lower strength properties. Readily treated with preservatives. Its other uses include box manufacture, pitwood, fencing, fibreboard manufacture, chipboard manufacture, pulpwood and wood-wool. It is the preferred species for wood-wool slab manufacture.	It is important to obtain plants of true Corsican provenance, that is, plants raised from seed collected in Corsica, or their descendants. Produces timber faster than Scots pine. Shows some tolerance to smoke. More difficult to establish than Scots pine. 6—20 (11)

Table 3 *(continued)*

NOTES ON INDIVIDUAL SPECIES: MOST COMMONLY USED CONIFERS

Species and Native Country	Conditions Justifying Selection	Unsuitable Conditions	Notes on Timber	General Remarks and Yield (m^3/hectare/annum)*
Lodgepole pine *Pinus contorta* Dougl. ex Loud. Western North America	After suitable ground preparation Lodgepole pine grows relatively well on the poorest heaths, sand-dunes and peat where no other tree will survive. Stands exposure better than most other species. Fairly tolerant of air pollution. For optimum results the choice of correct provenance is important. (R. & D. Paper 114, 1976).	Tends to grow very coarsely on moist fertile sites.	Home-grown timber is used in the round for pitprops and fencing. The sawn timber has similar properties to Scots pine and can be used for the same purposes.	Is probably the best pioneer species in Britain and is now being widely planted, especially in the west and north. Coastal provenances generally have a higher yield than inland provenances, but are of poor form. 4—14 (7)
European larch, *Larix decidua* Mill. Mountains of Central Europe	Site requirements are exacting. Does best on moist but well-drained moderately fertile loams. A strong light demander. A good nurse tree. Has some tolerance of smoke.	Avoid damp, badly drained or very dry sites, frosty places, shallow soils over chalk, poor sands, peat soils, leached soils, exposed sites at high elevations or near the sea, areas carrying a dense growth of heather.	The timber is heavier and stronger than most other softwoods. The heartwood is naturally durable but any sapwood needs preservatives for outdoor use. It is widely used for fencing, gates, estate work and pitwood. Other uses include telegraph poles, rustic work, garden furniture and chipboard. Selected material is in demand for vat making, boat-building, and wagons.	Canker is a danger and it is essential to select really suitable sites for planting. Choice of origin of seed for plants is most important; home-collected seed (particularly Scottish), from a good stand, is the most reliable; seed from the high Alps (over 3,500 ft) must be avoided. Sudeten and Polish provenances are promising. Not a high yielding species. 4—14 (7)
Japanese larch, *Larix kaempferi* (Lambert) Carr. Japan	Thrives over a wide range of conditions including the high rainfall districts of the west and north. Suitable for upland sites including grassy and heathery slopes. Of great value in coppice areas and in fire belts as it quickly outgrows and suppresses adjoining vegetation. A valuable pioneer species and useful nurse with some resistance to smoke pollution.	Avoid dry sites and areas where the annual rainfall is low (under 30 inches); also badly drained sites, frost hollows and very exposed situations.	The timber is strong and resembles that of European larch. Grade for grade it can be used for the same purposes.	Resistant to larch canker. Gives a higher yield, up to middle age, than European larch or Scots pine. 4—16 (8)

TABLE 3 *(continued)*

NOTES ON INDIVIDUAL SPECIES: MOST COMMONLY USED CONIFERS

Species and Native Country	Conditions Justifying Selection	Unsuitable Conditions	Notes on Timber	General Remarks and Yield $(m^3/hectare/annum)*$
Hybrid larch, *Larix × eurolepis* Henry First raised in Scotland	Of special value on sites which are at the limits for the use of European or Japanese larch. Hardier and more resistant to disease. On good sites can grow even more quickly than Japanese larch. Shows some tolerance of smoke pollution.	Similar to Japanese larch.	Resembles the timber of European larch and grade for grade can be used for much the same purposes.	Characteristics are intermediate between European and Japanese larch, but depend on the particular parents of the hybrid. First generation hybrid from selected parents is outstanding; second generation hybrid is also valuable, but third generation is poor. 4—16 (8)
Douglas fir, *Pseudotsuga menziesii* (Franco) Mirb. Western North America	Likes a well-drained soil of good depth and of moderate fertility. A tree for valley slopes. Particular care is needed in site selection. A moderate shade bearer for a few years.	Unsuitable for exposed situations, heather ground, wet soils and shallow soils. Liable to windblow on soft ground except where drains are well maintained. Suffers from frost damage when young.	An excellent constructional timber with a high strength to weight ratio in compression and bending. Takes preservatives reasonably well. It is used for fencing, pitwood, flooring, joinery, building, packing case manufacture, telegraph poles, flag poles, chipboard, fibreboard and pulpwood.	On suitable sites Douglas fir grows rapidly and produces a high volume of timber. Thinning at too late a date can render crop unduly susceptible to windblow. Good drainage is important. 8—24 (14)
Norway spruce, *Picea abies* (L.) Karst. Europe	Moist grassy or rushy land, and shallow, less-acid peats. Succeeds on old woodland sites and most soils of moderate fertility including heavy clays. Can withstand light shade for a few years. Somewhat sensitive to exposure.	Fails on heather land and does poorly on dry sites, particularly on the eastern side of Britain. May be checked by frost in hollows and by occasional grazing by roe deer and sheep, but eventually grows away from this.	A good general purpose timber with a clean white colour. It works and nails well, and has a wide range of uses. It is stable during changing conditions of humidity, and is therefore particularly suitable for building. Its other uses include joinery, kitchen furniture, boxes and packing cases, pulpwood, chipboard, pitwood, fencing, fibreboard, wood-wool, ladder poles and scaffold poles. The 'whitewood' of the imported timber trade. Seldom used out of doors as the heartwood is hard to	Where it is really at home, Norway spruce produces a high volume of timber. Good drainage is essential if windblow is to be avoided. The young trees, and often tops of thinnings, can be sold as Christmas trees, but only in November/December. Choice of provenance is important. East European origins have grown well. 6—22 (12)

TABLE 3 *(continued)*

NOTES ON INDIVIDUAL SPECIES: MOST COMMONLY USED CONIFERS

Species and Native Country	Conditions Justifying Selection	Unsuitable Conditions	Notes on Timber	General Remarks and Yield (m³/hectare/annum)*
Norway spruce, *(continued)*			treat with preservative, but small poles take enough preservative in their sapwood to fit them for fencing.	
Sitka spruce, *Picea sitchensis* (Bong.) Carr. Western North America	Damp sites, generally, including exposed high land. Stands exposure better than any other common conifer, very suitable for high rainfall districts especially on the west coast.	Avoid all dry sites. Honey fungus is a risk in some scrub and coppice areas. Not a tree for the dry east nor for southern and midland England. Can suffer severe damage from frost when young.	Properties and uses are similar to those of Norway spruce. A first class pulpwood and readily accepted for chipboard, boxboards and many building jobs but not for high grade joinery.	A faster grower than Norway spruce and a very large volume producer. Useless as a Christmas tree. Wide provenance variation. Queen Charlotte Islands (B.C.) is a safe choice but on southern sites Washington and Oregon are preferred. 6—24 (12)
Western hemlock, *Tsuga heterophylla* (Raf.) Sarg. Western North America	No well marked climate preferences. Does well in the west. May be highly productive in quite low rainfall areas. Acid mineral soils and the better peats. A strong shade bearer and excellent for underplanting. Most competitive with other shade bearers on dry brown earths.	Rather difficult to establish pure on bare ground, and does better with a nurse. Dislikes heather competition and is slow to establish on heaths, where it may eventually grow well. Sites where previous conifer crops have suffered from *Fomes annosus* and *Armillaria mellea* should be avoided, as hemlock is prone to butt rot from this fungus.	Home-grown hemlock has good prospects as a building timber and – if graded for the purpose – as a joinery timber. Also for pitprops and general estate work. A good pulpwood.	Is best established under some shade. 12—24 (14)

TABLE 4

NOTES ON INDIVIDUAL SPECIES: PRINCIPLE BROADLEAVES

Species and Native Country	Conditions Justifying Selection	Unsuitable Conditions	Notes on Timber	General Remarks and Yield (m³/hectare/annum)*
Oaks: Pedunculate oak, *Quercus robur* L., and Sessile oak, *Quercus petraea* (Matt.) Lieb. British Isles and Europe	Well-aerated deep fertile loams. Grow well on fertile heavy soils and marls. Strong light demanders. Sessile oak tolerates less rich soils than does Pedunculate oak.	Avoid all shallow, ill drained or infertile soils, and exposed areas.	Oak is both hard and resistant to abrasion. It has a naturally durable heartwood, but the sapwood needs preservative treatments when small poles are used out of	Both species are very windfirm. 2—8 (4) Bark is still harvested as tan-bark in southern England.

TABLE 4 *(continued)*

NOTES ON INDIVIDUAL SPECIES: PRINCIPLE BROADLEAVES

Species and Native Country	Conditions Justifying Selection	Unsuitable Conditions	Notes on Timber	General Remarks and Yield (m³/hectare/annum)*
Oaks *(continued)*			doors. Prime clean oak is used for veneers, furniture, gates, flooring and barrel staves for tight cooperage. Lower grades of oak are used for fencing, weather-boarding, engineering, wagon construction and repair, sawn mining timber. Round oak is used for hardwood pulpwood and chipboard. Small poles are valued for cleft or round fence stakes.	
Beech, *Fagus sylvatica* L. Southern England, South Wales, and Europe	Chalk and limestone soils. Good loams of all types if well drained. Likes a mild sunny climate. A good shade-bearer. Tolerant of smoke pollution.	Avoid frost hollows, heavy soils on badly drained sites, and leached soils.	Beech has a wider range of indoor uses than any other home-grown hardwood, but is rarely employed out of doors. It is strong, works well to a good finish, and is easily stained. Its uses include furniture, particularly for kitchens and schools, turnery, flooring, veneers, bentwood and pulpwood. It is a good wood for charcoal making and firewood.	Benefits from a nurse on exposed areas; Scots pine is a suitable species. Useful for underplanting. Grey Squirrels can be very destructive to young beech. Stem form often poor. Dense planting gives better chance of selecting individuals for final crop. 4—10 (6)
Ash, *Fraxinus excelsior* L. British Isles and Europe	A most exacting species which demands good soil conditions. Likes sheltered situations and deep calcareous loams, moist but well drained. Thrives on chalk and limestone but only where soil is deep. Benefits from shelter in youth.	Not a suitable species for large-scale planting or for use on open ground. Avoid dry or shallow soils, grassland, heath or moorland, ill-drained ground, heavy clays. Frost hollows and ex-posed situations are also unsuitable.	Ash has a high resistance to shock and is thus used for oars, hockey sticks and other sports equipment, vehicle framing, tool handles and turnery and fur-niture. Also for pulpwood.	It is no use planting ash unless there is local evidence that first-class timber can be produced. It is rare to find suitable conditions except in small patches, and it is necessary to choose these sites with great care. 4—10 (5)

TABLE 4 *(continued)*

NOTES ON INDIVIDUAL SPECIES: PRINCIPLE BROADLEAVES

Species and Native Country	Conditions Justifying Selection	Unsuitable Conditions	Notes on Timber	General Remarks and Yield (m³/hectare/annum)*
Sycamore, *Acer pseudoplatanus* Central Europe	Fairly frost hardy. Stands exposure and smoke pollution very well.	As for ash but stands exposure.	A white timber especially suitable for use in contact with food (kitchen utensils, butchers' blocks, bread boards, etc.). A good turnery timber; used for textile rollers and bobbins. Figured sycamore is much sought after for veneer and furniture manufacture. Also for pulpwood.	A useful tree as a wind-firm mixture for conifers in shelterbelts. Grey squirrels can be very harmful. 4—12 (5)
Sweet chestnut, *Castanea sativa* Mill. Mediterranean	Needs a deep fertile soil, and it does best in a mild climate. Profitable as coppice in the south of England.	Unsuitable for the less fertile soils, frosty or exposed sites, badly drained ground or heavy clays.	Coppice - grown material is used for cleft fencing and hop poles. Sawn timber is used for furniture and coffin boards.	Treatment as coppice is discussed in Forest Record 30. When grown for timber, should not be left to reach large size, owing to risk of shake. As coppice. 4—10 (6)
Poplars: Black hybrids (*Populus x euramericana* (Dode Guinier) *P. 'Eugenei' P. 'Gelrica' P. 'Laevigata' P. 'Robusta' P. 'Serotina'* Europe, etc.	Very exacting; suitable sites are limited. Loamy soils in sheltered situations. Rich alluvial or fen soils, both well-drained and well-watered. Banks of streams.	Avoid high elevation, exposed sites and shallow soils. Stagnant water is fatal but occasional floods do no harm. Avoid acid peats and heathland.	Large clean poplar is peeled for matches and veneer packages (chip baskets). Used for wagon and barrow bottoms because of its high resistance to abrasion. Good pulpwood.	Poplar growing is a specialised job and is dealt with in Leaflet 27 (*Poplar Cultivation*). Poplars should be considered for planting when dealing with derelict or smoke polluted areas. 4—14 These yields are for plantations established at their usual spacings. Higher yields can be obtained by planting the trees more closely together.

TABLE 4 *(continued)*

NOTES ON INDIVIDUAL SPECIES: PRINCIPLE BROADLEAVES

Species and Native Country	Conditions Justifying Selection	Unsuitable Conditions	Notes on Timber	General Remarks and Yield (m³/hectare/annum)*
Balsam poplars: *P. trichocarpa* Torr. & Gray. *P. tacamahaca* x *trichocarpa* hybrids North America	Often susceptible to a bacterial canker and only clones generally resistant in practice should be used. They withstand slightly more acid soils than the Black hybrids and are more suited to the cooler and wetter parts of Britain than those.	As above.	As above.	As above. 4—16

TABLE 5

NOTES ON INDIVIDUAL SPECIES: OTHER CONIFERS

Species and Native Country	Conditions Justifying Selection	Unsuitable Conditions	Notes on Timber	General Remarks and Yield (m³/hectare/annum)*
Lawson cypress, *Chamaecyparis lawsoniana* (A. Marr.) Parl. Western North America	Soil requirements are not exacting, but does best on a deep fertile soil preferably in a sheltered situation. Stands shade well, is fairly frost hardy, and is sometimes of value in areas associated with chalk.	Avoid heather ground.	There is too little homegrown timber of this species on the market for it to be considered for any special purpose. It finds an outlet as a general-purpose softwood.	Of limited value; has a tendency to fork and is liable to suffer from snow break. Foliage is valued by florists. 12—24 (13)
Austrian pine, *Pinus nigra* var. *nigra* Harrison Austria	Limestone sites in exposed areas. Useful for shelterbelts near the sea. Tolerates smoke better than other conifers.	Not suitable for wet soils, or for planting in the north and west generally.	Very knotty owing to large branches.	Only worth planting where sea, limestone, or smoke rule out other conifers, and then only as a shelterbelt or for amenity.
Californian redwood, *Sequoia sempervirens* (D. Don) Endl. California	Deep, fertile soils in high rainfall areas. Sheltered situations. Tolerates a great amount of shade.	Avoid infertile soils, dry ares, exposed situations and frosty places.	Has mainly been used for fencing, owing to its high natural durability. A valuable timber in its homeland, but British grown timber has exceptionally low density and only moderate strength.	Usually slow in establishing itself. Best planted under tall cover. 16—30

C

TABLE 5 *(continued)*

NOTES ON INDIVIDUAL SPECIES: OTHER CONIFERS

Species and Native Country	Conditions Justifying Selection	Unsuitable Conditions	Notes on Timber	General Remarks and Yield $(m^3/hectare/annum)^*$
Wellingtonia, *Sequoiadendron giganteum* (Lindley) Buch. California	Deep moist, fertile soils in sheltered situations. Tolerates drier and more acid soils than the California redwood.	—	Timber is similar to Californian redwood.	Windfirm. A hardy tree. 16—30
European silver fir, *Abies alba* Mill. Central Europe	Not safe to plant owing to damage caused by the insect *Adelges nüsslini*. A strong shade bearer.	—	The timber has generally the same appearance and texture as Norway spruce, or 'whitewood', and is used for the same purposes under the same trade name of 'whitewood'.	— 14—22
Grand fir, *Abies grandis* Lindl. Western North America	Well-drained, moist, deep soils. Useful for underplanting. Often grows well on sites following a crop of larch.	Avoid frost hollows and poor soils, particularly really acid ones. On exposed sites older trees suffer crown damage.	Similar to spruce.	In favourable situations, produces a large volume of timber rapidly. Is more resistant to *Fomes annosus* than Sitka spruce, Norway spruce, Western red cedar and larches. Provenance choice is critical.
Noble fir, *Abies procera* Rehd. Western North America	Flourishes on well-drained, deep, moist soils. Tolerates fairly acid soils and is less frost tender than other silver firs. Stands exposure well. Can be used for underplanting and is as resistant to *Fomes Annosus* as Grand fir.	Avoid poor soils and dry sites.	Similar to spruce.	Has proved a useful shelterbelt tree under west coast conditions, particularly in Scotland. A high volume producer. 10—22 (15)
Omorika spruce, *Picea omorika* (Pancic) Purkyne Yugoslavia	Similar to Norway spruce, but tolerates poorer soils and is frost hardy.	Similar to Norway spruce, but is more frost hardy.	Similar to Norway spruce.	Useful in frost hollows where other spruces fail. 10—20

TABLE 5 *(continued)*

NOTES ON INDIVIDUAL SPECIES: OTHER CONIFERS

Species and Native Country	Conditions Justifying Selection	Unsuitable Conditions	Notes on Timber	General Remarks and Yield (m^3/hectare/annum)*
Western red cedar, *Thuja plicata* D. Don Western North America	Moderately fertile soils, even if rather shallow, and fairly heavy clays. Stands shade well; succeeds on chalk. More competitive with other shade bearers on heavy lowland soils.	Avoid poor or very acid soils and exposed sites.	A lightweight timber with heartwood of good natural durability, and so suitable for exterior work. Its uses include roofing shingles, ladder poles, weather boarding, greenhouse construction and seed boxes.	Liable to attack by the Keithia disease, caused by the fungus *Didymascella thujina*, in nursery seedbeds (See Leaflet 43). Foliage is valued by florists. 12—24 (13)
Mountain pine, *Pinus mugo* Turra. Mountains of Central Europe	Will grow on the poorest sites and will stand great exposure. Not a timber tree but can be valuable as a margin to very exposed shelterbelts.	Not worth planting on other than the very worst sites.	Not a timber tree.	No timber yield. Two distinct types — erect and prostrate. Tendency to needle diseases after 20–30 years.
Maritime pine, *Pinus pinaster* Ait. Mediterranean	Thrives on sandy soils, especially in the south and west of England.	Not recommended elsewhere.	Resembles Scots pine. Much is imported as pitwood and some for box making.	Windfirm, and a useful shelterbelt tree in exposed places in the south-west. Some forms often poor.
Radiata pine, *Pinus radiata* D. Don California	Grows well on a wide range of soils especially sandy types, but including loams and clay loams. Mainly suitable for the south and west coasts at low elevations.	Avoid very wet soils and shallow calcareous soils over chalk. 'Yellows' condition can reduce the stocking of all the stands. Avoid frosty sites.	Resembles Scots pine, but is usually coarsegrained owing to rapid growth.	Windfirm, and useful for shelterbelts. Grows very quickly where conditions suit it. Good seed producer, but collect only from trees holding three years' needles. 6—22
Bishop pine, *Pinus muricata* (Blue form D. Don) California (coast)	As Radiata pine but somewhat hardier inland, perhaps up to 300 metres. More tolerant of poor soils.	Avoid calcareous soils. Not liable to 'Yellows'. Essential to use 'blue' form and **not** 'green'.	Timber is not well known in UK, but New Zealand experience suggests that it is similar to *P. radiata*.	Very high yields possible. Good and early seed producer, retaining cones on trees. 6—24

TABLE 6

NOTES ON INDIVIDUAL SPECIES: BROADLEAVES OF LIMITED FOREST VALUE

Species and Native Country	Conditions Justifying Selection	Unsuitable Conditions	Notes on Timber	General Remarks and Yield (m³/hectare/annum)*
Birches: Silver birch, *Betula pendula* Roth. White birch, *Betula pubescens* Ehrh. British Isles and Europe	Not worth planting for their sakes but often useful as nurses for frost-tender conifers or for beech or oak. Prefer light soils in the drier parts of the country, but these species are ubiquitous as natural growth on felled woodlands.	Should not be planted on any site where they are not clearly wanted for silvicultural reasons or for beauty.	Mainly used in turnery work, e.g. for bobbins, toys, tool handles and brush backs. Have good strength properties and could find a wider range of uses if grown to saw log size. Pulpwood.	Natural growth is often worth keeping as shelter for a new crop. Must be cut out before it damages the crowns or leaders of more valuable trees. Makes useful fire-brooms. 2—10 (4)
English elm, *Ulmus procera* Salis. England (introduced)	Fertile, deep, moist, light loams. Frost hardy. Resists sea winds.	All infertile soils.	Field elm is our most valuable hedgerow timber. Uses include coffin boards, furniture, weatherboarding, box ends, packing case manufacture, dock piles and fenders. Pulpwood and turnery.	Field elm is usually grown only as a hedgerow tree. Dutch elm disease now makes it unsafe to plant this species.
Wych elm, *Ulmus glabra Huds.* Britain and Europe	As for English elm. Stands town smoke well.	As for English elm.	As for English elm. Also in boat building.	Wych elm thrives under forest conditions, particularly in northern and western valleys. Also susceptible to Dutch elm disease.
Grey poplar, *Populus canescens* (Ait.) Sm. Britain and Europe	Grey poplar merits retention in woodlands	—	As for Black hybrid poplars. See Table 4.	Very vigorous, suckers widely.
Aspen, *Populus tremula* L. British Isles and Europe	Seldom a good tree in the British Isles.	—	As for Black hybrid poplars. See Table 4.	—
Alders: *Alnus glutinosa* L. Gaetn. Europa *Alnus cordata* Desf. Italy *Alnus incana*	Very hardy and accommodating species, but prefers wet soils to dry ones. Can stand flooding. Loam over chalk. Used on industrial waste sites.	Not suitable for very acid peats, badly aerated soils, or dry acid sands.	Used for hat-blocks, clog soles, and general turnery, also as pulpwood. Some timber is used as a substitute for softwood.	Will grow in conditions of wetness of soil which no tree, other than willow, will tolerate. Very rapid growth. 4—12

TABLE 6 *(continued)*

NOTES ON INDIVIDUAL SPECIES: BROADLEAVES OF LIMITED FOREST VALUE

Species and Native Country	Conditions Justifying Selection	Unsuitable Conditions	Notes on Timber	General Remarks and Yield $(m^3/hectare/annum)$*
Limes: *Tilia cordata* Mill. *Tilia platyphyllos* Scop. *Tilia vulgaris* Hayne. Britain and Europe	Fertile soils. Useful as a hedgerow tree to replace elm.	All infertile soils.	Good for turnery, and is a favourite timber for wood-carving and as pulpwood.	Of limited value. Windfirm. Viable seed is produced only rarely. ·
Norway maple *Acer planatoides* Europe	Fertile soils. Useful as a hedgerow tree to replace elm.	All infertile soils.	A hard strong smooth-textured wood used for furniture and carving.	Amenity tree.
Cricket bat willow *Salix alba* var. *coerulea* Sm. England	Margins of flowing streams or water courses with alluvial soil or similar highly fertile land.	No good anywhere else.	Used for cricket bats, artificial limbs, chip baskets. Pulpwood.	Growing Cricket bat willows is a highly specialised business. For details see Bulletin 17, *Cultivation of the Cricket bat willow.*
Gean, or **Wild Cherry** *Prunus avium* L. Britain and Europe	Fertile woodland soils, particularly over the chalk.	All infertile soils.	A valuable turnery and furniture wood.	One of the few trees to produce good timber and showy blossoms.
Red oak *Quercus borealis* Michx. Eastern North America	Fertile sandy soils.	Very infertile soils.	A general-purpose hard wood with good strength properties.	Valued as an amenity tree because of its autumn colour. Grows rapidly. Nursery treatment resembles common oak. Takes wood preservative well. 4—10
Horse chestnut *Aesculus hippo-castanum* L. Greece and Albania	Fertile soils.	All infertile soils.	A soft white timber of fine texture used to a limited extent in turnery work and in making moulders' patterns and fruit trays, and as pulpwood.	Valued for amenity because of its showy white flowers.

TABLE 6 *(continued)*

NOTES ON INDIVIDUAL SPECIES: BROADLEAVES OF LIMITED FOREST VALUE

Species and Native Country	Conditions Justifying Selection	Unsuitable Conditions	Notes on Timber	General Remarks and Yield (m³/hectare/annum)*
Nothofagus spp: *N. procera,* (Poepp. and Endl.) Oerst L. *N. obliqua* (Mirb.) Blume Chile	These species are not too exacting regarding soil and have given good growth on quite a wide range from deep sands to heavy clays. *N. obliqua* performs better than most broadleaf species on poor soils. Below 30 inches of rainfall *N. obliqua* appears to be more suitable, but both species grow well in up to 60 inches of rain.	Impeded drainage, frost and exposure to particularly cold winds. There is some evidence of weakening attacks of *Armillaria mellea.*	*N. procera* is probably the better and comparable with beech. Little home-grown *Nothofagus* has been available for testing.	These species may be very suitable for growing coppice for pulping. 10—18

PREPARATION OF SITE—BARE LAND

Much of the land available for afforestation is remote, roadless, suffers from adverse climatic conditions and is almost without exception infertile. It includes wet peats, dry heaths and hard stony ground, all of which provide difficult rooting for the young trees. This is frequently accompanied by competition from the natural vegetation that is encountered. The forester must endeavour to improve such sites to enable his tree crop to become established. He must plan the preparation of the site with care, his aim being an optimum balance between drainage, soil aeration and cultivation, together with the suppression of the vegetation already present.

Operations which improve the site can be time-consuming and expensive, and are therefore best carried out by machinery whenever possible. The use of ploughs can be particularly quick and cheap. However, where terrain is difficult, or areas small and remote, hand methods may be the only ones available to achieve the necessary cultivation. Broadly these are three:

Site Preparation by Hand

SCREEFING

A 12 to 18-inch square is cleared of vegetation with a spade or mattock in order to expose the soil. Planting is made easier and some relief afforded to the plant from competition of the existing vegetation for nutrients, moisture and physical growth below and above the ground. The mattock is a stronger tool, used where the ground is stonier and the vegetation tougher, e.g. heather. Further cultivation is obtained during the actual planting.

INVERTED TURVES

Where vegetation and turf are particularly thick and screefing may result in pits which will hold water, a square turf with 12–18 inch sides 6 inches deep is cut. This is lifted out, inverted and placed back in the hole. In addition to relief from the physical competition, newly planted trees may derive some benefit from the buried vegetation as this rots.

RAISED TURVES

On some sites, particularly on wet ground, it may be desirable to provide a raised or perched planting position. Here, procedure is the same as with the inverted turf except that the cut square is turned over and placed alongside the hole and not in it. A variation is to make a 'hinged' turf, by cutting only three sides of the square and folding the turf back with the uncut side of the vegetation providing a link. Hinged turves are of special use on steep slopes where there is some danger of their sliding and washing down the slope.

In all of the methods described involving turves and associated holes, thought must be given to the position of the turf. On slopes, the shelter that it may provide and the way in which it may affect local drainage are both important. On water-logged sites the production of raised turves can be combined with draining. An 'ace' or 'rutter' is used to cut peat from the drain. This is sectioned and a 'drag' or 'hack' used to pull the cut turves to the required planting positions. (See Plate 3).

Ploughing

Each site has its own soils, vegetation, topography and climate, and these should determine which of the various ploughs available is best suited to its cultivation.

Soils can be broadly divided into four groups; freely draining soils; soils with pans or compacted layers; soils composed of poorly draining materials and soils which are skeletal or on too steep slopes and make ploughing extremely difficult. Soils in the last group should not be ploughed.

Ploughing provides a planting position and maximum weed suppression by producing a continuous turf placed upside down beside the furrow. A certain amount of soil disturbance will also increase nutrition, even if only temporarily.

Soils with pans or compacted layers are made freely draining to a greater depth by subsoiling with a 'tine'. Poorly draining soils, made up of impermeable material such as amorphous peat or clay, cannot be improved by the general disturbance of ploughing because of a high water table. Drainage is difficult and, here, ploughing is to provide a raised planting position and to rapidly remove water from those shallow but freely draining layers of the soil above the impermeable material.

Forest ploughs consist of a mouldboard assembly attached to a beam, which may be either part of a carriage trailed behind the tractor or mounted directly on the tractor. There are two forms of mouldboard assembly: those used for digging and disturbing soil and those used for producing clean draining furrows.

For freely draining soils a double or single mouldboard tine plough should be used to give a furrow depth of between 20–45 cms. For soils with pans or compacted layers ploughing with a single mouldboard tine plough is recommended to give a furrow depth of 45–60 cms and tine channel 60–90 cm deep. On poorly draining soils with impermeable materials, a double mouldboard plough producing a clean furrow 60 cms deep is recommended.

Nutrition

Marginal bare land sites are often lacking in three basic elements, nitrogen, potassium and phosphorus. The last named is the most essential for tree species in that it promotes root growth, and whilst most species, especially conifers, do not demand a high nutrient content in the soil, competition on infertile sites from existing natural vegetation is often very fierce and particularly detrimental to the growth of tree species not yet acclimatised to the conditions. Frequently young trees will establish themselves, and whilst not dying, will stop growing and go into 'check'. To avoid this, and to remedy it if it occurs, it is advisable to supply the appropriate phosphate fertiliser by hand, tractor or air according to the extent and remoteness of the site. Details of fertiliser applications are given later in this chapter under 'Planting'.

An alternative form of nutrition may be obtained by killing other vegetation with chemicals. Thus the use of 2,4–D has proved to be highly effective in reducing the competition for the limited nutrients available, as well as removing the physical competition at the time of planting and weeding.

PREPARATION OF SITE—WOODLAND

This section deals with replanting of sites upon which trees have grown in the recent past or are re-establishing themselves as coppice or natural regeneration. These sites retain to a greater or lesser extent what is, in fact, a woodland ecosystem. This is further reinforced if the area to be replanted adjoins other woodland. Some of the ground vegetation and fungi are of woodland origin and form part of the weed species in the new planting. Many insects on the area may be woodland orientated and the new planting will be attractive to insects from adjoining woodland. Some disturbance of the fauna is inevitable, and these will move to adjoining areas with resultant pressure on the populations there, leading, not unexpectedly, to the reinvasion of the site when woodland conditions are restored. The existing drainage system may well be insufficient for a new crop and will have to be returned to the condition needed for the establishment of young trees.

Protection

Attention must be given to the protection, by fencing or other controls, of the area being planted. What may appear to have been a quite innocuous fauna before replanting may prove to be insupportable afterwards unless special protective measures are taken. If possible, notes should be made of the tree species growing in the previous crop, their quality, and the pests, insect, fungal and animal, that affected their growth. These points should be among those borne in mind when selecting species for replanting. Examination of the site and the stumps of any trees felled thereon will indicate the extent to which there may be danger from pests, particularly fungi. Adjoining woodlands, especially if these are mainly coniferous, mean the almost certain presence of weevils which can have a devastating effect on any replanting unless precautions are taken at the time of planting.

Expenditure

The problems and expenses of reafforestation depend almost entirely upon the condition of the ground. This may be completely clear, in which case these problems relate to the characteristics of the site such as soil fertility, exposure and the previous vegetation growing upon it. Attention is then only required for fencing, draining and necessary tidying up.

The efficiency of the earlier felling operations will largely dictate expenditure here. If lop and top has been thoroughly disposed of and necessary ditch repairs reduced to a minimum, then the work involved in the preparation of the new planting site and its subsequent weeding is minimised. A large amount of lop and top left on the ground results in the regrowth of weeds, which are not only difficult to control but provide a safe harbour for pests. On the other hand the area may already carry scrub or a coppice crop. This is more likely on old broadleaf than on old coniferous sites. The latter tend to have more acid soils, and are less productive of weeds than broadleaf sites, and such scrub growth as occurs generally involves fewer and less vigorous species. Normally the presence of a scrub type of crop means more expensive replanting.

Methods

If possible, it is important that reafforestation should follow closely on clear felling. This ensures a rapid return to woodland conditions and prevents a heavy invasion of weeds. Decisions have to be taken about the species to be planted but, if the area being dealt with is already carrying broadleaved regrowth, there are many ways in which it can be treated, viz:

(a)   it can be completely cleared and replanted,
(b)   Some of the existing crop may be good enough to grow on and the remainder cleared,
(c)   the existing tree cover may be thinned and underplanted,
(d)   combinations of (a) to (c) may be appropriate.

(a) Complete Clearance has simplicity and ease of supervision as its main advantages. The work is easily done by contractors, who may be prepared to carry out what would be an expensive clearing operation relatively cheaply if they can profit by the sale of small-sized material, box wood, mining timber etc., obtained from the site. Alternatively a herbicide can be employed to give a complete kill of all the scrub. This is quick and relatively cheap provided that planting can proceed easily, but care must be taken that conflict does not arise with amenity/conservation interests. Disadvantages are that complete clearance is very labour-consuming for an estate, the area is open to every sort of exposure (frost, sun, wind), and weed growth thrives. Here too there may be disadvantages to amenity and conservation/sporting interests.

(b) Partial Clearance may be considered when a crop of acceptable quality can be obtained from natural regeneration and selected coppice shoots in parts of the existing crop. Possible advantages are smaller cleaning costs, not too much supervision, the retention of woodland conditions and some advantages to amenity,

conservation and sporting. Groups of 1/20th hectare or over can usefully form part of the crop. Where coppice stems are acceptable these must be straight and vigorous. Only one or two shoots should be left on each stool. Large individual trees are not usually acceptable because they occupy a great deal of room and are expensive and difficult to handle in due course. Disadvantages include the fact that no change of species or improvement of productivity can be effected on that part of the area where the existing crop is accepted.

(c) Thinning and Underplanting is attractive to the forester. Less labour and only normal supervision are required during preparation once a start has been made. Other advantages include the relative shelter from frost and insolation, together with reduced weed growth. A smaller number of plants is normally required to complete the planting, and the maintenance of a woodland habitat is assured. In this method the height of the overhead cover, the density of its crowns and the species to be used in underplanting must all be considered. Only shade-bearing species can be used. Small trial areas of about 1/20th hectare can be thinned to different standards for consideration and, if need be, for further expert advice. Workers soon appreciate the stem spacing that is required, and should be instructed regarding the type of tree to be removed. Generally speaking, larger and more heavily crowned trees should not be left in the overhead cover but rather those with lighter and higher crowns. This can help to avoid damage at a later stage when the shelter crop is removed.

It is in the treatment during the few years after planting that mistakes often occur. Many growers fear the damage that they think may be caused to the young trees when the over-storey is felled into it. This possibility is naturally greater when the over-storey is heavily crowned, and should be avoided by care in the thinning out stages. Skilled workers and contractors can reduce damage by care in their felling and stacking and, if extraction is intended, by using a small number of clearly defined extraction routes.

(d) Alternative Methods. Many of these problems can be avoided by the use of herbicides, of which more will be said later. The arguments in support of herbicides include the labour saving achieved, and the value of the gradual diminution of shade obtained. A good deal depends upon whether the overhead cover has any commercial value as a timber crop. Many variations of (a) to (c) above have been tried in the past, and variously sized strips and groups have been cleared and planted, particularly in dense scrub. The main object has been to achieve a planting programme with limited labour. Fast-growing species have been tried in the groups or strips with the object of defeating the adjoining scrub, but these methods have generally required   close   supervision   for   both   their

implementation and subsequent management, and the planting is continually at risk of being overgrown by the adjoining scrub. Moreover, much of the area is unproductive until it can be treated in turn. However, there may be other advantages relating to visual amenity, sporting or conservation.

Natural Regeneration

This may be considered where it may be desirable and there are good chances of success. Regeneration can only be of as good a quality as the parent trees, and satisfactory results cannot be expected if the latter are of a poor genetic strain. If natural regeneration appears appropriate then great care should be taken to leave only trees with better genetic qualities to supply the seed.

Few species growing under our climatic conditions produce copious seed annually or biennially. Those which do include Scots pine, oak and sycamore. Beech is not such a species and many years (five to ten) may separate good masts. Whilst awaiting a good mast the grower must expect heavy weed growth, which can give much competition for the seedlings when these do arise. There is continuous pressure from squirrels, rabbits, pigeons and other fauna that feed on the seed and seedlings, and awaiting natural regeneration is generally lost time as far as woodland economics are concerned.

Herbicides

Something should be said about the use of herbicides, which can greatly reduce costs and labour requirement. Herbicides must be used in conjunction with, rather than instead of, manual and mechanical means as a method of dealing with unwanted weed species. It must be emphasised that great care should be taken in choice of chemicals and the methods employed. On woody weeds they may be applied to stumps to prevent coppice regrowth, to the bark of standing trees or as foliar sprays. Herbicides may or may not be selective between planted trees and the surrounding shelter scrub. Selectivity may, in fact, depend on the time of year at which the control is carried out, i.e. whether or not the planted trees are dormant. Some herbicides are selective between particular 'weed' species. This knowledge can be used when the thinning out of scrub consisting of more than one 'weed' species is required.

Before taking a decision on the chemical to be used, a careful study must be made of up-to-date literature and of makers' instructions. New developments are constantly taking place in this field. Detailed advice on herbicides in current use is given in the section on Weeding and Cleaning.

DRAINING

Tree roots require oxygen and moisture in order to survive. The lack of either produces a worsening state of health, leading, in anaerobic and waterlogged conditions, to death. Water loving species such as poplars and willows cannot exist in stagnant conditions. In intermediate stages where good air/moisture conditions are only available in part of the soil, poorer and shallower root growth and windblow result.

The condition of the soil may be improved by drainage, but all drainage operations must be planned with the knowledge that any system that is introduced will be present for the whole of the rotation. Thought must therefore be given to planning a system that will fit in first with any cultivation carried out during establishment, fence lines etc., and then, at a later stage, with intended road lines and extraction routes. Mechanical maintenance is desirable. Trees should be planted far enough away from drains to allow for mechanical maintenance, and it must be remembered that tree roots tend to go towards drains and may be damaged during the mechanical maintenance of the latter. This may lead to windblow.

Because of the long-term nature of this operation, it is important to know the local geology, topography and catchment area for all the water coming onto the site. It is also advisable to know the probable destination of water that is drained from the site, particularly when the afforestation of a large wet area is involved. Unexpected run-off can prove an embarrassment to adjoining owners. Soil maps (geological drift maps), nearby quarries and ditches should be studied, and it is well worth while to sink a few soil pits about a metre in depth on the area. The latter, in conjunction with an inspection of local drain sides, will sometimes reveal abrupt changes of soil from light sand to heavy clay or vice versa.

Drainage is expensive whether done mechanically or by hand. Hence the importance of not over-draining. Some drainage is necessary in all parts of the British Isles at those times when evaporation/transpiration is exceeded by rainfall, or when there is heavy flooding. A great deal depends upon the geological background of the soil and hence its permeability. Even in the driest parts of the country some waterlogging of clays and similar impermeable soils takes place during the course of the year.

Drainage Systems

When dealing with drainage on an area to be (re) planted any existing drainage must first be considered because it is to this that the new system is being added. Into this natural drainage is fed the output of the 'cut-off' drains that intercept water normally running onto the area from outside and the 'collecting' drains that deal with excessive rainfall. Very local drainage for the planted trees is provided where necessary by ploughed or hand-cut turves. (See Plate 3). There are three general types of drainage provided for a tree crop: the local individual tree drainage, the drainage of excessive rainfall on the planting area, and the interception of run-off from adjoining land. All three must be correlated. Drains, particularly those carrying a large quantity of water, should not have long straight runs, deep gradients or sharp bends. These all lead to erosion, bank collapse and flooding. Drains that pass under roads should be well piped to ensure that all the water can be carried at flood times. A drainage system that has recently been introduced will tend to have more than expected run-off, particularly on peaty sites.

As a general rule, all main drains should be aligned so that they are slightly off the contour. Drains on steeper ground should lie nearer to the contour than those that are put on gentler slopes. The outfall of main drains into natural stream lines is thus maintained at a reasonably gentle level.

Before discussing the density of drainage on different soil types in Britain it is probably worth mentioning Scandinavian, Dutch and other European practices. Frequently their drains are wider spaced than ours, but this is partly because of the need for control of the summer water-table for horticultural purposes. Also, in winter, the ground is frozen and winter waterlogging is avoided. The density of drainage depends on the particular soil type. More will be required on naturally impermeable soils according to the proportion of organic material and mineral soil. Broadly, there are six main types, which are given in Figure 1.

Problems

Drainage problems arise on a site from two main sources. These are the soil particle size which determines the permeability of the soil, and the rainfall on the site plus any run-off onto the area from adjoining land. Under natural circumstances either or both of these can result in the formation of a peat layer, a process that may have been going on for many years. The peat can in itself achieve such a depth that it becomes the only medium in which trees planted on the area can be said to be growing. Other complications may be caused by the development of a podzol in which, as a result of leaching, an impermeable mineral layer or pan may have been formed by the deposition of leached materials.

When a pan is the main cause of the drainage problem (a. and b. of Figure 1) and the soil is more or less impermeable, then the use of a tine plough to break the pan and obtain some vertical movement of moisture gives immediate improvement. All that is then required is such surface drains as are necessary to remove any surplus of surface water. In higher rainfall areas with finer textured parent material, there is a development of peaty gleys. Where the parent material can be leached, a podzol may develop (see c. and d. in Figure 1). The deeper the peat becomes in the soils, the less important the parent material is to eventual tree growth. A pure peat soil may be defined as one in which the peat above

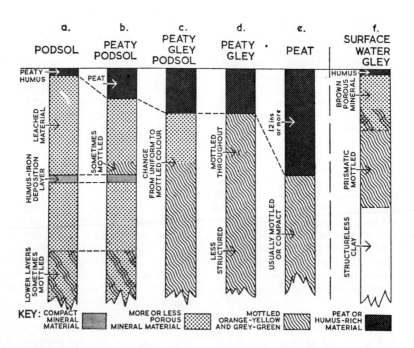

Figure 1 Drainage soil types.

the parent material is 30 cm or more in depth. Any importance that the parent material plays in eventual tree growth depends largely upon its permeability and base status. If it is fine textured it can probably only be drained with difficulty and will not be used by roots. All of the foregoing are, of course, sites upon which afforestation is intended. Similar sites where afforestation has been carried out are numerous, and an examination of these will show the extent to which the drainage applied has been successful. Because of variations in soils, rainfall and run-off from adjacent land, no two sites are exactly the same and the best specification for a drainage scheme in terms of numbers of drains, depth and alignment can probably be made by inspection of local sites that have already been treated.

It is important to realise that the provision of drains, even in quantity, in no way guarantees that the land drained will be dried up quickly. This is especially so in peats and clays, where the moisture retained by the soil particles does not move horizontally through the soil at all. An approach to drier conditions is only achieved when the transpiration/evaporation from the site exceeds the direct rainfall.

Maintenance

Drains maintenance is an on-going aspect of forest work. This can represent an important part of the annual labour requirement and, in the case of large afforested areas, it may be advisable to have a drains plan in order to ensure that no areas are missed out. As the tree crop grows, local drainage will be dealt with by the trees and evaporation as described in the previous paragraph, and only the main drains will require regular maintenance. Time will also indicate those areas of excessive wetness from springs and other sources where the drainage has been too light.

Apart from silvicultural requirements, drains maintenance should be aimed at ensuring that water is cleared quickly from the site and that there is no damage to roads, banks, bridges or fences because of flooding or blockages. Drainage maintenance programmes should take into account all thinning, felling and brashing programmes, because it is at these times that drains become blocked either from debris or because of the activities of timber fellers and their equipment. Drainage systems should be examined carefully before felling programmes take place, to assess them and decide whether they have proved adequate. If a felled-over site is to be left for any time after felling, the drains should be left clear and free running. This can be written into a felling contract if it is thought necessary.

FENCING

In forestry the cost per hectare of fencing, even to a simple specification, amounts to a large part of the early capital cost on a rotation. Within an estate where the owner has reasonable control of operations on both sides of the fence, the cost must be balanced very carefully against the losses that are to be expected if the fencing is not carried out. However, where the fence concerned lies between different ownerships then some fencing may be a legal requirement, and one cannot expect to control a neighbour's treatment of his property and livestock. Other matters may arise concerning rabbit control, public and private rights of way, prevention of public danger and sporting including hounds. Each of these may have its own legal connotations.

Assuming some freedom of choice, the forester must first be certain of the probable cause of damage and the likely cost involved by not fencing. He must also consider the cost and effectiveness of alternative measures such as additional control by stalkers and trappers, or the use of an alternative species which will be less attractive to, or damaged by, the animals concerned. When the decision is taken to erect the fence, thought must be given to the shape of the area being enclosed, the line that the fence will follow, its specification and intended life.

Area

Basically the larger the area enclosed and the more its shape approximates to a square, the cheaper the cost per hectare becomes. Costs are further reduced by using fewer intermediate posts. The shape of the area is something which should be considered before felling plans are prepared.

Fence Line

The actual line the fence will follow must depend to some extent on the fence specification, but other factors should be borne in mind. The pressures to which a fence may be subjected may result from man and his vehicles (tractors), or from animals both domestic and wild. Sometimes the movement of a fence by a few feet will relieve this pressure, i.e. where tractors are turning or stock is regularly driven. Where fairly local movement of deer is involved, a slight curve in the fenceline may suffice to change their intended line of movement. But in the case of a periodic migration, as from lowland to mountain pasture, the provision of an unfenced way is probably imperative if reasonable conservation of deer stock is intended and extreme damage to the plantation is to be avoided. It may be both difficult and expensive to control the movement of the general public between two points, but much can be done to obtain their acceptance of a particular route by judicious fencing.

The fenceline should avoid rough stony ground which offers easy access to rabbits (e.g. the line of an old dry stone wall); adjacent banks or walls which provide easy 'jump-ins' for small mammals; and, if possible, situations where the fence will be easily buried under

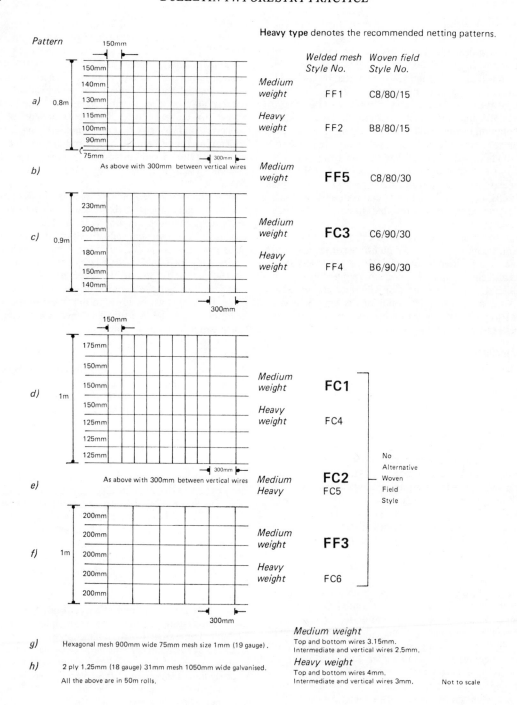

Figure 2　Fence netting specifications.

DEER FENCE

	Roe.	Fallow, Sika & Red.
Woodwork		
Top diameter sizes	10 − 13 cm	12 − 18 cm End posts
Lengths − see text	8 − 10 cm	10 − 13 cm Struts
	5 − 8 cm	8 − 10 cm Stakes

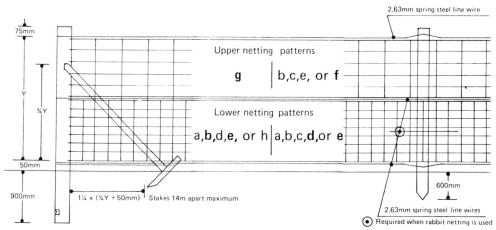

Distance Y is the sum of the widths of the two nets and will range from 1.6m to 2m.

STOCK AND RABBIT FENCE

	Stock	Rabbit
Woodwork	10 − 13cm	10 − 13cm End posts
Top diameter sizes	8 − 10cm	8 − 10cm Struts
Lengths − see text	8 − 10cm	5 − 8cm Stakes

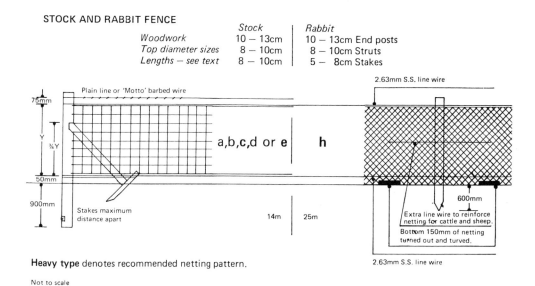

Heavy type denotes recommended netting pattern.

Not to scale

Fencing specifications and construction.

Figure 3 (top).   Deer fence.

Figure 4 (bottom).   Stock and rabbit fences.

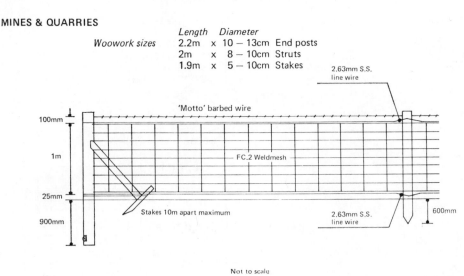

Figure 5   Specification of fence suitable for use under the Mines and Quarries Act.

snow. Both wild and domestic animals will walk over snow-covered fences to be trapped in plantations when the thaw comes.

Specification

Every effort should be made to ensure a high standard of work. Gates must be easy to open and shut, fence wire and netting taut with no loose ends to snag body or clothing. This attention attracts a greater sense of responsibility from the visitor when he realises the woodland is being looked after.

The use of spring steel wire and welded mesh netting for forest fence construction has resulted in very reduced costs compared with older methods. Details of the construction of the various types of fences can be obtained from Forest Record 80. The specification charts (figures 2 to 4) provide a guide to the various net combinations that can be used and show the recommended netting patterns that will give an effective barrier at the lowest cost (based on prices current at December 1977). The top diameter sizes of posts, stakes and struts are also given in the diagram. Their lengths will depend on the widths of the netting to be used and can be calculated from the figures as follows:

(a)   Posts and stakes. The combined width of the two nets (y metres) plus the depth in the ground (0·9 m for end posts and 0·6 m for stakes), plus 125 mm (75 mm above the top of the net and 50 mm between the bottom of the net and the ground).

(b)   Struts. The length of the strut must be at least 1·6 times the distance, at the end post, that the strut is from the ground, i.e. $1·6 \times (\frac{3}{4}y + 0·05$ m).

A specification for security fencing around quarries and disused mines to meet the requirements of Section 151 of the Mines and Quarries Act 1954 is shown (Figure 5). The specification should have the approval of the regional senior inspector of HM Inspectorate of Mines and Quarries for enclosing such hazards on forest areas where public access is encouraged. The spring steel wire is manufactured by Rylands Whitecross Ltd and is specified as 2·63 mm diameter, 1550 N/mm^2 (100 tons/sq in) tensile strength and galvanised to BS 443. This wire once strained remains taut, fewer straining posts and stakes are required with resultant savings in labour and material (see Plate 5). Spring steel is rather different to handle than the mild steel that was used in older fences. Because of this, some investment must be made in special tools to work with it. These include strainers, a wire bending tool and wire cutters. Details are given in Forest Record 80. Their cost is very small when compared with the savings effected in other ways.

Intended Life

The forester should ensure that the fence is designed so that its various components will last for approximately the same time. There is little point in erecting a fence with untreated stakes and posts that will only last for four to five years, and using wire and netting on the same fence that will last many times as long. Equally, if there is some factor such as smoke pollution that causes deterioration of metal work, then some action should be taken to obtain thicker material galvanised to British Standard 443.

Entrances

When barbed wire is used for any purpose the top of the fence should not be completely impassable. Entrance can be provided at points at the forester's discretion by placing a light smooth pole, easy to get over, along the top of the fence between two posts. On rights of way which are not bridle paths, stiles may be preferred because they cannot be left open. Stiles are invaluable for shooting-parties, and are the better for having a good hand-hold. Thought should be given to the passage of invalid chairs and disabled people along rights of way.

When woodland is being fenced in hunting country, close liaison between the hunt and the forester will do much to ensure that the gates provided into the plantation are adequate and in selected places. It is much quicker to check that gates have been closed after a day's hunting than to carry out a complete fence inspection and necessary repairs after the field has gone.

PLANTING

The success of planting depends upon good planning and preparation before the planting is carried out. Success also depends upon the selection of the species and plants that are used, together with efficient arrangements for their collection and eventual storage, handling and planting.

Site

In his selection of tree species the forester will have to consider the site characterisitics. As far as possible his choice will have taken account of problems arising from rainfall, soil variations and geographical position. He will know the location of the supplying nursery relative to the planting site. This is not important in the long term but it can be an important factor during the planting season. For example, it is possible to have young trees flushing in nurseries in the south of the country when the planting site is in the north and the area concerned is still under snow or likely to meet with frosty conditions. However, as this is only a temporary problem it should be met by the forester during the current season, and can often be solved by early ordering and good storage, possibly in a cold store.

Type of Plant

The size of plant that is used depends a lot upon the site. Ground preparation and soil conditions may very well determine what size of plant can be safely and efficiently planted. Large spreading root systems or long tap roots are of little value if the site for planting cannot be adequately prepared for them. Topography and associated exposure are also important. Smaller trees can more easily be given some local shelter during the first year or two of their life. Weed growth has also to be considered and for this, rather larger transplants are desirable. Luckily those sites where weed growth is rampant are usually more fertile and relatively sheltered, and thus can support a larger plant.

Transplants or their equivalent in undercut plants are normally preferred in most species because of their balanced root-shoot development. If it is large enough, the 1 + 1 type of transplant is the most popular because it is less costly. A considerable area is being planted using plants grown in containers (See Plates 6 and 7). Such plants are raised in controlled conditions in polyhouses and it usually takes some 12–16 weeks from sowing to planting out in the forest. This technique involves smaller seedling stock, re-emphasising the importance of good site preparation.

It should be noted that under the Forest Reproductive Material Regulations, cuttings and plants of the listed species, if they are intended for the production of wood, may not be marketed unless they have been derived from sources approved and registered by the Forestry Commission in Great Britain or by the relevant authority in another EEC country or Northern Ireland. If plants or cuttings are to be marketed under the description 'EEC standard', then they must satisfy specified conditions. Persons marketing plants or young plants of the listed species must comply with certain packaging/labelling requirements and must provide the buyer with a Supplier's Certificate, giving certain stipulated information, in respect of any plants sold. An explanatory booklet, *The Marketing of Forest Tree Seed and Plants within the European Economic Community*, is available from the Forestry Commission and gives a fuller outline of the Regulations.

Transport of Plants to Site

Some losses have always occurred in the past, and are still occurring, through inadequate treatment of the plants from the time when they are lifted in the nursery to when they are planted. When plants are transported in polythene bags they must be placed in the bags with their foliage in a relatively dry state and kept cool and shaded to avoid drying out and overheating. Polythene bags can be a danger if plants are exposed to the sun whilst in them, and this can easily happen on a planting site. The forester must ensure that they are kept in a shady spot. The plant roots must be kept as free from the sun and drying wind as possible in the planting process by the careful use of planting bags etc. Where polythene bags are not used, tree roots should be 'heeled in' on the planting site as soon as they arrive.

Time for Planting

Much debate takes place between foresters about the optimum time for planting. There is general acceptance that this is best done when the plants are dormant, although there has been some successful planting 'outside the season' when ground moisture, rainfall and plant storage have been good, and particularly when 'container' stock has been used.

Opinion is divided as to whether planting should be carried out in the autumn and early winter or in late winter and early spring. To a certain extent the decision is forced by the size of the planting programme, the labour force that is available to carry it out, and the number of weeks that are available for planting during the planting season. Those who argue against planting at the end of the year tend to point out that the young plants are left standing in a planting site throughout the winter, when they face all the dangers that may arise as a result of bad weather in one form or another, and damage from birds and animals. Advocates of this method claim that if the planting is carried out soon enough whilst there is still some warmth in the soil, then some root growth takes place and the trees are relatively safe. Those who favour 'spring' planting support their preference by citing the absence of a waiting period between planting and the beginning of growth when the soil warms up. The practical forester must decide on the basis of his programme, his labour force and his local knowledge of the weather and the site being planted.

Techniques

Assuming the availability of good plants, successful planting is achieved by the provision of a hole large enough for the roots, with some cultivation below and around to give the root system a good chance to develop. The plant is held so that the soil replaced round it is kept level with the root collar, and firmed down hard whilst avoiding damage to the plant in the process. Soils all vary in their behaviour both at the time of planting and afterwards. Air spaces, that can readily lead to the death of the tree, are easily left round the roots in clay soils and some fibrous peats. Clay soils are particularly liable to crack open near recently planted stock during periods of drought or extreme frost, when the roots may become exposed to the air. Fibrous peats are as bad or worse than clays in the way in which they do not 'marry' together after cutting. They have the same problems from shrinkage in dry weather and frost lift. The forester must always bear in mind the probable water requirements of the plant and how the site may vary in this respect as a result of ground preparation, draining etc.

Tools

Various spades are used for planting, including the Schlich and Mansfield foresters' spades which have tapered blades set in line with the handle. An ordinary garden spade in which the blade is not at too great an angle to the shaft is probably used more than most for tree planting. Sometimes, in a new spade, the blade is too long and may need to be worn a little before it provides the right depth of cut to suit plant roots and normal planting ground conditions. It may be impractical to use spades on stony ground amongst tough vegetation or on steep gradients. A mattock is used on such sites. The blade of the mattock is used to scrape away the vegetation and make the cut in which the plant root is placed, whilst the pick end provides cultivation for planting. In peat a semi-circular planting spade is often used. This cuts a truncated cone from the turf which is replaced after the tree's root has been comfortably sited in the hole. Care should be taken to ensure that the turf is of such a depth that it is completely penetrated by the spade. This ensures ready access for the roots to a zone between the turf and parent material, and provides some insurance against frost lift or shrinkage by drought.

A special tool (Plate 7) has been developed for use with Paperpot planting stock.

Methods of Planting

Many methods of planting are used and these appear to depend upon the forester's personal experience of different sites. (See Plates 8 and 9.) The simplest is probably slit notching in which a single, vertical cut is made with the forester's spade. The spade is then pushed backwards and forwards to break up the soil at the bottom of the notch, the plant is inserted with the roots as well spread as possible, and the ground pressed back into position with the heel of a boot to clench the soil around the tree root. Planters with garden spades favour a great variety of notches. The latter may be in the shape of a T, L, V, or H. The preferred shape probably arises from local experience. Notch planting of this type is designed to provide a slit which can be easily opened by leverage to enable the plant to be introduced with good root distribution. An effort is made to avoid over-compression of the soil or large air spaces where cuts have been made. Similar principles of good root distribution, hard firming down and the avoidance of air pockets are used with both the semi-circular spade and the planting mattock.

No hard and fast rule can be given about the planting position, which will vary between sites according to method of ground preparation, expected weed competion, moisture regime and exposure. On dry ground, particularly if a pan has been shattered by tine ploughing, planting is generally done in the furrow thereby benefiting from cultivation and maximum moisture. Only rarely in these conditions is the planting position at ground level or on the inverted turf. When this occurs, it is usually on rather moister sites suffering from excessive weed growth. On wet, peaty sites the planting position is normally on the top or the side of the inverted turf. The latter situation arises when the turf is very thick or the need for shelter is acute. The turf is then cut to provide a suitable 'step' position, in which case the tool is chosen that provides most promise of successful growth.

Pit planting is not used a great deal in forestry, and usually only involves small numbers of plants whose roots are too large for normal notch planting. The holes are dug large enough in width and depth to accommodate the roots, the surrounding soil cultivated and the tree roots spread carefully across the pit. The earth is then returned and firmed up in layers until all the loose soil is back in place. It is a method more applicable to the planting of ornamental standards and semi-standards.

Spacing

Apart from the normal differences between species and the variations in growth potential of one species between different sites, there are many other factors such as rotation length, thinning regime if any, and length and type of bole required, which determine the spacing of plants. Improved plant supply, ground preparation and weeding during recent years have had their influence, and planting distances have increased over the last 25 years from 25 to 40 per cent according to both species and site. As a rough guide spacings of about $2\,m \times 2\,m$ are now commonly used. Occasionally, closer spacing may be used for special reasons on exposed and very poor sites or where weed growth is particularly heavy but, as with all forest operations, the forester must be satisfied that this is worth while.

PLANTING OUT

Plants must be regularly spaced out in definite lines. This will ensure that subsequent operations, beating up, weeding etc. can most easily be carried out. To achieve this, some organisation has to be undertaken at the time of planting. On ploughing, the planting lines will naturally follow the lines of the ploughing. Spaces between plants must be regular and the planter must learn how to gauge a set distance between plants. This ability is easily developed but can be helped in the first place by using a spacing stick. Where planting is in the open, a standard method of achieving straight lines is the use of fairly long straight sticks. Using these in pairs as sighting rods at opposite ends of the planting area or a convenient portion of it, the planter is able to maintain a remarkably straight alignment. By continually offsetting one pair of sticks by the distance between two rows the planter is able to proceed up and down the area continuously planting. As far as possible he should try to plant in the same position in the notch that is chosen.

Labour

In the organisation of his planting programme a forester must, above all, understand the quality and experience of his labour force, particularly if it is proposed to carry the work out on a piece work basis. Deficiencies should be met by training in plant handling, techniques and safety. His plans will be affected by the number of areas and site types to be planted. He must also consider how many and which species are being used, what mixtures are to be employed and on what sites. The priorities are important. Thus Corsican pine is particularly liable to suffer from drought about the time of planting. Larches and other frost tender and early flushing species are best planted on north facing exposures when there is a danger from frost at the time of planting. The forester must decide which areas are to be planted first, and to what extent he is able to split his labour force and divide his supervision. When mixtures, particularly group mixtures, are involved he must know the extent to which he can rely upon his labour force to carry out the work, or whether intensive supervision and/or careful marking out of the planting is the only way in which this can be achieved.

The forester should plan primarily to protect the plants being used. Time and expense are not the main criteria although very often both will be saved by good organisation.

Fertilisers

In Great Britain a small number of site types occur that are large in total area and on which the soils are poor, wet, acid and peaty. Such soils are largely deficient in essential elements, particularly phosphorus and, to a lesser extent, potassium. Available nitrogen may also be missing in some cases. Trees may not actually die when planted on such sites, but they can go on living and make very little growth for many years. A crop of this type is said to be 'in check'. Of the area fertilised by the Commission in recent years approximately two-thirds has required phosphorus. Almost one-third has required phosphorus and potassium, and a smaller area amounting to 1 per cent has been treated with a nitrogen fertiliser.

Phosphorus (P) has normally been applied as URP—Unground Rock Phosphate. Potassium (K) is applied as muriate of potash (KCl) the cheapest form. Potassium sulphate (K_2SO_4) can also be used, but it is more expensive. Nitrogen (N) is usually obtained for forestry purposes from urea, but this can lose its value in more moist conditions. Other sources of nitrogen include a mixture of ammonium nitrate NH_4NO_3 with ammonium sulphate $(NH_4)_2SO_4$ or calcium carbonate $CaCO_3$. Other and similar nitrate mixtures may be used but are not readily available.

Fertiliser may be applied by hand, by ground spreader, or from the air. Application over large areas,

D

particularly if these are in rougher country which is already carrying a young crop, is most cheaply accomplished from the air. Spreading from the air demands close cooperation with the aircraft pilot and his crew to determine the location and clearing of suitable landing/loading points, and the marking of the areas to be treated. Forest staff assisting with this work must be thoroughly drilled in all the safety aspects of working because they will be at the loading sites and near to the aircraft. They should appreciate the importance of safe, quick reloading as spreading from the air is highly dependent on favourable weather.

On the rare occasion when URP is applied by hand it should be broadcast around each plant. It has been found that very practical equipment for this purpose consists of two PVC coated hessian fertiliser bags, each of which holds up to 26 kg, which are supported on a 44 mm wide cotton webbing harness. This can be made more comfortable during warm weather by the use of shoulder pads when working without a jacket. It has been found that the measurement of a dose of fertiliser and its spreading is as accurate with the hand as with the hand-operated spreaders that are available. Workers quickly appreciate the weight of the fertiliser per plant, and a sample dose can be kept in a polythene bag for reference purposes. GMP, ground mineral phosphate, can be a dirty and uncomfortable fertiliser to spread by hand but the worker can be given some protection by the provision of goggles, face masks, gloves and, if necessary, over-trousers. Applications are usually made fairly soon after planting, but in some circumstances fertilisers are applied prior to ploughing so as to obtain a double dose in the 'sandwich' layer beneath the overturned turf.

The aerial treatment of many thousands of hectares of poor peaty moorland in northern Britain has been carried out with the application of 375 kg of GMP or URP per hectare (3 cwt per acre). Where potassium has been required the normal application has been 200 kg per hectare ($1\frac{1}{2}$ cwt/acre) of muriate of potash (KC1).

On the rare occasions when applications of nitrogen have been required, it has been applied as prilled urea at the rate of 350 kg/ha.

Beating Up

Beating up is the replacement of trees that have been lost in the early years. Usually losses of less than 25 per cent, provided they are evenly distributed, do not need replacement. There are, however, exceptions, e.g., in a mixture where a final crop species is planted as a small proportion and has suffered heavily and where wide spacing has been used at planting.

It is an expensive operation as planters have to cover a lot of ground looking for missing trees and have to use larger and more costly plants. Weeding then becomes necessary over a longer period. When delayed beating

up is necessary, consideration should be given to the use of another faster growing species to fill the gaps quickly.

WEEDING AND CLEANING

Weeding is the suppression of vegetation growing around young trees, and competing with them for nutrients, moisture and space, and tending to smother them in the autumn when it dies and collapses. It may be done manually, mechanically or by using herbicides. 'Cleaning' is an expression often used by foresters to describe the removal of 'woody weeds' such as Old man's beard, gorse, bramble and young coppice regrowth. Since weeding normally follows closely after the preparation of ground and planting, foresters have to be prepared for sudden and vigorous growth of previously unsuspected weed species. This is particularly so where mechanical cultivation (ploughing or rotovation) and associated draining have been carried out. A short grassy sward can, after ploughing, produce a dense crop of thistles 6 ft high followed in the next year or so by tall vigorous grasses. Sometimes this may result in a decision to change the tree species that has been planted when beating up or further planting in the area is being considered.

The need for, intensity and time of weeding should be given careful thought because these vary according to site, the species and condition of the planted trees, and the weeds involved. Weeds can give protection from sun, drying winds and unseasonal frosts, and weeding may often be limited in extent for these reasons. Manual, mechanical and chemical control of weeds should be used as appropriate. None is exclusive of the others. Thought must be given to the vegetation that will probably replace the weeds that are removed. Grass, for example, may replace broadleaved weeds and be much more difficult to manage.

Manual Weeding

Manual weeding is usually carried out by working along a line of plants. The quality of planting is reflected by the ease with which the young trees are found. Completely straight lines and even spacing mean quicker weeding and fewer losses from cut-off trees ('Sheffield blight'). For safety reasons, workers should never be allowed to work too closely together. The amount of weed cut is limited to that required to free the tree, give reasonable access, and limit damage caused by collapse of the dead weeds at the end of the growing season. Any vegetation that is left aids conservation and may give some small added protection to the young trees. Stiff-stemmed weeds, such as willow herb, do not normally cause damage to the young trees by collapsing on them.

The tool normally used for weeding is an ordinary hand sickle or reaping hook, but the type and length of blade and handle preferred varies greatly over the country. Many foresters also find it is useful to carry a hooked stick to help in locating and protecting the young trees when these are small.

Mechanical Weeding

Machine weeding is cheap and time-saving. Effectiveness is limited to some extent by the ground conditions, topography, and the quality of the pre-planting ground preparation. Some use of hand-weeding or herbicides may be needed in addition in order to control the weed growth close to the trees.

In general, machines can be considered as light and pedestrian-controlled or heavy and tractor powered. Both types are available to deal with grass, herbaceous broadleaves and bracken, or with woody weeds. Light equipment for grass and soft weeds is typified by the auto-scythe, whilst for woody weeds various forms of portable or pedestrian-controlled brush-cutter have been developed. Tractor-powered methods depend upon breaking and bruising the lighter weeds with rollers, rotating bars and chains, or, in the case of woody weeds, cutting with more powerful brush cutters or flails. One mechanical weeding is frequently cheaper than one herbicide weeding, but in the case of herbaceous weeds more than one treatment may be necessary during the season. A fairly complete 'kill' of weeds is eventually achieved by mechanical means, but there is the almost inevitable change in the weed species present on the site.

Herbicides

Herbicides are probably the most commonly employed form of weed control used in woodland in the United Kingdom today, particularly on larger planting areas. The other methods already discussed are used where weeds resistant to herbicides are present in quantity, or there are environmental reasons for not using herbicides. Herbicides are most commonly used as sprays (see Plate 10), but they are available as paints or granules.

Before using herbicides the forester should be satisfied that he knows the weed species that he wishes to control and the herbicide that he intends to employ. He must satisfy himself that there is no environmental reason against using the herbicide in question, and take into account the periods during the year when it is most effective. At the same time he must be aware of the pros and cons for pre- and post-planting treatments. These points can most readily be settled by reference to recent literature on the subject.

TYPES OF WEED

The forester is concerned with five main groups of weeds. Two of these represent a very broad spectrum of species, whilst the remaining three really consist of one species each. The first of the broad groups consists of perennial grasses and grasses mixed with herbaceous broadleaved weeds. The second consists of woody broadleaved weeds and mixtures of woody and herbaceous broadleaved weeds. The remaining three, which are heather, bracken and rhododendron, are considered separately as dominant weeds because of the relatively large areas they occupy; their overall ability to resist herbicides; and, in the case of bracken at least, the specific nature of the herbicide employed.

SPECIAL FOREST USES

Certain tree species and forestry activities require individual consideration. Norway spruce that are to be used as Christmas trees benefit by retaining all their branches and not being deformed by weeds, but may lose needles under some herbicide regimes. Sometimes the weedkilling effect of a herbicide may so encourage growth in Norway spruce that the long internodes produced make them unacceptable as Christmas trees. For poplar, where the maintenance of a fast early growth is vital, paraquat and dalapon are suitable, but chlorothiamid and dichlobenil depress the growth rate.

Another possible use of herbicides lies in the preparation of fire breaks. The vegetation can be killed off and burned during the period of minimum fire danger.

SPRAYING EQUIPMENT

Work on spraying equipment continues to develop. Effort has been directed towards decreasing the total volume of spray applied per hectare, thereby reducing the expense of moving large volumes of spray liquid or water into the forest. At the same time progress has been made to reduce the size of droplets, increase the area wetted by the spray and the ability of the spray to remain on vegetation in spite of rain.

Some idea of the volumes (herbicide plus dilutent) that have to be taken to the site for different types of sprayer is of value. Medium Volume (MV) sprayers, of which the MV Knapsack Sprayer is an example, require from 200 to 700 litres per hectare. Low Volume (LV) sprayers, which may be knapsack or tractor-mounted, are mistblowers and require 90 to 200 litres per hectare. Ultro Low Volume (ULV) sprayers, which are carried by the worker, use from 5 to 15 litres per hectare. The variations in transportation and storage problems are very obvious.

SAFETY

When using herbicides the forester must consider the safety of his workers, particularly if he is using LV or ULV equipment. Paraquat, for example, should never be applied at low volume or ultra low volume. Neighbouring crops must always be considered when there is a risk from spray drift which is increased with low volume and ultra low volume application of herbicides. As far as is known, the herbicides that are commonly employed and used as recommended by the makers will not have any ill effects on mammals, birds, insects or fish. The forester should ensure that he is aware of any interesting and rare species that occur in his woods, and obtain expert advice when he is considering weed control measures of this type. Before finalising his ideas about weed control the forester will be well advised to read Bulletin 48, *Weeding in the forest*, and Booklet 40, *Chemical control of weeds in the forest*. Both have considerable bibliographies attached to them. A valuable summary is given in Leaflet 66— *Guidelines to Forest Weed Control.*

BRASHING AND PRUNING

Brashing is a forest operation normally carried out prior to thinning. It consists of the removal of lower branches of the tree up to a height of about two metres. This may be done for a variety of reasons. For many years it was the practice to carry out complete brashing of plantations with the object of improving the amount of knot-free timber that would eventually become available during thinning and felling operations. However, as it became apparent that the practice was expensive and did not really achieve this aim, it has gradually been excluded or its form amended in normal forest operations. It has been found that for many uses knot-free timber is unnecessary, and fears of a serious reduction in the price paid for standing timber when this is completely unbrashed have often been unfounded. Modern felling and extraction methods have overcome many of the anticipated difficulties, and details of the way in which brashing is still employed are given in Chapter 8. In the past it has generally been considered that only dead branches should be brashed because of the dangers of fungal infection when branches are still green. However, this has not been found to be a serious matter, particularly in conifers. Some brashing is still carried out for reasons other than thinning. Access may be required for inspection purposes, not least before thinning, and it can be of great value for deer control and shooting parties. It is a useful fire protection measure.

Hand brashing of conifers is most frequently carried out with a 0·5 m curved brashing saw with a strapped head. The handle is normally a 0·6 m axe handle. In pine areas, bill hooks, such as the Yorkshire bill hook, or trimming axes are sometimes used instead of saws. In larches, the branches are simply knocked off with a pick handle or a suitable stick cut on site. Mechanical brashing can be carried out using lightweight chainsaws, but should only be done where damage to the trees can be kept to a minimum. It is particularly useful when access is required for line thinning. It then gives a cost advantage over normal hand methods.

Tree species, conifers in particular, vary a great deal in the extent to which they retain their branches. Those from Sitka and other spruces are very persistent and therefore expensive to work. Larches are probably the easiest, and pines mid-way between the two.

Whereas brashing normally refers to an operation carried out on conifers, pruning, which is normally carried out for a greater length along the stem, refers equally or more so to broadleaves. Pruning is directed at the production of knot-free timber, and the operation is planned to be done where rotation length and eventual timber value make this worth-while. It is not normally carried out in one operation, but rather in from two to four prunings according to the length of clear stem it is desired to obtain. Care needs to be exercised about the size of branches pruned, particularly in some broadleaves such as oak, in which it is important to prevent infection of the heartwood by fungi. It is an expensive and somewhat risky job and care should be taken to use the correct ladders and/or tree bicycles. The latter are frequently used in Europe for pruning poplars. Pruning wounds can be given additional protection from fungal infection by the application of an appropriate fungicide/sealant, a number of which are marketed under British Standard BS 3998: 1966, *Recommendations for tree work*. Some include callus inducing hormones.

BIBLIOGRAPHY: ESTABLISHMENT AND MAINTENANCE OF PLANTATIONS

Forestry Commission Publications

BULLETINS

No. 17 *The cultivation of the Cricket bat willow.* 1968.
No. 28 *Sitka spruce in British Columbia. A study in forest relationships.* 1957.
No. 29 *Shelterbelts and microclimate.* 1957.
No. 30 *Exotic forest trees in Great Britain.* 1957.
No. 32 *Afforestation of upland heaths.* 1960.
No. 34 *Chalk downland afforestation.* 1962.
No. 35 *Pruning conifers for the production of quality timbers.* 1963.
No. 36 *Mycorrhizal associations and* Calluna *heathland afforestation.* 1963.
No. 37 *Experiments on nutrition problems in forest nurseries.* 1965. Vol. 1 and 2.
No. 40 *Rooting and stability in Sitka spruce.* 1967.
No. 43 *Nursery practice.* 1972.
No. 45 *Windblow of Scottish forests in January, 1968.* 1971.
No. 48 *Weeding in the forest.* 1974.
No. 49 *The potential of Western hemlock, Western Red Cedar, Grand fir, and Noble fir in Britain.* 1974.
No. 52 *Influence of spacing on crop characteristics and yield.* 1974.
No. 53 *Production and use of tubed seedlings.* 1975.
No. 55 *Aspects of thinning.* 1976.

No. 57 *Safety of the Herbicides 2, 4–D and 2, 4, 5–T.* 1977.

BOOKLETS

No. 40 *Chemical control of weeds in the forest.* 1975.
No. 41 *Fertilisers in the establishment of conifers in Wales and Southern England.* 1974.
No. 44 *Landscape of Forests and Woods.* 1978.

LEAFLETS

No. 20 *Watermark Disease of Cricket Bat Willow.* 1977.
No. 27 *Poplar cultivation.* 1963.
No. 43 *Keithia disease of Western red cedar,* Thuja Plicata. 1974.
No. 57 *Replacement of elm in the countryside.* 1973.
No. 61 *Tubed seedlings.* 1975.
No. 62 *Ultra low volume herbicide spraying.* 1975.
No. 63 *Fertilisers in the forest: A guide to materials.* 1975.
No. 64 *Control of heather by 2, 4–D.* 1976.
No. 66 *Guidelines to forest weed control.* 1976.
No. 67 *Rabbit management in woodlands.* 1976.
No. 68 *Badger gates.* 1976.
No. 70 *Forest Ploughs.* 1978.

FOREST RECORDS

No. 22 *Shelterbelts for Western hill farms.* 1963.
No. 30 *Growth and yield of Sweet chestnut coppice.* 1956.
No. 43 *Establishment methods for poplars.* 1960.
No. 49 *The development of Douglas fir plantations in relation to site conditions.* 1963.
No.50 *Wind-loosening of young trees on upland heaths.* 1963.
No. 51 *The use of flags to estimate the relative exposure of trial plantations.* 1963.
No. 53 *Studies in the mineral nutrient status of heather,* Calluna Vulgaris. 1965.
No. 62 *Plantations on mediaeval rigg and furr cultivation strips.* 1967.
No. 69 *Guide to site types in forests of North and Mid-Wales.* 1977.
No. 71 *Soil groups of upland forests.* 1970.
No. 73 *Ploughing practice in the Forestry Commission.* 1970.
No. 79 *Nothofagus plantations in Great Britain.* 1971.
No. 80 *Forest fencing.* 1972.

No. 88 *Cold storage of forest plants.* 1973.
No. 97 *Forest site yield guide to upland Britain.* 1974.
No. 114 *Terrain Classification.* 1977.

RESEARCH AND DEVELOPMENT PAPERS

No. 26 *Forest drainage.* 1963.
No. 34 *Practice and research in spacing, thinning and pruning.* 1967.
No. 39 *Slash disposal to aid regeneration.* 1967.
No. 51 *Experiments in the rehabilitation of uneconomic broadleaved woodlands.* 1967.
No. 75 *Restocking windthrown forest.* 1968.
No. 76 *Bibliography on international provenance experiments begun in 1938.* 1976.
No. 77 *Treatment of Christmas trees.* 1974.
No. 87 *Production and use of ball-rooted planting stock in Sweden and Finland.* 1972.
No. 91 *Silviculture and good landscapes in British forestry: The improvement of planning and practice.* 1972.
No. 98 *International Norway spruce experiment at the Bin, Huntly Forest, Aberdeenshire: Results up to twenty-five years.* 1973.
No. 99 *Inventory provenance test with Norway spruce in Britain: First results.* 1973.
No. 101 *Flushing time for Norway spruce.* 1973.
No. 105 *Summary report on the IUFRO 1938 Provenance experiments with Norway spruce Picea Abies.* 1974.
No. 108 *Tree growth on the South Wales coalfield.* 1974.
No. 109 *Fertiliser effects on the growth and composition of Sitka and Norway spruce nursery transplants and on the composition of a podzol profile after 15 years cropping.* 1974.
No. 110 *Initial spacing in relation to establishment and early growth of conifer plantations.* 1974.
No. 114 Pinus Contorta *provenance studies.* 1976.

Other Publications

Anderson, M. L. (1950). *The selection of tree species.* Edinburgh: Oliver & Boyd.
Bridgeman, P. H. (1976). *Tree surgery, a complete guide.* Newton Abbott: David & Charles.
British Standards BS 3998: 1966, *Recommendations for tree work.* HMSO.
Brown, G. E. (1977). *The Pruning of Trees, Shrubs and Conifers.* London: Faber.

Chapter 4

DISEASES AND INSECT PESTS

This Chapter deals briefly with the commoner diseases and insect pests which the forester may encounter in Britain. Many of the diseases and insects have been dealt with in detail in other Forestry Commission publications and these are noted in the text.

DISEASES

Diseases in woodland are best controlled by avoidance, and over the years such control has to some extent been achieved, not as a result of knowledge of tree diseases, but simply by the commonsense planting of tree species that have been found to thrive, in preference to those that have not. No tree, however, is immune from all disease, and it is obviously useful to know something about diseases and their control.

The majority of tree diseases can conveniently be divided into two clearly separable groups: diseases caused by non-living agencies, and those caused by parasites. Susceptibility to parastitic disease is, in the main, genetically determined, and the theory that parasites are generally best able to attack trees debilitated by adverse physical factors is erroneous. In some cases, of course, physical factors and parasites may cumulatively cause serious disease.

Much remains to be discovered about tree diseases, and several that cause lasting damage have yet to be explained. Only the more important or conspicuous diseases of known cause are described below. In the selection of these, some regard has been given to the amenity and recreational aspects of trees, as well as to the ultimate economic production of timber.

DISEASES DUE TO NON-LIVING AGENCIES

Frost causes various forms of injury to trees. In winter the foliage of evergreens may be damaged when there are sudden changes from mild to freezing conditions, or when long periods of frost with bright sunshine cause repeated and fairly rapid freezing and thawing. In hard winters, cracks may develop in the stems of trees where freezing and thawing cause unequal expansion of the wood. Early frosts in autumn may damage shoots that have not hardened off, but the most troublesome damage is that caused by late frosts in spring, when the tender developing shoots and sometimes the bark and cambium of young trees in the establishment stage are particularly liable to injury. Early and late frosts occur mainly on clear still nights, when air in contact with surfaces rendered cold by outward radiation is in turn cooled and, being relatively heavy, gradually flows down slopes to collect in valleys and hollows or on shelves on hillsides. Frost injury is liable to occur in such situations. On level ground, small plants are more likely to be damaged where there is a grass mat or some similar cover than where there is bare soil. Heat lost by radiation from the bare soil surface is replaced by heat from the underlying soil, provided it is moist (dry soil lacks thermal conductivity), whereas grass insulates the soil and has no large store of heat to replace that lost from its surfaces by radiation.

On sites where late frosts are likely to be frequent and severe, hardy species such as Scots pine should be planted in preference to frost-tender species such as Sitka spruce. Where suitable woody growth is present, however, underplanting with shade tolerant species, as described in Chapter 3, can be used to get shelter from frost. On level ground, ploughing for planting, with its concomitant reduction of surface vegetation and exposure of bare soil, appreciably reduces the severity of late frosts.

Tree roots require oxygen and are liable to be killed where soil aeration is lacking, as in boggy ground, or where aeration has been drastically reduced. Such reductions occur where soil becomes waterlogged after flooding or blockage of drains; where the surface layers of soil are compacted by machinery or by trampling by man or animals; or where thick layers of heavy soil or impervious covers such as concrete are laid down over the rooting area of trees.

In summer the heat of the sun sometimes scorches seedlings at soil level, causing them to collapse and wither. It can also kill patches of bark on the stems of thin-barked species such as beech if they are suddenly exposed to full light after having been shaded. Drought may cause cracks in the stems of fast-grown conifer dominants, and also wilting and dieback of trees, especially on sand, gravels and very shallow soils over rock.

On limestone and chalk soils, where the high lime content prevents the absorption by roots of certain other minerals, induced nutrient deficiency is liable to cause yellowing, dieback and death of some trees, particularly Scots pine, larches and Douglas fir. Usually symptoms do not appear until trees start to close canopy or even later. An abundance of nitrogenous matter in very calcareous soils appears to intensify lime-induced deficiency, and even beech, normally a lime tolerant species, may be damaged where there are rabbit warrens or where starlings have roosted.

Wind, snow and the weight of ice can cause breakage in trees, leading to the entry of decay-causing fungi. Lightning, as well as shattering individual trees, can also kill groups of trees in woodland. Sometimes, but not always, one or two trees in such groups show spiral scars on their stems.

Industrial and domestic pollution of the atmosphere with smoke and fumes can damage and sometimes kill trees. Where acute injury occurs after severe exposure to fumes in the vicinity of the source of pollution, the cause is fairly obvious, but the extent to which trees are harmed by relatively low concentrations of pollutants well away from sources is problematical. In the latter situation, damage and poor growth caused by other agencies is quite often wrongly attributed to pollution. In general, conifers are more susceptible to pollution injury than broadleaves, and among the latter, sycamore, elm and poplar are particularly tolerant.

Salt from roadside dumps for use on icy roads often kills trees where it is carried to their roots by rainwater, and, in summer, salt-laden gales from the sea sometimes cause conspicuous browning of foliage for several miles inland. Damage to trees by weedkillers mostly occurs where recommended precautions have been ignored.

FUNGAL AND BACTERIAL DISEASES

Nursery Diseases

While protective control with fungicides would in most cases be prohibitively uneconomical in woodland, in nurseries it is generally justified.

To avoid later repetition, where any disease described here is also a serious disease of established trees, that information is given in this section.

DAMPING-OFF

Various soil-inhibiting fungi cause losses at a very early stage of germination (pre-emergence damping-off), and they also infect the roots and cause the death of young seedlings (post-emergence damping-off). Post-emergence killing usually occurs before the end of June, and is most serious in dense seedbeds under warm, moist conditions. Infected seedlings may be either scattered through the seedbed, or in irregularly distributed groups. On light or medium loam soils, soil sterilization with formalin or dazomet, before sowing, is effective, but in most nursery soils, drench treatment, with captan, as soon as possible after the damage first appears, will prevent further serious development of the disease. Where soil is sterilized, particularly with dazomet, dispersal of fumes from the soil must be ensured before sowing. Details on application are given in Chapter 7 of Bulletin 43, *Nursery Practice.*

GREY MOULD (Leaflet 50)

The aerial parts of a wide variety of conifer seedlings may be attacked by Grey mould (*Botrytis cinerea*), usually in late summer, autumn and early winter. The disease is recognisable by a typical 'grey mould' that develops on killed tissues. Spraying at about ten-day intervals with Bordeaux mixture, thiram or captan gives protective control, and should be a routine measure with seedbeds of *Sequoia, Sequoiadendron, Cryptomeria* and *Cupressus* species, as these are very susceptible. Other conifers, particularly Japanese larch, Sitka spruce, Western hemlock, Douglas fir and Lodgepole pine, may be attacked under dense, humid seedbed conditions, when the fungus colonises shaded needles and then infects the lower stems, causing death of entire plants. The disease may also become established on parts damaged by frost. Dense stocking of seedbeds should be avoided, and spraying should be instituted at the first sign of infection.

LEAF CAST OF LARCH (Leaflet 21)

This is caused by the fungus *Meria laricis*, which infects young needles, causing them to turn yellow and wither. European and Hybrid larch are susceptible, and Japanese resistant. Infection proceeds up the shoot, the tip of which remains green. The disease rarely kills plants, but it may seriously weaken them and greatly increase the proportion of culls. Leaf cast is best avoided by raising larch in nurseries not adjacent to standing larch, which acts as a source of infection. In susceptible nurseries, spraying with colloidal sulphur at the time of flushing and at intervals of three or four weeks gives good control.

KEITHIA DISEASE OF WESTERN RED CEDAR (Leaflet 43)

This disease is caused by the fungus *Didymascella (Keithia) thujina*. Infection causes browning of individual scattered leaflets and, where infection is severe, death of whole shoots. The fructifications, which are small, round or oval structures produced on leaflets, are slightly swollen and olive-brown when mature, but when moribund appear as blackened cavities in dead leaflets. The disease can cause very heavy losses in Western red cedar nursery stock. Infection is rarely seen on first-year seedlings, but rapidly increases in severity on older stock. Spraying with cycloheximide (Acti-dione Ferrated is the only commercial formulation available in this country) at the end of March and a month later gives good protective control in areas of low rainfall; in wetter areas a third application should be made in mid-June.

OAK MILDEW (Leaflet 38)

This is caused by the fungus *Microsphaera alphitoides*, which grows mainly on the outside of succulent leaves and shoots, covering them with a white bloom. It causes distortion, poor growth and dieback of lammas shoots rather than complete death. The fungus overwinters between bud scales, and the shoots emerging from these buds are the first affected in spring. Later, the disease is spread by wind-dispersed spores. Spraying with colloidal sulphur at the start of flushing, and later at intervals of two or three weeks if secondary infections appear, gives good control.

VERTICILLIUM WILT

In tree nurseries this disease is usually caused by *Verticillium dahliae*, and infrequently by *V. albo-atrum*, both soil-inhabiting fungi. It can cause severe losses of various broadleaved trees, especially species of *Acer*. In summer, the leaves on some or all branches of infected trees wilt, and usually the wood of wilted branches shows a diffuse green to brown staining. Laboratory techniques are required for detection of the fungus. Infested soil can be cleaned by sterilization with chloropicrin or dazomet. Ground previously used for potato crops is particularly liable to be infested.

On established trees the disease is of no importance in forestry, but it can be lethal to ornamentals such as *Catalpa bignonioides* and *Cotinus coggygria*, and to some of the maples.

PHYTOPHTHORA ROOT ROT

This rather misleadingly named fungal disease—on woody species it kills roots and does not decay them—is caused by various soil-inhabiting species of the genus *Phytophthora*. It is uncommon in forest nurseries, but it can cause heavy losses among plants of various species, including Lawson cypress, Douglas fir and Sweet chestnut. Roots are infected by spores that are motile in water, and development of the disease is dependant on wet soil conditions in summer. The damage may easily be mistaken for that caused by waterlogging, particularly as the fungus cannot be detected without the aid of laboratory techniques. As yet no simple means of control has been found, though complex measures have been devised for nurseries specialising in the propagation of susceptible ornamentals. There is circumstantial evidence of a link between this disease and the use of farmyard manure.

In woodland, the roots of Sweet chestnut are frequently attacked, especially on heavy clay soils. On this species, the disease is known as Ink disease, from the inky discoloration of dead roots, which is not, however, a symptom of this disease alone. Large trees may be rapidly killed, but often only part of the root system is killed, together with a patch of bark in the form of an inverted V at the base of the stem. Beech on heavy soils may be similarly attacked. Susceptible trees, including Common lime and Horse chestnut, may be attacked under parkland conditions, particularly where livestock can create wet boggy conditions by congregating under trees, and can carry infected soil from tree to tree on their hoofs. The disease can be very damaging to ornamental cultivars, screens and hedges of Lawson cypress. Any measures to prevent wet conditions round the bases of trees will reduce the risk of infection.

FUNGICIDES

In view of the wide range of proprietary fungicides now available, no directions are given for their preparation. Instructions are always given on the container, and it can be assumed that most trees will be unharmed by the average dose recommended for horticultural plants. *Approved Products for Farmers and Growers* lists fungicides sanctioned for use by the Ministry of Agriculture, Fisheries and Food and is published annually by HMSO.

Diseases of General Importance

HONEY FUNGUS (Arboricultural Leaflet 2)

Honey fungus (*Armillaria mellea*) attacks the roots of a wide range of coniferous and broadleaved trees. Most infection is by means of brown to black bootlace-like strands (rhizomorphs) that grow through the soil from infected wood, often that of broadleaf stumps. Rhizomorph tips can penetrate the bark of live roots with which they come into contact, after which disease development may vary from gradual and limited root decay to fairly rapid death of roots and, consequently, of trees. Where trees are killed, white or cream coloured sheets of mycelium, sometimes streaked with brown or black, can be found between the bark and wood of the bases of their stems. Later on, rhizomorphs may develop under this bark (See Plate 11). Honey fungus, however, often invades trees killed by other agencies, so its presence is not necessarily proof that it was the cause of death. In autumn, the fungus produces clusters of variably honey coloured toadstools at the bases and above the roots of infected trees and stumps.

In their early years, plantation conifers are particularly liable to be killed on old broadleaf sites. Usually deaths are so scattered that appreciable gaps are not formed, but sometimes they do occur in groups, in which case the gaps can be replanted with more tolerant trees, such as most broadleaves and Douglas fir or species of *Abies*. With increasing age, commonly planted conifers become more resistant to killing by the disease, but root decay may render them liable to windthrow. In some conifers, particularly spruce, decay progresses a little way up the stem, but does not cause much loss of utilisable timber. Such decay has a characteristic wet stringy appearance.

Honey fungus is ubiquitous but rarely troublesome in broadleaved woodland. It is, however, a destructive parasite in gardens, ornamental plantings, arboreta and the like, where many of the more susceptible species are likely to be planted and where individual trees are of great value. In such places the stumps and large roots of felled trees should never be left in the ground to act as sources of infection, and any infected trees should be removed with all their major roots. Commercially advertised claims that stumps can be destroyed, or that the disease can be controlled, by chemical means alone should not be accepted without proof that the claims have been impartially verified.

Diseases of Conifers

FOMES ANNOSUS (Leaflet 5)

This fungus is the most serious cause of disease in British forests. It can attack virtually all coniferous species, usually through their roots. Once in a root, it may progress through the heartwood to the stem and cause butt-rot. The larches and spruces are very liable to butt-rot, and Western hemlock and Western red cedar are the most susceptible species of all. *Fomes* may also cause death of trees by killing their roots. The pines, which are resistant to butt-rot, are particularly susceptible to root killing on alkaline soils and on former arable land. Douglas fir and species of *Abies*, which are not particularly susceptible to butt-rot or to extensive killing of roots, may be rendered liable to windthrow by partial decay of their roots.

The fruit bodies of *Fomes* are perennial and easily recognised (See Plate 12). They occur as brackets on stumps and at the base of killed trees, usually at soil level and often under fallen needles and vegetation. They are reddish-brown above with a conspicuous white margin, the underside being white and perforated by minute pores.

Fomes is present in most areas that have previously carried coniferous crops. In new plantations on previously treeless ground, *Fomes* is nearly always introduced by means of airborne spores deposited on freshly cut stump surfaces. The fungus invades the stumps and spreads to standing trees via root contacts, and in the same way infection spreads from tree to tree. The development of the disease in first rotation crops and its further development in the second rotation can be greatly retarded by the prompt treatment of freshly cut stump surfaces with a solution of urea. Pine stumps, but not those of other conifers, can be treated with commercially produced spore suspensions of *Peniophora gigantea*, a fungus that prevents invasion by *Fomes*, and that readily decays stumps but not standing trees.

PHAEOLUS SCHWEINITZII (Booklet 13)

Butt-rot of conifers caused by the fungus *Phaeolus schweinitzii* is of low incidence and occurs mainly on sites that previously carried broadleaves or pines. In Sitka spruce, the species most frequently attacked, decay may extend 3 m or so up the stems of 30- to 40-year-old trees. Douglas fir, Scots pine and the larches are also attacked, but in these extensive decay tends to develop later when the trees are mature or nearly so. Decayed wood is dry, crumbly, pale yellow-brown darkening to mahogany in the final stages. It cracks radially and across the grain, forming roughly cubical blocks, and has a characteristic turpentine smell. The fructifications are annual, appearing as brackets at tree bases, or on the ground above infected roots, when they have a short central stalk. A fully grown specimen is about 30 cm across, and has a deep rusty-brown upper surface with a yellow margin. The underside is yellow-green, and has angular irregular pores. Little is known of the biology of this fungus.

GROUP DYING OF CONIFERS (Forest Record 46)

This disease is caused by the fungus *Rhizina undulata*, the spores of which readily germinate in the soil after they have been subjected to relatively high temperatures. In plantations, the fungus usually appears first where fires have been lit on the ground, often by workers at tea-breaks during the course of thinnings. The fungus spreads through the litter and upper soil, damaging or killing roots as it progresses. This spread may continue for six or seven years before the fungus dies out, by which time large groups of dead trees may develop in Sitka spruce, which is particularly susceptible, and large gaps may be created from which windthrow may develop. The fructifications of *Rhizina* are annual, shallow, inverted cup-like structures, dark brown above, appearing mainly around the periphery of groups. In plantations the disease can be prevented by prohibiting the lighting of fires on the ground. Some loss of coniferous planting stock can result where fires have been lit during ground clearance, but usually the damage is slight, and the fungus does not persist for more than one or two years.

LARCH CANKER AND DIEBACK (Leaflet 16)

This disease of European larch is caused by the fungus *Trichoscyphella willkommii*, a not very active parasite that infects the bark and causes it to become exceedingly frost-tender in a narrow zone just beyond that invaded by the fungus. When temperatures fall below freezing point, tissues in this zone are damaged, the fungus advances into the damaged zone when the tissues thaw, and another frost-tender zone is created. In this way the fungus advances each winter, causing cankers to form on twigs, branches and stems. Its fruit bodies appear on active cankers, and are small saucer-shaped discs, the concave upper surface being apricot-orange to light buff with a white rim. Susceptibility to canker is related to the origin of the larch, high alpine provenances being the most susceptible, and Carpathian provenances, such as Sudeten larch, the least. Hybrid and Japanese larch are generally resistant.

Where cankers girdle twigs, branches or stems, the dieback and occasional deaths ensue, but a much more damaging and epidemic type of dieback follows severe infestations by the insect *Adelges laricis* (p. 47) whether canker is present or not. As high alpine provenances are those most susceptible to epidemic dieback as well as to canker, these two disorders often occur together. Carpathian provenances are the least susceptible to both disorders and, on the evidence available in this country, if European larch is to be planted, Sudeten larch is the best choice.

DIEBACK OF CORSICAN PINE (Forest Record 61)

This disease, sometimes called Brunchorstia disease, is caused by the fungus *Scleroderris lagerbergii*, which infects the developing shoots of Corsican pine during protracted periods of high humidity in summer. Infected shoots continue to grow normally, and the disease develops after they have become dormant, causing damage varying from death of buds to complete death of shoots. Small, pin-head, blackish-brown fruit bodies of the fungus develop on buds, needles and shoots. The disease is particularly damaging in the north and west of Britain, especially at higher elevations.

RESIN TOP DISEASE OF SCOTS PINE (Leaflet 49)

This is caused by the rust fungus *Peridermium pini*, and is most prevalent on Scots pine in north-east Scotland, but does occur elsewhere. The fungus causes cankers that commonly girdle the main stem and branches. Cankers are usually seen as large, blackened, resin-soaked areas on the upper part of the stem. Dieback of the crown above large cankers frequently occurs, and is commonly followed by death of the tree. Vigorous crops are the most susceptible, and dominant trees the worst affected. During May and June, large numbers of blister-like fructifications are produced on the cankers. Unlike many rust fungi, *Peridermium pini* does not require an alternate host, and can spread directly from pine to pine. Infected trees should be removed in the course of thinning.

TWISTING RUST OF PINE (Booklet 4)

The cause of this disease, *Melampsora pinitorqua*, is a rust fungus that requires two hosts, pine and aspen. It causes distortion and dieback of the current year's shoots of Scots pine, and it produces bright yellow, mealy fruit bodies on the distorted shoots in early summer. Later, small orange spots appear on the aspen leaves. The disease is virtually confined to south-east England, where Corsican pine, which is resistant, should be planted instead of Scots pine on sites where aspen is present. Where Scots pine has already been planted, the disease can be controlled by early and frequent cutting of aspen suckers, but generally it does not cause appreciable losses in the long run, even where attacks are severe. Once the canopy has closed, the pine suppresses the aspen, and the disease dies out.

NEEDLE-CAST OF PINE (Leaflet 48)

Several fungi can cause needle cast of pine. In plantations, the most spectacular damage is caused by *Lopherdemella sulcigena*, which attacks the current year's needles, particularly those of Corsican pine. By the end of October, the needles are killed to within about one cm of the sheath, the dead parts being first brown and later pale grey. Severe outbreaks are normally confined to western and northern parts of the country, and are usually too infrequent to cause lasting injury.

In nurseries, attacks by *Lophodermium pinastri*, which causes browning and shedding of needles, can result in heavy losses. Severe attacks are normally confined to nurseries in the near vicinity of older pines, and the disease is best avoided by raising pines at least 200 m away from older trees.

Diseases of Broadleaved Trees

BACTERIAL CANKER OF POPLAR (Leaflet 27)

This, the most important disease of poplars in Britain, is caused by the bacterium *Aplanobacter populi*, which gains entry through fresh leaf scars and wounds in the bark. The first signs of the disease are splits in the bark of twigs, branches or young stems, from which a whitish bacterial slime oozes in spring. According to the variety of poplar, cankers varying from rough, blackish excrescences to open, smooth sided 'target' cankers may develop on branches and stems, and extensive dieback may occur. Losses from the disease can be reduced by the use of resistant varieties, and by removing all older cankered trees on or next to ground that is to be planted with poplars.

BEECH BARK DISEASE (Forest Record 96)

This disease affects beech from the pole-stage onwards. It develops where bark first infested by an insect, the Felted beech coccus (p. 48), is subsequently invaded by a fungus, *Nectria coccinea*. Infestation by the insect is revealed by the white woolly wax that it secretes, and if the fungus gains entry, large vertical strips of bark on infested stems may be killed and severely affected trees may decline and die within a few years. Once bark has been killed, fungi that can cause rapid decay of the underlying wood usually gain entry, and the stems of affected trees that remain alive are rendered very liable to snap. The minute, red, globular fruit bodies of *Nectria coccinea* appear in clusters on more recently killed bark. Prompt felling of affected trees is required if their timber is to be utilized, and recently infected trees and those markedly infested by the insect should be removed during thinnings. On specimen trees, the insect can be controlled by the thorough application of a tar-oil winter wash.

DUTCH ELM DISEASE (Forest Record 115).

During the 1960s, some 40 years after it first appeared in Britain, this disease became markedly more destructive in some regions following the introduction of a more lethal strain of the causal fungus, *Ceratocystis ulmi*, probably on imported logs. The fungus grows mainly in the water-conducting vessels of the outer ring of wood, causing a patchy to extensive wilting of foliage in summer, followed by partial or complete death of wilted parts and often of the entire tree. If the bark of a recently wilted small branch is peeled back, a streaky brown discoloration of the wood is usually revealed, and if the branch is cut across, a fairly clearly defined dark brown staining of invaded vessels can be seen.

The disease is spread by the Elm bark beetles *Scolytus scolytus* and *S. multistriatus*, which breed under the bark of diseased trees. Many of them bear spores in and on their bodies, and they then fly to the crowns of live trees where, by feeding on the bark of twigs, they create wounds that are readily infected by the spores they carry. Control by reduction of the beetles' breeding grounds can be practised by felling recently killed and severely diseased trees, followed by destruction or insecticidal spraying of the bark before spring. To be effective, this needs to be done very thoroughly over a wide area.

WATERMARK DISEASE (Leaflet 20)

This important disease of Cricket-bat willow is caused by the bacterium *Erwinia salicis*. The disease appears as a browning of leaves followed by dieback of twigs and branches. The wood of affected parts shows a diffuse watery stain. In the principal willow-growing area of East Anglia and the neighbouring counties, owners are required by law to fell and dispose of diseased willows. These measures have restricted the spread of the disease. Sets for planting must always be taken from healthy trees or stool beds.

Decay and Safety (Arboricultural Leaflet No. 1)

A great number of different fungi cause decay in trees, and little is known about many of them. Some enter heartwood exposed by breakage, pruning and the like; some invade sapwood where bark has been removed or killed by other agencies; and some, particularly amongst those that decay roots, can invade through live bark. Microscopic fungal threads (hyphae) penetrate the wood and feed on it, and when these are well established, often after many years, fruit bodies connected to them may grow on the exterior of invaded trees, or on the ground over infected roots. Some of these fungi have perennial fruit bodies that persist for years, and others have annual ones. The risk of decay developing from small, cleanly cut wounds, such as those created by brashing, is negligible and, in woodland, control of decay—other than that caused by *Fomes annosus*—is largely a matter of avoiding more extensive injuries, such as those caused to the bases of trees where logs are extracted by dragging.

Decay involves considerable loss of mechanical strength in wood, and is therefore particularly important in trees retained for amenity by roadsides or in places to which the public have access. Public safety must take precedence over amenity, so such trees should be regularly inspected for signs of decay, preferably in autumn, when annual fungal fruit bodies are generally most evident, and any unsound trees should be removed or made safe by other means. Fungal fruit bodies on and cavities in trees are the most obvious indicators of decay, while dead limbs, dead bark, large wounds and cankers are signs that decay could have entered. Whether advanced decay is present can be determined by probing or boring. The fruit bodies of fungi that decay roots often do not develop until most of the roots that provide anchorage have been destroyed, and underground decay is often not evident until trees are blown over and their decayed roots are revealed. Root decay may cause the crowns of trees to become sparse and sickly, but these symptoms alone are not diagnostic, and confirmatory evidence can be sought by digging for decayed roots. In such cases, extensive root decay may not be evident except at depths of 40 cm or more. By the time crown symptoms develop, especially in the case of large beech, the tree may be in imminent danger of falling.

There is a misapprehension that decay in the trunks of trees can readily be cured by cutting out decayed wood and by treating the resulting cavity in various ways that leave it either filled with some substance, or open, ventilated and drained. In fact, it is almost impossible to eradicate well established decay, and such treatment should be avoided where safety is involved. Large pruning wounds often provide entry for decay, and systematic research is needed to determine how these should best be treated. On general grounds, large wounds should best be treated with a wood preservative such as Solignum or Cuprinol, and a tough bituminous cover should then be applied to prevent weathering of the preservative. This cover should be inspected annually and maintained intact.

INSECT PESTS

Introduction

The afforestation programmes of the past 50 years or so have been completed in Britain without major limitation by insects. From time to time there have been outbreaks of moth, sawfly and aphid defoliators, bark beetles and weevils with resulting economically important damage, but these have been local in occurrence. The underlying reasons for our relative freedom are as likely to have stemmed from the youth, vigour and extent of these new woodlands as to any special character of our environment inimical to insect outbreak. It is certainly true that as the estate has grown older and larger so have some indigenous forest insect species found conditions in our new forests compatible with population increase and have changed their status from forest inhabitant to forest pest. Similarly there are foreign insects, which may or may not have arrived on these shores before, but at any rate now find conditions congenial for settlement and increase. Visitation from these alien species should in no way come as a surprise to us since, as exotic tree planters, it is from exotic pests that we might, on general principles, expect the more difficult and important problems to arise.

Often in forestry, quite evident insect damage has to be tolerated simply because control action would be uneconomic, or ecologically or tactically undesirable. Artificial control becomes urgent where crop survival is in jeopardy, and examples may be found both in the nursery during the establishment phase of new crops and in older crops. The abundance of some insects and the damage they do is directly related to the general health condition of the crop. By observing the rules of good sylviculture and maintaining the crop in a sound condition, the scale of damage inflicted by many pests can be considerably reduced. A very important example may be found in pine woods where the maintenance of forest hygiene and the correct planning of thinning and felling operations do much to restrict damage by bark beetles and weevils. It should not be thought that good silviculture alone, embracing correct choice of species and careful subsequent tending of the crop, will result in immunity from all insect troubles. Such measures may well help to ward off 'secondary' pests whose increase is dependent upon the appearance of some predisposing factor. But a number of insect pests, including some of the most harmful species, are capable of attacking and seriously damaging if not destroying apparently healthy and well tended stands. The latter type of insect is commonly referred to as 'primary'.

Different insect pests are associated with different ages of the host crop, and it will be convenient therefore to consider in this section the main enemies which are of common occurrence in the various stages of crop development. Obviously in such a brief review it is possible to do no more than quote a selection of examples and indicate which species of insect are of importance.

Within the Forestry Commission it is standard practice to use insecticides other than DDT when practicable. However this chemical has been approved by the Agricultural Chemicals Approval Scheme and is given as a method of control in many instances.

Insects Attacking Tree Seed

Many insects live in the developing seeds and cones of forest trees and their attacks can sometimes result in appreciable losses. One particularly damaging species is the chalcid seed wasp, *Megastigmus spermotrophus*, whose larvae hollow out the seeds of Douglas fir (Leaflet 8). Infestations by this insect are sometimes very heavy and can cause near total loss of the seed crop. It is therefore advisable to make an assessment of

the seed to determine its soundness before cone-collecting is carried out. Other species of *Megastigmus* infest Silver fir, larch and Norway spruce seeds.

The caterpillars of a number of moth species such as *Dioryctria abietella, Laspeyresia strobilella* and *L. conicolana*, the larvae of the weevil *Pissodes validirostris*, and the maggots of some dipterous (two-winged) flies, feed upon and destroy the seeds of various conifers. Their attacks, however, are not often serious. The grubs of the weevils of the genus *Curculio* attack and hollow out acorns, whilst beech-nuts are similarly infested by the caterpillars of the moth *Laspeyresia grossana*. Again the attacks are not usually of a serious nature, but they may on some occasions affect the success of natural regeneration schemes or the economics of seed collection.

Other types of insect infestation can produce indirect effect on seed production. For example the defoliation of oak by the oak leaf Roller moth, *Tortrix viridana*, or of the winter moth, *Operophtera brumata*, may result in marked reduction in acorn yield.

Nursery Pests

The most important nursery pests are soil-inhabiting insects and sap-suckers. Leaf-eating insects are not usually troublesome in the nursery, but occasionally some moth and sawfly caterpillars and species of leaf beetle damage broadleaf stock. These pests can easily be controlled with insecticides applied at the rates recommended in normal horticultural practice.

CUTWORMS AND CHAFER GRUBS

Two important groups of soil insects are cutworms and Chafer grubs. Cutworms are the caterpillars of various species of noctuid moths which remain in the soil during daytime and emerge at night to feed upon the seedlings. The damage consists of gnawing at the root collar region, usually resulting in the young tree being cut off at or about soil level. When damage is detected the identity of the pest can be confirmed by digging up the caterpillars or looking for them on the surface of the soil at night with the aid of the torch. The caterpillars are dirty grey-green in colour and measure about 25 mm in length; their reaction to handling or disturbance is to roll themselves up into a coil. Another check on the identity of the pest is the presence of holes—the entrance to the burrows—in the surface of the seedbed. A practical control can be achieved by using either gamma HCH or DDT applied to the seedbed. Chafer grubs are white, curved and wrinkled and measure up to 40 mm in length when full grown. They are the larvae of various species of scarabeid beetles of which the best known is the large May bug, *Melolontha melolontha*. A smaller species, *Serica brunnea*, is common in the north. The grubs live in the soil for from one to four years and during this period feed on the roots of seedlings and transplants. The roots are either stripped of bark or chewed through. The first obvious symptom of attack is browning of the foliage, and the death of the plant is a common result of attack. Chafer grubs used to be the most important of pests in old agricultural-soil nurseries, but with the change to the heathland type they do not appear to be so troublesome. Control is with gamma HCH 'Wireworm Dust', which is either worked into the top few inches of the soil between the rows or incorporated during the last cultivation before planting or sowing.

SPRINGTAILS

The collembolon (springtail) *Bourletiella hortensis*, another soil dweller, can cause heavy losses amongst conifer seedlings; Lodgepole pine seems particularly susceptible. The attack takes place on the hypocotyl and cotyledons of germinating seeds. Death of the seedling can occur before emergence from the soil or, where damage to the hypocotyl has not been great, the shoot and needles may be deformed. At the end of the growing season the surviving plant has a normal stem (often showing brown specks of dead tissue), on top of which is a bush of swollen distorted needles. After a second year's growth the small trees appear perfectly green and healthy but bear four or five leaders—the kind of plant which will normally be rejected without thought by the nurseryman. It is possible that collembolon damage on a small scale may be quite common and could account in part for the wide differences between laboratory-determined germination percentage and survival in the field. These tiny jumping wingless insects are easily controlled by spraying with malathion. The use of DDT or gamma HCH or other chlorinated hydrocarbon, often recommended for control of springtails in pot plants, will in the field result only in a temporary depression in numbers and the population will be found to have recovered within a short time if not actually to have increased.

SAP-SUCKING INSECTS

Aphids and adelgids are fairly common in nurseries, and their attacks may check and stunt the growth of plants. Adelgids are restricted to coniferous trees and their presence can be detected by the patches of white wool which they produce to cover themselves. *Pineus pini* on Scots pine, *Adelges cooleyi* on Douglas fir, *A. abietis* on spruce and *A. laricis* on larch are perhaps the most common and sometimes damaging. *Cinaropsis pilicornis* feeds on the new shoots of spruce and sometimes causes local needle loss and a degree of distortion. *Phyllaphis fagi* on beech and *Myzus cerasi* on cherry are also often found feeding on the leaves of their hosts and bring about leaf curl and stunted growth. Another interesting aphid species namely, *Stagona (Prociphilus) pini*, may be found on the roots of nursery pine and is often associated with poor and dry conditions of growth; plants grown in clay pots tend to be particularly prone to infestation by this species. Most of the aphid species are controlled by the use of either malathion or lindane sprays such as are used to combat the attacks of green or black fly in gardens. In the case of the adelgid species, however, which protect themselves under wool and have spring and summer egg stages, some difficulty may be experienced in reducing damage to an acceptable level. Careful timing of treatment and a suitable prevailing temperature are critical factors in adelgid control; a warm period in late autumn, winter or early spring provides optimum conditions for spraying.

The mite *Paratetranychus ununguis*, the Conifer spinning mite, can be a serious pest of young conifers, particularly the spruces in rather dry growing conditions. This tiny relation of the spiders sucks the sap from the needles causing them to turn a dirty brown colour and leaving them netted with fine silk. Good control can be obtained through the use of Kelthane (dicofol).

Occasionally small weevils such as *Otiorrhynchus*, *Phyllobius*, and *Barypithes* cause damage in the nursery by feeding upon bark and leaves. These insects are controlled by the use of DDT or gamma HCH sprays or dust.

Insect Attacks in Young Woods

ROOT AND BARK FEEDERS

Generally speaking the first few years in the growth of a conifer crop are much more critical from the point of view of insect damage than in the same period in the life of a broadleaved stand. This is particularly true when the new conifer crop is a replacement for another one recently removed. In such a case pests which have multiplied in the stumps of the previous crop emerge to feed upon the young trees and may bring about heavy mortality if no protective measures are taken. The insects concerned in such situations are the well known Pine weevil, *Hylobius abietis*, and the Black pine beetles, *Hylastes* spp. (Leaflet 58). The Large pine weevil breeds in conifer stumps. The grubs, which burrow beneath the bark of the roots and stump buttresses, measure about three-quarters of an inch in length when full grown and are white, curved and legless. Development from egg to emergence of young adults takes between one and two years, depending on local climatic conditions. In particularly cold sites it may even take longer than this. On emergence the weevils, which can live in the adult stage for two or occasionally more years, feed by gnawing the bark of newly planted conifers (See Plate 13). When the stem-bark of young transplants is ringed the tree dies. Total loss of the crop is not an uncommon result of neglect to carry out protective measures. All of the commonly grown conifers appear to be susceptible to attack by this weevil. Damage by the Pine weevil was traditionally avoided by allowing the site to lie fallow for a period of three or four years after felling. The time-lag between felling and replanting allowed the weevil population to breed-up and exhaust the available breeding material; this was followed by intensive billet-and-spray trapping, intended to mop up the vastly increased population and return it to normal level prior to replanting. The method had disadvantages in that the ground was lost to use for the period, soil deteriorated, and weed growth often become rank. In modern terms the cost of trapping alone, in any case, would be prohibitively expensive. Insecticidal control has replaced the old method throughout Europe and wherever this weevil is to be found as a forest pest. DDT emulsion or wettable powder formulation, applied as a dip of aerial parts, was the first of such materials to provide effective and cheap means of transplant protection. DDT has now been to some extent superseded by gamma HCH, mainly on environmental grounds. In Britain a water-suspension rather than the emulsion formulation is normally used, and it is applied as a total dip for the joint control of Pine weevil and Black pine beetle, or as a dip of aerial parts only for Pine weevil control. Both DDT and gamma HCH emulsions may be used as emergency, topical sprays of already planted crops, against either one or both of the two pests mentioned above, when sudden outbreaks of them occur and no prior protective measures have been taken, or when such measures have not been full effective.

The Black pine beetles also breed in conifer stumps and later emerge to attack young coniferous trees. Damage is caused by the small bark beetles burrowing beneath the bark at and below the collar region of the young tree. The attack frequently causes the death of trees through girdling. Symptoms of attack are externally not so obvious as that by Pine weevil, but it is an easy matter to carefully lift and examine obviously unhealthy and dying trees to determine if *Hylastes* is responsible. Pine appears particularly prone to *Hylastes* attack and, somewhat less so, spruce. Serious outbreaks are most common where annual or continuous fellings take place in contiguous coups. The Clay-coloured weevil, *Otiorrhynchus singularis*, like the Pine weevil can also bring about serious loss in new plantings. The larvae feed on the fine roots of various herbs, and the adults upon the aerial parts of forest trees and other plants. Western hemlock seems particularly prone to attack. The adults not only eat off triangular chunks from the needle, but also remove the bark from the finer twigs and branches in a manner similar to that of *Hylobius* feeding on the main stem. The creatures are dormant during the daytime but may be looked for just under the soil surface at the base of the stem. Adult activity usually starts at the end of April or early May and continues throughout the summer months into September. Almost identical damage, particularly to larch, is sometimes caused by the small brown weevil,

Strophosomus coryli. Indeed these two very often work together. Effective control of both species may be obtained by spraying with gamma HCH or DDT.

DEFOLIATORS

In the first decade after establishment a number of insect pests make their presence felt, especially in coniferous crops. The sap-sucking adelgids (Bulletin 42 and Leaflet 7) are usually conspicuous on Douglas fir, the larches and the spruces. Although such attacks can be demonstrated to bring about a reduction in growth it is seldom economically worthwhile to attempt control artificially. One species, however, *Adelges nordmannianae*, so severely cripples the Common silver fir *Abies alba* that the planting of this tree species has seldom been attempted on a forest scale in this country (Bulletin 26). The so-called Pineapple gall forming species *A. abietis* is a noteworthy pest of Norway spruce grown as Christmas trees. Here winter or early spring treatments with gamma HCH emulsions can provide effective control (Forest Record 104).

Pine sawflies, *Diprion pini* and *Neodiprion sertifer*, are conspicuous on young pines and occasionally defoliation may be almost complete (Leaflet 35). Defoliation seldom brings about death of the tree although there may be a noticeable decrease in height increment. Outbreaks seldom persist on Scots pine for more than two or three seasons before they collapse naturally, through parasites in the case of the former species and a nuclea polyhedrosis virus (NPV) in the latter. Artificial dissemination of the virus gives an extremely efficient and worthwhile control of *N. sertifer*. Long experience has shown that the 'home' production and application of this NPV (one of a type of virus specific to insects) material can be carried out without known hazard to man. Preparation of the material is a somewhat tedious process and requires a degree of 'know how'. Despite all the difficulties the virus has provided a very useful weapon for combating sawfly attacks upon the highly susceptible Lodgepole pine. However, it should be mentioned that all forms of virus control have, in recent years, come under question as to possible side-effects upon man and other animals. It is a moot point at the moment whether or not the *N. sertifer* virus should be regarded as an indigenous biological control agent, or a form of pesticide. If the latter, of course, it would require some form of clearance under the Pesticide Safety Precaution Scheme by intending users.

In broadleaf crops of up to 10 years of age, defoliation by leaf beetles and by the caterpillars of moths and sawflies is sometimes encountered. Serious damage is rare and recovery is normally very good. Exceptions to this rule are the attacks made by the leaf-beetles *Phyllodecta vitellinae* and *P. vulgatissima* on poplar stool-beds. In the interests of increasing productivity of propagating material, sprays of DDT or gamma HCH are commonly applied. Aphid attacks, too, may occur, but again they do not seriously interfere with the growth of crops.

Insects in Older Woods

Many species of leaf-feeding insects cause damage of varying degrees of severity in older woods of all types. Some of the most harmful forest pests are included in this group and, although crops in Britain have, by comparison with similar ones in other countries, remained fairly free from serious outbreaks in the past, it is essential to appreciate that some species have by no means yet reached their full potential as pests. The list of insects having achieved pest status has grown as our forest estate has increased in size, and the crops have become older. Since 1953, at least two species on spruce and three each on pine and larch, have, without obvious reasons, found conditions ecologically suitable for outbreak. It is wise to remember, therefore, that we are still very much a developing country as far as plantation forestry is concerned, and our quickly expanding, largely exotic, forest holdings must still be considered vulnerable to ecological change and to chance import.

DEFOLIATORS

The most important forest defoliators in old crops are the caterpillars of moths and sawflies, but some examples also occur in groups other than these. For instance, beech leaves are often damaged by the weevil *Orchestes fagi*, the adults of which eat holes in the leaves whilst the larvae mine the interior of the leaf. Again, Sitka spruce is frequently defoliated by the aphid *Elatobium abietinum*, but, although recovery from attack is normally good, that is unless site conditions are particularly adverse, considerable loss of increment may result from severe defoliation. Outbreaks are invariably associated with mild winters, $-8°C$ being a threshold low temperature for winter survival (Forest Record 84). Control measures against this aphid have never, in fact, been recommended, partly due to difficulties of forecasting severe attack, and thus of taking timely action, partly for the doubtful economies of such action, and partly for ecological objections to wholesale insecticide applications. In the nursery and in research plots malathion has given good control. Again *Adelges laricis* is now recognised as not only responsible for wholesale canopy discoloration and degrade, but may also be the prime factor in bringing about the condition known for many years as 'dieback of European larch'. Alpine provenances of larch are found to be particularly susceptible to this malaise, whilst Carpathian provenances and Hybrid larches are less so, and the Japanese larch is virtually resistant. The grey aphid-like creature may easily be spotted on the needles of larch often accompanied by white waxy wool. This, together with the sooty-mould blackened honey-dew produced by the species, is often conspicuous, and causes the foliage to appear a bluish-green by mid-summer.

Examples of defoliators among the moths may be found in the Pine looper, *Bupalus piniaria* (Leaflet 32); *Semasia diniana* on larch, pine and spruce; *Coleophora laricella* on larch; the Winter moth *Operophtera brumata* on oak and many broadleaf trees; and the Oak leaf roller moth, *Tortrix viridana* (Leaflet 10). The Pine Beauty moth, *Panolis flammea*, (Forest Record 120), though long known as a pest on the continent reached infestation level for the first time in 1976 on Lodgepole pine in the North of Scotland. The sawflies on pine have already been mentioned as has the fact that their attacks occur usually in young stands. Larch and spruce also carry a varied sawfly fauna with seven species occurring on the former tree and eight on the latter. These larch and spruce species are of particular interest since they must all be foreigners to Britain, all being specific to exotic tree hosts.

Space allows only brief reference to the forest status of the above insects. Most of them occur in some numbers in woodlands containing their host tree but will indicate their presence through visible damage in restricted areas only. The Winter moth and Oak leaf roller moth are wellknown pests which periodically cause damage to older oak woods. The trees usually recover fairly well, assisted by heavy Lammas shoot production, but a distinct loss of timber increment results. It is interesting to note that the later flushing Sessile oak is less susceptible to heavy infestation than is Pedunculate oak. The Pine looper (See Plates 14 and 15), also known as the Bordered white moth, was regarded as of little importance until 1953 when the first serious epidemic requiring artificial control occurred. Since then the moth has had to be controlled from the air on five separate occasions. On larch the Larch web-spinning sawfly, *Cephalcia alpina*, caused widespread damage of Japanese larch for the first time in 1972, having been first recorded in Britain only in 1954. Among the spruce sawflies *Gilpinia hercyniae*, (Forest Record 117) first recorded in Britain in 1906, made its debut as a serious pest of Sitka and Norway spruces in 1968 in north and central Wales. The small spruce sawfly, *Pristiphora abietina*, for a longer time recognised as a pest in Britain, has also the capacity to cause quite serious defoliation and die-back of shoots, with consequent crown distortion following. Two other larch feeding species, *Anoplonyx destructor* and *Pristiphora westmaeli*, also occasionally caused heavy crown browning and needle loss. In general the control of defoliators is a complicated operation, since usually fairly large areas are affected, and special equipment has to be used. The best advice that can be given is that when trouble arises expert guidance should be sought. The Forestry Commission Research Division is always interested in reports of outbreaks and will readily offer advice.

BARK AND WOOD FEEDERS

Bark and Ambrosia beetles and weevils are, in the main, secondary pests whose numbers are dependent on the provision of suitable breeding sites in the form of debilitated or damaged trees or felled produce. Multiplication normally takes place beneath the bark. When numbers of these insects are high they can under certain circumstances attack and damage healthy growing crops. The most important British problems are connected with Bark beetles on pine and larch, and also weevils on the former tree. The insects concerned are the weevils, *Pissodes* spp. (Leaflet 29), and the Bark beetles *Tomicus piniperda* or Pine shoot beetle (Leaflet 3), and *Ips cembrae*. The last is a fairly recent introduction to this country, having first been recorded in 1956, and is so far confined in distribution to east and central Scotland. The young adults of these two species feed by boring into twigs or branches. In the case of *Tomicus*, they bore up the centre of young, usually one-year-old shoots, and in *Ips* in the cambium and wood, girdling branches up to four years old. These damaged parts break off and, since the leading shoot is often involved, permanent and serious distortions of the main stem can result. Control can be achieved by maintaining a good standard of forest hygiene, and it is thus a managerial rather than a strictly entomological problem. As a general rule, it is wise to ensure that stems which are felled in thinning and clearing operations are not left in the forest long enough for a brood to be produced from them. Material, therefore, should not be left in the forest for more than six weeks from the time of felling, during the period from April through to July, in case of *Tomicus*, and rather later in the year for *Ips*. If removal within this time limit is not feasible, the bark beetle brood should be destroyed, either by disbarking the timber or by spraying it with gamma HCH. Leaflet 3 gives further details of the methods which should be employed. Good forest hygiene is also effective in controlling numbers of *Pissodes* weevils.

STEM FEEDERS

Another category of insect which may be the cause of direct or indirect loss are those that feed on tree stems. The more important species belong either to the family of so-called Scale insects or to the Woolly aphids or adelgids. The well-known Felted beech coccus, *Cryptococcus fagi* (Leaflet 15), may produce unsightly quantities of waxy wool on the stems and branches of forest and amenity beech trees. Its association with the fungus disease, *Nectria coccinea*, however, is not so well known. A joint attack of these two organisms can cause a serious canker and die-back condition in beech crops (Forest Record 96). Again the Ash scale, *Pseudochermes (Fonscolombia) fraxini*, is associated with, and may be a contributory cause of, a debilitated condition of ash. Among conifers conspicuous stem infestation may be seen on *Abies* spp., particularly on *A. grandis* by *Adelges piceae*, is well as on *Pinus strobus* by the species *Pineus strobi*. Infestations on *Abies* sometimes lead to a form of timber degrade or reaction wood termed Rotholz. Infestation on *Pinus strobus* appears to have no noticeable direct effect although stems affected are often also attacked by the pathogenic rust fungus *Cronartium ribicola*.

Insecticides

Approved Products for Farmers and Growers is an annually-prepared list of chemicals sanctioned for use under the Agricultural Chemicals Approval Scheme of the Ministry of Agriculture, Fisheries and Food.

It is important to follow closely the advice given by the makers on the containers or associated literature for each product. *The Insecticide and Fungicide Handbook*, published by the British Crop Protection Council, is a mine of information as to prescription and treatment of specific pest species.

BIBLIOGRAPHY: DISEASES AND INSECT PESTS

Forestry Commission Publications

BULLETINS

No. 26   *Adelges insects of Silver firs.* 1956.
No. 38   *The Great spruce bark beetle* Dendroctonus micans. 1965.
No. 42   *Conifer woolly aphids (Adelgidae) in Great Britain.* 1971.
No. 43   *Nursery practice.* 1972.

BOOKLETS

No. 3   *Chestnut blight caused by the fungus* Endothia parasitica. 1951.
No. 4   *Rusts of British forest trees.* 1956.
No. 13   *Principal butt rots of conifers.* 1965.

LEAFLETS

No. 2   Adelges cooleyi, *an insect pest of Douglas fir and Sitka spruce.* 1960.
No. 3   *Pine Shoot Beetles.* 1977.
No. 5   *Fomes annosus.* 1974.
No. 6   *Honey fungus.* 1971. (Also Arboricultural Leaflet No. 2—below).
No. 7   *Adelgids attacking spruce and other conifers.* 1968.
No. 8   *Megastigmus flies attacking conifer seeds.* 1961.
No. 10   *Oak-leaf roller moth.* 1961.
No. 15   *Felted beech coccus.* 1956.
No. 16   *Larch canker and dieback.* 1969.
No. 18   *Two Leaf-cast diseases of Douglas fir.* 1956.

Plate 1 Tripod steps. The collector is removing cones from seed orchard trees of larch. The cones are being put straight into the cone-collecting bag. (p. 3).

Plate 2   Lining out by hand in long lines. Note board on right. Bagley Wood Nursery, near Oxford. (p. 5).

Plate 3 (top) Planting on overturned turves cut from a shallow drain with a rutter and set out in a regular pattern with a drag or hack. (p. 23 and 25).

Plate 4 (below) Repair of drainage in a plantation using rutter and drag. A bottoming spade provides a clear run-off for water.

Plate 5   Spring steel forest fencing, against deer and sheep. Note long distance between posts. (p. 30).

Plate 6 (top)   Tray of 440 eight-week-old Lodgepole pine tubed seedlings ready for planting. (p. 31).

Plate 7 (below)   Special tool for planting tubed seedlings in peat, with seedling in position. Note cut-away portion of tube, and depth gauge. (p. 32).

Plate 9 L–Notch planting on overturned furrow. (p. 32).

Plate 8 Planting on old woodland. Note planting bag and straight spade. Sighting rods on left are being used by an adjoining planter. (p. 32).

Plate 10   Herbicide being applied from a knapsack sprayer. (p. 35).

Plate 11 (top)   Young fructifications of Honey fungus, *Armillaria mellea*. Right can be seen the sub-cortical rhizomorphs after the bark has fallen off. (p. 40).

Plate 12 (below)   Fructifications of *Fomes annosus* at the base of a dying 27-year-old-pine. (p. 41).

Plate 13 Adults of the Large pine weevil, *Hylobius abietis*, feeding on the bark of a young Scots pine. (p. 45).

Plate 15   Pine shoot defoliated by larvae of Pine looper moth. (p. 47).

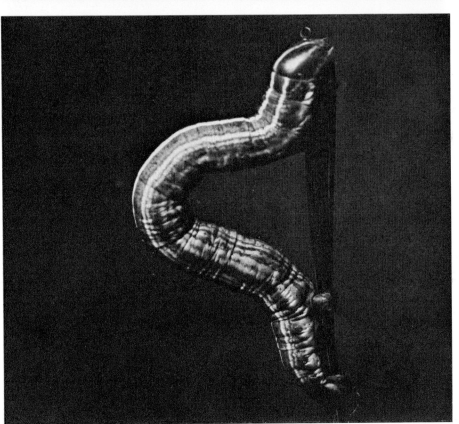

Plate 14   Larva of the Pine looper moth, *Bupalus piniaria*. (p. 47).

Plate 16 A Forestry Commission picnic site, showing information kiosk and car park. (p. 59).

Plate 17 After widening the road formation to make a timber loading bay, the dozer spreads and consolidates the road metal delivered by tipping lorry. (p. 121).

No. 20 *Watermark disease of the Cricket bat willow.* 1977.
No. 21 *Leaf-cast of larch,* Meria laricis. 1963.
No. 27 *Poplar cultivation.* 1963.
No. 29 *Pissodes weevils.* 1952.
No. 32 *Pine looper moth,* Bupalus piniaria. 1966
No. 35 *Pine sawflies.* 1955.
No. 38 *Oak mildew.* 1956.
No. 43 *Keithia disease of Western red cedar*, Thuja plicata. 1974.
No. 48 *Needle-cast of pine.* 1964.
No. 49 *Resin-top disease of Scots pine.* 1964.
No. 50 *Grey mould in forest nurseries.* 1969.
No. 53 *Blue stain of coniferous wood.* 1968.
No. 58 *The Large pine weevil and Black pine beetles.* 1974.
No. 65 *Group dying of conifers.* 1976.

FOREST RECORDS

No. 54 *Decay in standing conifers developing from extraction damage.* 1965.
No. 55 *Death of Pedunculate oak and variations in annual radial increments related to climate.* 1965.
No. 57 *The relationship between resin pressure and Scolytid beetle activity.* 1966.
No. 61 *Brunchorstia dieback of Corsican pine.* 1967.
No. 82 *Dutch elm disease survey, 1971.* 1972.
No. 83 *The Pine shoot moth and related species.* 1972.
No. 84 *Winter temperatures and survival of the Green spruce aphid.* 1972.
No. 96 *Beech bark disease.* 1974.
No. 100 *Dutch elm disease survey, 1972–1973.* 1974.
No. 104 *Towards integrated control of Tree aphids.* 1975.
No. 105 *Experiments with insecticides for the control of Dutch elm disease.* 1975.
No. 111 *Some Important Foreign Diseases of Broadleaved Trees.* 1977.
No. 115 *Dutch Elm Disease.* 1977.

No. 116 *The EEC Plant Directive and British Forestry.* 1978.
No. 117 *Gilpinia hercyniae—a pest of spruce.* 1978.
No. 119 *Pine looper moth,* Bupalus piniaria. 1978.
No. 120 *The Pine Beauty Moth.* 1978.

Other Publications

Arboricultural Leaflet No. 1—*External signs of Decay in Trees.* 1977, HMSO.
Arboricultural Leaflet No. 2—*Honey Fungus* 1977, HMSO.
Arboricultural Leaflet No. 3—*Sooty Bark Disease of Sycamore.* 1978, HMSO.
Arboricultural Leaflet No. 4—*Virus and Virus-like Diseases of trees.* 1978, HMSO.
Arboricultural Leaflet No. 5—*Common Decay Fungi in Broadleaved Trees.* 1978, HMSO.
Bridgeman, P. H. (1976). *Tree surgery, a complete guide.* Newton Abbot: David & Charles.
British Crop Protection Council (1972). *Insecticide and fungicide handbook for crop protection.* Ed. H. Martin. 4th edn. Oxford: Blackwell Scientific Publications.
British Standards BS 3998: 1966, *Recommendations for tree work.*
Ministry of Agriculture, Fisheries and Food. *Approved products for farmers and growers.* Annually, HMSO.

LEGISLATION

Under the Plant Health Act 1967:
The Importation of Forest Trees (Prohibition) (Great Britain) Order 1965 (SI 1965 No. 2121), as amended by SI 1974 No. 1.
The Importation of Wood (Prohibition) (Great Britain) Order 1974 (SI 1974 No. 2).
The Watermark Disease (Local Authorities) Order 1974 (SI 1974 No. 768).
The Dutch Elm Disease (Local Authorities) Order 1974 (SI 1974 No. 830), as amended by SI 1974 No. 1816 and SI 1975 Nos 55, 1163 and 1905.
The Dutch Elm Disease (Restriction on Movement of Elms) Order 1975 (SI 1975 No. 1904).

E

Chapter 5

WILDLIFE MANAGEMENT

WILDLIFE MANAGEMENT PHILOSOPHY

Foresters live in a rural environment and work with nature, not against it, to produce their crops. This is reflected in their approach to the problems that come from the wildlife which inhabit the same environment. The emphasis is upon the *management* of wildlife, and to control those animals and birds which cause damage, not to eliminate them.

The forests are the natural habitat of many wild species, and the forester is well aware of their value to man. Their presence is not only a considerable amenity, providing an important interest for countryside lovers and pursuers of natural history studies, but they are of a special educational value with examples of rare and common forms of wildlife. They are important scientifically as a reserve of natural types (sometimes called 'gene pool'), and as a source of new zoological discoveries of benefit to mankind. Finally they often have a monetary value where the particular species concerned is prized for its sporting, or even for its meat. People will pay surprisingly high prices for the opportunity to use a gun to shoot animals or birds, to collect trophies (e.g. the antlers of deer) and to be able to dine on game (e.g. pheasant and venison).

Where a forester has to take steps to control wildlife he should endeavour to carry out the necessary measures *humanely*. By this it is meant that he should be prepared to accept a limited amount of damage, and not attempt to completely exterminate the offending beasts. He should concentrate his attention on those areas where the crops are suffering the greatest damage. He will study his population, and by doing so learn how best to reduce the amount of damage. Above all, where it is necessary to kill animals he will do it quickly, without pain and without terror.

TYPES OF DAMAGE

Wildlife can harm forest crops in a variety of ways. Primarily damage results from their feeding off trees, and the extent will depend upon the size of the tree concerned. Young trees, if heavily grazed, or 'browsed', can be completely killed. Larger trees can be so heavily pruned that they barely grow at all from year to year, while if the bark is stripped away from stems or branches as the animal goes for the juicy cambial layers underneath, parts of the tree will die, resulting in malformation and poor timber.

Sometimes damage can be caused by activities other than feeding, such as the harmful effect of droppings from starling roosts. Particularly heavy damage can be sustained in areas carrying a high deer population

where the bark of young trees is scraped off or 'frayed' by the males rubbing their freshly grown antlers. This activity is necessary to remove the skin or 'velvet' from the antlers as they mature.

METHODS OF CONTROL

There are a number of approaches which will meet with varying success depending on the species concerned, the local situation and the expertise required. Natural methods are most acceptable to the conservationist. By providing alternative food, either planting or encouraging the regrowth of plants more palatable than forest trees, or even bringing in hay and other feedstuffs, damage can be minimised. The encouragement of predators (e.g. by erecting perches for owls in vole infested areas) is another method.

The introduction of barriers in the form of fencing may be necessary, especially where domestic stock as well as wildlife have to be guarded against. Chemical barriers, or repellants, have a limited success; when applied to living trees, for instance, subsequent growth is unprotected.

Elimination may be the only effective remedy. It should always be carefully controlled, restricted to the precise locality where unacceptable damage is suffered, and should cease as soon as trees grow out of a vulnerable stage. Shotguns, rifles, cage and spring traps, poison bait and poison gas, are the main methods used. There is, though, always the necessity to consider whether other non-damaging animals will be affected by the method chosen.

DAMAGING SPECIES

Deer

There is a variety of wild deer in our forests which can cause unacceptable damage amongst young plantations from their browsing and fraying.

Control: Control of deer is best effected by first estimating the population of deer, deciding the number which can be sustained by a given forest area without unacceptable damage, and eliminating the difference between these two numbers as a 'cull'. Careful consideration must be given to which beasts will be removed (keeping the best specimens and taking out the sick and weakly), and to establishing the correct balance of sexes. Culling should be carried out by a skilled rifleman, using a high velocity rifle and telescopic sight. Where woodlands are scattered, or adjoin neighbouring woodlands, an integrated plan of control should be drawn up with the cooperation of adjoining owners (Leaflet 52 and Forest Record 99).

Rabbits

Although the incidence of damage by this animal has been greatly diminished by myxamatosis, population levels are beginning to rise in many parts of the country. Damage is usually confined to freshly planted trees, though older trees may suffer, particularly in hard weather.

Control: Shooting with shotguns, snaring and spring traps are all effective. Where rabbit populations form burrows, they can be dealt with either by ferreting or by the use of poison gas (Leaflet 67).

Squirrel

There are two species, red squirrels and grey squirrels. The former cause damage in conifer plantations, the latter in broadleaved stands. Damage is suffered in the crowns of the trees when squirrels tear off the bark to feed on the juicy cambial layers. Red squirrel damage is very limited, confined to certain parts of the country, and rarely results in the need to take active control measures. Grey squirrels are profuse over most of the country, and the damage, which results in the mutilation and death of the crowns and branches, of often highly valuable timber trees, is unacceptable.

Control: These animals are easily trapped in spring traps and cage traps, provided the techniques are well understood and properly carried out. If the correct feeding hoppers are used it is now permissible to use poison bait in areas where red squirrels do not exist (Leaflet 56 and Forest Record 101).

Voles and Mice

In thick, grassy areas, which provide a safe habitat for the small mammals, fresh plantings of trees can suffer severe damage from their feeding. Populations are not constant, and reach peaks in certain years when the bark may be stripped off at ground level by feeding voles and mice.

Control: When populations are found to be on the increase it may be necessary to use poison bait placed in the 'runs' through the grass, setting the bait systematically on a grid system throughout a young plantation (Forest Record 90).

Starlings

Damage is rare, localised, but extremely serious when it does occur. Massive flocks congregate in the crowns of pole-crops and the blanket of extremely strong droppings that build up on the ground can kill trees over a substantial area.

Control: Flocks may be dispersed by use of guns, noisy drums and rattles, fireworks or tape recordings of the birds' alarm call. Each of these methods calls for extreme patience and persistently frightening the birds as they come in to roost. Eventually they can be persuaded to leave the area. (Leaflet 69.)

Finches

Flocks of finches can create havoc in nurseries by feeding on newly emerging seedlings.

Control: Netting with wire or plastic small mesh material is the only really successful method, though somewhat costly.

Other Species

Damage can be caused to forests by birds such as capercaillie and crossbills. Other species of wildlife, including badgers, pine martens and butterflies, while causing no appreciable damage must nevertheless be taken into account in forest management.

BIBLIOGRAPHY: WILDLIFE MANAGEMENT

Forestry Commission Publications

BOOKLET

No. 29   *Wildlife conservation in woodlands.* 1972.

LEAFLETS

No. 52   *The fallow deer.* 1971.
No. 56   *Grey squirrel control.* 1973.
No. 67   *Rabbit management in woodlands.*
No. 68   *Badger gates.* 1976.
No. 69   *Starling Roost Dispersal from Woodlands.* 1977.
No. 73   *Chemical Repellants.* 1978.

FOREST RECORDS

No. 64   *Pine martens.* 1968.
No. 65   *Butterflies in woodlands.* 1974.
No. 66   *Blackgame.* 1971.
No. 76   *Polecats.* 1975.
No. 77   *Hedgehogs.* 1973.
No. 80   *Forest fencing.* 1972.
No. 85   *The coal tit.* 1975.
No. 86   *Crossbills.* 1973.
No. 89   *Titmice in woodlands.* 1973.
No. 90   *Voles and field mice.* 1974.
No. 91   *Birds and woodlands.* 1974.
No. 92   *Woodpeckers in woodlands.* 1975.
No. 98   *The crested tit.* 1974.
No. 99   *The roe deer.* 1974.
No. 101   *Red squirrel.* 1975.
No. 103   *Badgers in woodlands.* 1975.
No. 109   *The capercaillie.* 1976.
No. 118   *Woodland mice.* 1978.

RESEARCH AND DEVELOPMENT PAPER

No. 104   *Public demands on forests in relation to forest wildlife.* 1973.

Chapter 6

FIRE PROTECTION

The size, location and nature of a woodland estate dictate the level of fire precautions and fire fighting capacity which can be justified. Here are described the kind of options open to an estate, but it is the owner's responsibility to try to assess his own overall situation, and to select the most appropriate scheme. It is possible to insure against fire losses, but Insurance Companies usually expect reasonable precautions to have been taken to reduce fire danger, and it would be a mistake to rely solely on insurance cover.

Fire danger is a combination of *fire risk* and *fire hazard*. Fire risk is whether a fire is likely to be started. It increases with the presence of people, especially holiday-makers or day trippers, or if other possible fire starting elements are present, like neighbouring moorland during heather and grass burning seasons, or a harvested corn field if stubble burning is practised. Fire hazard is how susceptible vegetation is to burning if a fire spreads to or starts in it. It depends on the kind of vegetation present, its flammability, wind force, and relative humidity. There is obviously no fire danger even if fire hazard (the condition of fuel) is critical, if there is no remote risk of a fire being started. There is extreme fire danger in areas which are in a most hazardous condition when there is a high risk of a fire being started.

FIRE PLANS

Plan layout

The first thing an owner must do is to assess fire danger in his estate and in each particular block of woodland. He will then follow, perhaps after advice, with decisions on the level of fire precautions he will take, and set up some system for calling out fire fighting assistance. If he sets all this down in a logical manner, in a **fire plan**, it will help him make his decisions, and will be a useful medium for passing information to outside bodies, such as the Fire Service, who may be involved with fire protection measures. A small estate may be able to enter the whole of its plan on a few sheets, including maps, which can be used in the field under emergency conditions. Larger estates may consider having two plans, an **emergency plan** consisting of Fire Location Maps and a brief statement of telephone numbers and fire fighting arrangements, and an **organisation plan** which would be an office-based planning document.

Comprehensive fire plan layouts can be found in the booklets:

Fire Protection in Forests and Woodlands issued by the Home Office.

Fire Protection for Forests and Woodlands issued by the Scottish Home and Health Department.

Consultation with Fire Service

An integral part of any planning should be consultation with the local Fire Service. Fire Services are willing, within the limits of staff availability, to help owners by discussing the best means of prevention, and the best arrangements for tackling fires on their properties. Certain times of the year are less busy for Fire Service personnel, and an owner should arrange a mutually suitable time for discussion of his problems. An annual contact is to be recommended.

FIRE PROTECTION METHODS

Fire Protection methods are aimed at reducing risk or hazard. There are two main ways of doing this:

to try to prevent fires starting, and

to try to reduce the possible size of a fire when one starts.

Methods Aimed at Prevention

PUBLICITY

Statistics indicate that the public, by accident or intent, are responsible for over 60 per cent of Forestry Commission fire outbreaks. It is not known if this is also true of privately owned woodlands, but it is a reasonable supposition. A high proportion of the remaining Forestry Commission fires is caused by the carelessness of neighbours—muirburning or hedge burning farmers, railways and the like. The Commission makes use of all opportunities offered by the Press, radio and television, at both national and local level to make the public more aware of forest fire danger, concentrating its attack during the seasons of highest fire danger. Information on fire statistics, and on the damage done to faunal and floral populations during fires, is released, to bring more public awareness. Staff involved with the public stress the risk of fire and describe the hazards involved, be it at a school or college talk on forestry or merely a recreation ranger meeting a party in a picnic site or on a forest walk. A private owner has less opportunity for this form of publicity, and generally has to rely on the Forestry Commission. He can, however, make an approach through **fire warning signs** or beater stands. Good quality signs are not cheap and should be used only where their message will achieve maximum impact— i.e. in hazardous areas where the public have a right to or are invited to enter, and in especially dangerous areas. A better impact may be achieved by only putting up warning signs during the fire danger season, and removing them when the danger ceases. Most fire warning signs simply warn, but some tell the public what action to take in case of fire, locating the nearest telephone and giving the appropriate number to ring. Beater racks or stands have also been used as a visual reminder to the public of fire danger, as well as being a local store for immediate fire fighting.

An owner should personally cultivate good relations with his neighbours rather than warn them of fire danger by a formal letter. People generally take more care in burning waste material when they appreciate the danger, and good neighbours become a source of help if a fire breaks out—either by quicker intimation of an outbreak, or by actual help in fire fighting.

WOODMEN AND CONTRACTORS

It should be impressed on every individual who works in the woods that he is at all times responsible for taking the utmost care with fires in every shape and form. Estate and woodland staff should be continually reminded of fire danger, especially when fire hazard increases after a spell of little or no danger. Contracts for the sale of timber, or for carrying out other forest operations, should always include clauses defining responsibility for fire precautions, and compensation for any damage incurred.

In practice, it is useless to try to stop all smoking by workmen in the woods, or to prohibit the lighting of fires to brew up tea. A more practical line is to lay down times and places where men may smoke or light fires, give the precautions to be observed, and insist that these rules be followed.

REDUCING THE RISK OF A FIRE SPREADING FROM NEARBY GROUND

Apart from achieving maximum cooperation from neighbours, some physical means of stopping fires on neighbouring ground from spreading into plantations can be employed.

Fire Breaks. These are permanent features of a forest, with at least a 10 metre width kept clear of inflammable vegetation. Their surface should be firm and level enough to allow access and movement of

TABLE 7

FIRE BREAKS—COMPARISON OF ALTERNATIVE METHODS

Method	Appropriate Situation	Advantages	Disadvantages
Cultivation: plough, hand tool, bulldozer or discs, usually smoothed later by tine harrow or discs.	Particularly dangerous situations and infertile ground unsuitable for pasture.	No Risk. Can be done in any season.	Unless cambered and on suitable soil type can hinder access. Unsightly.
*Chemicals (paraquat) by knapsack sprayer.	Steep or rocky ground where mechanical equipment cannot work.	May have protection for 2 seasons.	Expensive. Not effective on calcarious soils or on all types of vegetation.
*Burning.	Where cultivation is difficult, and neighbours are likely to burn adjoining land.	May be integrated with agricultural practice.	High risk. Dependent on season. Needs annual repetition. If left unburned because of weather can be higher hazard next season.
Mowing: Large gang mower.	On soils which will carry pasture grasses, and where a reasonable surface can be obtained.	Good appearance. Low maintenance cost. Good access.	Initial formation cost usually high.
*Grazing	On soils which will carry pasture grasses.	May be integrated with estate management.	Stock management problems e.g. fencing. Initial cost can be high.

*See notes below.

CHEMICALS

Herbicides can be used to kill off vegetation, but have the disadvantage of often increasing hazard until the dead material is removed. Paraquat has proved effective against grasses especially *Molinia*. Booklet 40, *Chemical Control of Weeds in the Forest* describes its application. Spraying is usually done in early summer, and the dead material burned off 3 to 4 weeks later while surrounding vegetation is still green and less flammable. The break produced can be used as an additional safety barrier if controlled burning is contemplated the following spring. Treatment of heather or gorse is not recommended as surrounding untreated growth is seldom in a safe condition.

PROTECTIVE BURNING

Burning off dry vegetation in early spring, around the margins of plantations provides a temporary fire proof break that is effective through the following summer. It has to be repeated annually, however, and if weather prevents this in any particular year, problems of increased hazard can develop. The operation is always risky since a change of wind can quickly bring disaster. A proper fire line should be made, either by the use of herbicides as indicated above, or by setting a continuous line of vegetation alight and beating out the side nearest the plantation as soon as the flames separate into 2 lines. In planning and carrying out protective burning a number of points should be borne in mind.

 a. Compliance with statutory requirements. Under the Heather and Grass Burning (England and Wales) Regulations 1949, a licence is required other than during the period 1 November–31 March. In Scotland the situation is controlled by the Hill Farming Act 1946 which stipulates that muirburn is lawful only from 1 October to 15 April, though there are provisions for extensions in certain circumstances.

 b. Burning must only be carried out in daylight hours.

 c. Neighbours must be notified of the intention to burn.

 d. The local Fire Service should be warned of your intention.

 e. Calm conditions are essential. Wind should never exceed Force 2, Beaufort Scale, and should be away from the plantation.

 f. There must be adequate men and equipment to control the operation. An internal Forestry Commission instruction specifies that the burning fire line should not exceed 5 metres per man, with an overall limit of 60 metres, at any one time.

Protective burning is always risky. It can be made a little safer by the use of some form of 'sticker' to hold water on vegetation. Water sprayed directly on vegetation drips off, and drains away from the site. The addition of sodium alginate increases the water's viscosity several hundred times and prevents run-off from the foliage. The mixture, termed **viscous water** can be sprayed on a strip some 2 metres wide and used as a secondary safeguarding fire line. However, a special mixer/dispenser unit is needed to apply viscous water, and this is unlikely to be available to the smaller private estates. The use of foam making appliances by adding concentrate to water is also being tried. Medium-expansion foam expands approximately 30 times, and the foam will persist on foliage for about an hour before drying off.

Certain other chemicals when added to plain water aid dispersal of water through and over certain types of vegetation and soil, where plain water runs off in globules. These **wetting agents** are most effective on peaty ground, or on bracken, heather and tussocky grasses. They do not 'stick' water onto foliage, and are probably better employed in damping down the plantation edge of the burned strip than in making a secondary fire line. Various commercial wetting agents are available but household washing up liquid can be used in an emergency. Wetting agents are poisonous to fish and slightly corrosive. To avoid pollution care should be taken to flush out equipment well away from water courses.

GRAZING

This is a logical development from mown breaks, and is possibly a better form of integrated land use. However fencing off the plantation may be the biggest drawback and prove uneconomic. In many sheep rearing areas, stock is kept to the level which can survive the winter in sheltered in-bye parts of the farm, and is insufficient in summer to make full use of all the grazing available on higher ground. The 'surplus' grazing material builds up and increases the hazard where plantations are nearby. The production by the forester of improved grazing on his surrounds could hold sheep on the higher ground into the winter, and could well be dangerous for the farming stock. The forester must be careful to integrate his practice with the local farming one and this can only be done with good local cooperation.

---

vehicles and equipment for fire fighting. Quite often a feature of a fire spreading from adjoining land is that it has had time to build up in size, and fire fighting teams may have to be deployed to dampen down or put out outbreaks on the plantation side of the break. Fire breaks are an expensive form of protection, and an attempt should be made to assess the danger a break is intended to counter, and the value of losses if a crop was burned, and to reconcile these with the annual cost of producing the break. There are various means of forming and maintaining breaks, and these are described and compared in Table 7.

Breaks should be set out in the best possible position. Sometimes the boundary dictates this but topographical features can be used to reinforce their effectiveness. Ridges, brows of hills, physical barriers like streams, and sheltered parts of the forest have advantages, although the effect of the proposed barrier on the landscape must also be borne in mind. On occasion a break can be set up some way inside a plantation, if there are clear cost effectiveness or landscape benefits to be gained, and the higher risk accepted of losing the plantation left between the break and the boundary.

Fire Belts and Barriers. Belts of trees that do not themselves readily catch fire can be helpful in many cases. Broadleaved trees may be retained in a continuous strip, and enriched if need be with other broadleaves, or if bigger gaps occur, with larch. If the site is silviculturally suitable, larch can be planted to form a strip, and possibly four rows of trees would give a minimum width. Care must be taken at the planning stage to integrate these belts with the landscape, and it may be possible to vary the width so that the broadleaved or larch bands run up into any natural gullies or by some other means to break up their unnatural banded appearance while maintaining a continuous barrier.

Other forms of barrier worth preserving include hedges, walls, ditches and water courses. These, and indeed all other fire breaks, should never be regarded as fire proof, but only as obstacles to the rapid spread of a blaze where fire fighters might be able to check it.

Brashing. Where outside ground vegetation grows up to the forest edge, the removal of all the side branches to a height of 2 metres on the trees in a 10 metre-wide strip may stop a fire travelling into the tree canopy. The aim is to create a gap between ground vegetation and branches, and all cut material must be dragged inside the plantation, well away from the strip.

Methods aimed at reducing loss when a fire occurs

BREAKING UP A PLANTATION INTO SMALLER BLOCKS

If a plantation is sub-divided by means of internal fire breaks, or belts or other forms of barrier, possible losses, if a fire takes hold, will be reduced. The means of doing this are basically similar to those employed in preventing a fire spreading from adjoining land, and the only points worth repeating are the need to appraise the annual cost against the possible savings, and the need to look at the effect the barriers may have in a future landscape. Two additional suggestions for breaking up a crop are:

Breaking up the woods with different types of crop. It is a common experience when fighting a forest fire to find that its progress goes unhindered through a crop of one species and age of tree, but is checked as soon as it meets woods of another species or age class, thus giving fire fighters a chance to defeat it. Where the layout and scheme of management of the woods permit, it is therefore a good plan to break up large homogeneous blocks either by breaks in the species or in the age class.

Roading. When roads are being designed for timber extraction, it is worth bearing in mind that they can serve as useful internal fire breaks, It is worthwhile on occasion to consider additional features such as fire breaks or belts, to continue a road line to the edge of a plantation so that it can contain a fire. On the other hand, roads can increase fire risk by encouraging visitors into the woods, or even increase hazard by opening up areas to weed growth which might be highly inflammable.

RECEIVING AN EARLY WARNING OF A FIRE

The smaller a fire is when it is first tackled, the easier it is to extinguish.

Fire Lookouts and Patrols. The use of men to watch specifically for fire outbreaks is so expensive that it can only be considered for exceptional times such as Bank Holidays, if conditions are dangerous, and even then only for the most dangerous hours of the day. Lookouts must be equipped with some ready means of reporting an outbreak, and the means of communication is usually expensive. Fixed structures, such as towers, allow the installation of telephones, but have the disadvantages of either not covering the whole forest area, or of covering a hazardous section which can grow out of that condition in a few years. Mobile patrols may do some good by warning people or even of putting out small outbreaks. They must be equipped either with a radio pocket set (Chapter 12) or a vehicle so that they can reach a telephone quickly. Patrols must know the locality well enough to locate a fire, and should be instructed to report at regular intervals to keep the Control Centre aware of their position.

Neighbours. Good relations with neighbours are very worthwhile. By definition they live in or near the estate, and are therefore in a good position to see and warn the Centre of any fires. They can be put to good use too, if the position of a smoke report needs verification, or to confirm its cause. A list of neighbours' telephone numbers should be maintained, and their cooperation sought for describing and locating possible fires.

Public. Members of the public should be encouraged to report outbreaks of fire, and even to help fighting them.

PROVISION OF ACCESS AND WATER SUPPLIES

Common sense and experience dictate that easy access to a forest is an important factor in containing any fire which may occur within it. It can, however, be expensive to invest capital in roads and culverts years before they could be justified for major usage. Access provision must therefore be carefully assessed, and it may be possible to carry out inexpensive operations to improve access, while not providing the highest quality roads. Fire Services depend on good access to carry their equipment to a fire, and it is important not only to consult them fully, but to ensure that they are acquainted with any entrances from public roads which may not always be obvious.

The provision of static water supplies can be simple, and these can be invaluable in fire fighting or damping down after a fire. The minimum useful static supply is considered to be 2000 litres (440 gallons) and the smallest reliable flowing supply, about 5000 litres per hour with a one metre depth at the pumping point.

Wherever possible the damming of streams is to be preferred to the erection of water tanks which are often unsightly and difficult to maintain. Forest Record 75, *Design, Construction and maintenance of earth dams and excavated ponds* may help an owner considering the provision of dams. An owner should consult the local Water Authority or Regional Water Board before he impounds water as a licence may be necessary. He should bear in mind the risk that children or other visitors may find these attractive, and possibly dangerous.

Where ponds, lochs, or large streams already exist, they can often be brought into a fire protection scheme by making a short access route possible by lorries or fire appliances.

The desirability of seeking the advice of the local Fire Service on all aspects of provision of access and water supplies cannot be overstressed.

PROVISION OF BEATERS AND OTHER FIRE FIGHTING EQUIPMENT.

A small readily available supply of fire fighting equipment is essential to allow an immediate 'first-aid' attack before a fire grows too large to be easily extinguished. What equipment is needed depends on the scale and nature of the estate woodlands. For the commonest type of fire, where ground vegetation and small trees are alight, some form of beater is used, backed up if possible with knapsack sprayers or larger quantities of water. If fires occur in the crowns of older crops, fire fighting is usually restricted to containing a fire from prepared fire lines using large quantities of water.

Fire Beaters. A number of different types are used. **Birch brooms,** made by wiring freshly cut birch twigs together in lengths of 0·6–0·9 metres (2–3 feet) onto a springy birch pole some 1·8 m (6 feet) long are the most common. They are of most value in rough heather or tussocky ground. Their drawbacks are that if left in the open they only remain serviceable for one year. It is therefore best to only leave a few out in the forest for propaganda and immediate fire fighting purposes, and to maintain a larger stock in a covered store, where they will remain serviceable for 2 years, and are less likely to be borrowed by visitors. **Conveyor belting,** in pieces about 0·4 × 0·5 m (15 × 18 inches) can be attached to poles with small bolts. If the poles are of longer lasting wood like ash, they will last for a number of years. Alternatively, a doubled or tripled piece of **rabbit netting** can be attached to the pole, usually by threading spring steel wire through the outer edge of the netting, and binding the ends to the pole. Both belting and netting types are best used on *Molinia* ground, or where there are not too many tussocks or rocks, as they cannot be used to poke out embers in awkward corners. A **hessian sack,** especially if it can be dampened from time to time, is a very simple and very efficient beater,

and has the advantage that a small supply can be carried in a car boot. **Shovels** are another option, and can be used for digging embers and scattering soil as well as in a beating action.

Other Equipment. Even in a small estate some items of equipment in addition to beaters are considered essential. There should be a supply of usable torches for night work. Wire cutters are often required for speeding up access, and knapsack pumps are needed, not only for backing up beaters, but for damping down after a fire. A supply of wetting agent is a useful addition to the knapsack pump outfit, to allow better water penetration.

In a larger estate, or where the number of helpers would permit the cutting of fire lines, additional equipment would be

a. chain saws

b. axes for awkward obstacles which might damage chain saws

c. spades/shovels for clearing a trace

d. trailer or Land-Rover-mounted pumps may be useful, but only if there is a good enough access to the woods to allow the pump to be brought within reach of likely fires and if there are adequate water supplies to serve the pump's rate of delivery.

e. small portable pumps are mainly of value for bringing water closer to a fire site for damping down. In this connection, portable canvas dams holding about 450 litres, may be held in the fire store, and filled on site either by portable pumps or by the Fire Service tender before it leaves, and can be used in turn to fill knapsack pumps for damping down.

Whatever equipment is decided upon should be kept close to the vehicle's garage, not to be used for any other purpose, checked prior to the start of a fire season, and be freely available to estate staff (i.e. kept unlocked).

TRAINING FIRE FIGHTERS IN ADVANCE

A trained gang is far more effective than men pulled in only in an emergency. The possible saving in fire losses makes training well worthwhile, and it can often be tied in with controlled burning of particularly dangerous boundaries, or the actual testing of fire equipment. Training should be made as realistic as possible, and should include the reporting of the fire and the transport of men and tools to the scene. Any exercise should of course be discussed with the Fire Service beforehand. It could save them an unnecessary journey!

All estate staff should know what to do if they come across a fire. The most useful general rules are:

If you see a fire starting tackle it.

If after a few minutes it is clearly beyond your control (i.e. if the burning area is larger than when you started fire fighting), leave it and report immediately to:

a. The Fire Service
b. The Estate Fire Control Centre

If there are 2 or more of you, one should run to report the fire, the rest should tackle the blaze.

After any fire which occurs, the men should be brought together to discuss lessons learned about the sequence of events, the tools and techniques used, and to question future plans or actions.

CALLING OUT FIRE FIGHTING TEAMS

Whenever a report of a fire is received, the Fire Service and the Police should be informed, giving whatever details of location and type and size of the fire that are known. The Fire Service will wish to know even if you only have a smoke report which needs further investigation, and will take appropriate action.

The man in charge at the estate itself should gather as many men as he can find in a minute or two, and hasten to the fire, driving the vehicle carrying the fire fighting tools. He should not wait to muster a large gang—fires can grow faster than the band of helpers. A few determined hands soon on the spot will have a much smaller task to do, and can do more than a score or more, half an hour later. The rest of the staff should be under instructions to go at once to the scene of any suspected fire by whatever means is quickest. As a rule the word is soon passed around, or they see smoke rising. Some kind of audible warning, such as a siren, huntsman's horn or a loud whistle may be of help, depending on the size of the estate and the scatter of the workforce.

Fire Fighting Techniques

The way a fire is fought depends on the type and scale of fire involved. Three types of fire are recognised, but in any one forest fire all three may exist, and it is useful to recognise changes if they occur, and to change the fighting techniques if need be.

SURFACE FIRES

These are where all combustible material in contact with the ground, including ground vegetation and whole young trees, are burning. The beater is of most value in this situation backed up with pumps or knapsack sprayers.

Fires usually develop 2 flanks fanning from the point of origin, and the main tactic should be to work down each flank and gradually 'pinch out' the fire. The flank endangering the areas of highest value should be tackled first if manpower is not sufficient to fight two faces simultaneously. Some points to note are:

a. Beating should be an up-and-down motion, sufficient to smother the flames, but not so vigorous as to scatter embers.
b. Fighters should work as a team, advancing and beating together, especially where the fire front is too hot to work for more than a few seconds at a time.

c. If supplies of water are limited they should be saved for assisting at particularly hot spots.
d. In situations where beating is impracticable, areas of broken rocky ground for instance, the fire may be smothered at least to some degree by scattering spadefuls of humus-free soil.

Once a fire is established in a thicket stage or older plantation, a direct attack on the fire other than with large amounts of water, becomes impossible, and it is necessary to choose a good defensive position sufficiently ahead of the fire to ensure that advance preparations to meet it can be made. These would include:

a. clearing of humus and loose inflammable material to make a trace.
b. cutting (and removing) vegetation including trees.
c. damping down of vegetation in advance of the fire, possibly using some form of 'sticker'.

Vigilance is required on the 'safe' side of this trace or break to ensure that any sparks jumping over it do not allow the fire to cross to the new position.

As a last resort counter-firing may be attempted, i.e. the **controlled** burning of a strip in advance of the fire to act as a break. This should only be attempted in good ground conditions from a good fire break, and only on the instructions of the owner or a forester in charge. Adequate facilities for controlling the counter-fire must be available.

GROUND FIRES

These are fires which burn beneath the surface of the ground, usually in peaty soils or where organic content is high. They usually occur as a result of a surface fire, and can burn for days or even weeks. They can easily travel under the surface and cause further surface fires, and it is important to check after a surface fire that a ground fire does not exist. The two main techniques employed in fighting ground fires are:

a. by trenching, to cut down beneath organic layers to mineral soil, so that a fire is contained. This can be done with hand tools, ploughs or bulldozers, some way in advance of the fire.
b. by the use of water, preferably with a wetting agent to aid penetration.

CROWN FIRES

Fires burning in the crowns of trees usually start from surface fires. They can only be tackled by:

a. the direct application of large volumes of water usually only available from the Fire Service. Application as a spray outside the fire perimeter is often most effective.
b. the creation of a break in advance of the blaze.
c. aerial methods not economically justified in this country.

TACTICS FOR LARGE FIRES

Most fire outbreaks are small and can be extinguished fairly readily. Planning provision must be made for those which develop into larger conflagrations, and draw in possibly a number of brigades, neighbours, volunteers, police, and even the armed services. Organisation in a large fire is essential to ensure that incoming brigades are adequately briefed, fire fighting tactics planned, and progress monitored. Where large numbers of men are involved, they should be logged on and off duty so that rest periods and refreshments can be organised, and not least to ensure that fire fighters are safely accounted for. Arrangements should be made for refreshments to be made available.

The senior Fire Service Officer present is legally in charge of fire fighting operations, and joint liaison between him and the man in charge of the estate is essential.

ACTION AFTER A FIRE

The man in charge of fire fighting must walk the boundaries of the fire and check for himself that there is no danger of a further flare-up at any point before the fire fighting teams can be withdrawn. A few men must be kept on the spot to tackle chance new outbreaks and damp down remaining hot spots. They should regularly walk the boundaries of the fire.

The names and addresses of any outside helpers, including wives who helped on telephone or catering arrangements, should be noted. Payment should be offered for their services, even if they came as volunteers, and compensation offered for any damaged clothing. A letter of thanks later is always appreciated.

Finally he should try to investigate the probable cause of the fire, value the losses, and assess the fire fighting costs incurred. Any lessons learned should be noted for the future.

BIBLIOGRAPHY: FIRE PROTECTION

Forestry Commission Publications

BOOKLET 40. *Chemical control of weeds in the forest.* (Formerly Leaflet 51). 1975.

FOREST RECORD 75. *Design, construction and maintenance of earth dams and excavated ponds.* 1971.

REPORT

Holmes, G. D. and Fourt, D. F. The use of herbicides for controlling vegetation in forest fire breaks and uncropped land. *Forestry Commission Report on Forest Research.* 1960.

INFORMATION PAMPHLETS (free from Forestry Commission)

Concerning forest fires.
Forest fire fighting and protection.
Heath and forest fires: Instructions for fire fighting.

Other Publications

Home Office. *Fire protection in forests and woodlands in England and Wales.*
Scottish Home and Health Department. *Fire protection for forest and woodlands.* Edinburgh.

LEGISLATION

Fire Services Act 1947.
Heather and Grass Burning (England and Wales) Regulations 1949.
Hill Farming Act 1946.

Chapter 7

THE FOREST AND RECREATION

People in Britain are spending more of their leisure time in the countryside, and appreciating increasingly the values of the forest. Planners, too, recognise the capacity of the forest as an important resource for the pursuit of a wide range of recreational activities. The forest is able to absorb people and facilities more successfully than many other forms of land use, and with less adverse effect on the landscape.

The increased interest in countryside recreation over the last decade had been dramatic, and is a consequence of the affluence and mobility of people with more leisure time to enjoy. The Forestry Commission responded to public demand for recreation in the countryside many years ago by providing access to its forests and creating National Forest Parks. Its policy now is to permit public access on foot to all its forests where it is free to do so, taking into account considerations of land ownership and the interests of neighbours and lessors. Many of the Commission's forests have now been so developed for recreation, and a style of provision created which has a good reputation.

In 1973, the Commission was directed by the Government 'to give still further emphasis to recreational provision'. This exhortation applies to forestry as a whole. Under the new Basis III Dedication Scheme, the Government made it one of the conditions of grant aid towards the management of woodlands that 'such opportunities for recreation as may be appropriate' should be given.

The Impact on the Forest

Recreation schemes in the forest can affect companion objectives of management, and possible conflict between them must be taken into account at the planning stage.

Usually the restriction on the production of wood is not very significant. The greatest influence recreational development has in this respect is in the landscaping of small parts of the forest to provide access, and in clearing land for the development of car parks and picnic places. It might also be necessary to improve accessibility and landscape within the woodland by undertaking earlier thinnings where required. The scale and timing of clear felling might also be adjusted to maintain an interesting landscape or to create variety, but productivity would be lost if there were a significant departure from the optimum rotation. The interest of the forest might be improved by introducing a variety of tree species, which again could only be done at some cost to productivity.

No recreation scheme should be allowed to intrude on the beauty of the countryside, and all development in woodland should be planned from the start with this consideration in mind. The design should also prevent possible over-use of the facilities to be provided, otherwise there is the risk of endangering the very qualities of the woodland the public go there to enjoy.

Recreational Uses

Most people who visit a forest go there for quiet enjoyment of its intrinsic values, or for fresh air and exercise. There is much the forest has to offer if the visitor is prepared to leave the immediate neighbourhood of his motor car. He can be encouraged to do this, first, by providing him with stimulating information about the forest, its trees, flowers, streams, wildlife and history. Secondly, it should be made relatively easy for him to find his way about. Descriptive leaflets might be made available at the car park or picnic place, and waymarked walks set up through parts of special interest. (See Plate 16).

The forest can offer recreation for the specialist, such as the traditional field sports of shooting, deer stalking and fishing, with which the estate manager is likely to be familiar. For these activities a system of day permits may be used, issued at reasonable charges.

The forest is also an attractive place in which to ride, and horse riding and pony trekking are increasing in popularity. The Forestry Commission has created forest bridle tracks to cater for the increasing demand, but allows riding by permit only, for which a small charge is made. A permit system allows control of place and level of use, to ensure that possible conflict with other recreational uses of the forest does not arise. The recreation manager occasionally has to zone the forest to accommodate activities which are incompatible. Horse riding and walking is a case in point.

There are many other specialist recreational uses of the forest. Each has its own requirements with which the recreation manager must be familiar. A comprehensive list of these requirements is given in Table 8, against which may be judged the suitability of a particular forest.

Planning for Forest Recreation

It is essential to plan the various objectives before any start is made on the scheme. The private woodland owner is likely to require revenue from his provision for recreation, and at the same time he must aim at causing the minimum undesirable impact on his estate. He might also wish to preserve certain areas exclusively for his own privilege. A plan will enable the owner to identify the opportunities, to appraise their

TABLE 8

RECREATION US

Activity	Minimum space requirements	Distance from roads	Ground surface texture	Tree spacing	Stand layout	Stand penetrability	Tree preferer
CAMPING	9m²/tent. 6m spacing between tents.	Access road desirable.	Dry with short grass. Soil > 30cms. Not clay.	Not important on site.	Clumps of trees desirable on site.	Not important on site.	Tall tree for shel >5m.
CARAVANNING	14–15m²/van. 6 m spacing between vans.	Access road required.	Dry with short grass. Sometimes roads on site and hard standings.	Not important on site.	Clumps of trees desirable on site.	Not important on site.	All spec that gro well.
FIELD ARCHERY	Full size course ≏12 ha. Practice area < 1 ha.	Access road desirable.	Firm ground. Sparse vegtn. along shooting lane.	Wide.	Open shooting lane.	Penetrable along shooting lane and behind target.	Any wo land wit little ur growth
TARGET ARCHERY	130 m length. Targets spaced 3m centre to centre approx.	Access road desirable.	Dry ground, short grass.	Shooting area should be clear of trees.			
CLAY PIGEON SHOOTING Down the line	275×365m		Dry open area. Short grass.	Shooting area should be clear of trees.			
Skeet Universal and Olympic Trench	275×550m	Access road desirable.					
Sporting	275m in any direction of shooting.		Variable e.g. grassland rough ground, quarry.	Not important.	Individual and clumps useful.	Not important.	Not im portan
SMALL BORE SHOOTING Outdoor range	Up to 183m in length. Approx. 10m width.	Near to public road.	Firing point concrete. Rest of range low vegtn. bare ground etc.	Shooting area should be clear of trees.			
FULL BORE SHOOTING	Length up to 915m incl. safety area. Width up to 915m.	Access road desirable.	Short grass and other low vegtn.	Shooting area should be clear of trees.			

QUIREMENTS

Terrain and gradient	Natural water bodies	Minimum required facilities	Institutional, seasons etc.	Constraints		Advantages of Forest Environment
				Density, numbers taking part	Climatic	
at or undulating 6°.	Attractive on site.	Water. Sewerage. Toilets. Signposting. Refuse disposal.	Some sites closed in winter.	Maximum 75 tents/ha.	None	Screening of site from outside. Trees add to interest and appearance of site.
at or undulating 6°	Attractive on site.	Water. Sewerage. Toilets. Signposting. Refuse disposal.	Some sites closed in winter.	Maximum 60–65 vans/ha.	High winds	Screening of site from outside. Trees add to interest and appearance of site. May increase seclusion.
l slopes ceptable course. at practice area.	Stream attractive on course.	None.	Course avoids rights of way.	Several groups of 3–6 on course at same time.	None.	Courses have always been associated with woodland.
vel ea 2½°.	Water avoided.	Electricity. Gas. Water. Phone. Storage of equipment.	Restricted in winter.	6 archers may use 1 target in 2 details of 3.	High wind. Heavy rain.	Surrounding trees may increase tranquility of range.
vel. ght pes ceptable 2½°.	Water avoided.	Car parking space.	Site avoids rights of way. Conforms with bye laws and planning permission.	Maximum 5 people competing at one time on same layout.	Fog. Heavy rain.	Coniferous woodland provides a uniform dark background for shooting.
de ge of pes.	May add to visual appearance only.					Trees can hide traps and increase simulation of gaming conditions.
vel a 2½°.	Water avoided	Car parking	Ministry of Defence safety cert. required.	Variable.	Poor light. Fog.	None.
el a 2½°.	Water avoided.	Car parking.	Most areas owned by Ministry of Defence.	Variable. Average number of competitors is about 120.	Poor light. Fog. Heavy rain.	Trees surrounding range can absorb impact of noise.

TABLE 8 *(continued)*

RECREATION US[E]

Activity	Minimum space requirements	Distance from roads	Ground surface texture	Tree spacing	Stand layout	Stand penetrability	Tree preferen[ce]
WILDFOWLING AND ROUGH SHOOTING	Variable. 5% of woodland may be developed for game.	Not important. Access road convenient.	Depends on preferred habitat of each species.	Depends on preferred habitat of each species. Forest should be penetrable.			
PHEASANT SHOOTING	Variable. 5% of woodland developed for game.	Access road desirable.	Soils dry, pH > 7 Ground vegtn. and shrubs under trees. Grassy rides.	Wide to encourage undergrowth. Wide spacing at flushing points.	Compartments long and thin. 1-4 ha. Dense network of rides. Mixed woodland preferred. Several rising and flushing points in the forest.		
ROE DEER SHOOTING	Variable. < 8,000 ha for deer management.	Not important. Access road convenient.	Brambles and other shrubs and ground vegtn. for food and cover.	The layout should be planned to reduce browsing of plantations. Square compartments with surrounding belts of scrub. Good cover and food supply produce maximum densities of deer.			

GOLF
  18-hole course
  9-hole course
  Par 3 course
	35–60 ha. 14–30 ha. > 12 ha. for 18-hole course.	Access road	*Rough* Long grass, heather, shrubs
			
			Fairways Short grass, dry.
			
			Greens Short smooth grass
				4–5m	Clumps of trees between between holes.	Should be penetrable.	Conifer[s] are eas[ily] mainta[ined] also br[oad] leaves [with] small leaves. Pine, Birch prefer[red] species

Pitch & Putt	3½–5½ha			Not important.		Not important.	
ORIENTEERING	≃ 500 ha. > 3kms in length	Assembly point near road.	Roads, paths, uncultivated fields, woods etc.	All tree characteristics are acceptable.			
Wayfaring	200 ha.						
CYCLOCROSS	1–3km irregular slope.	Access road.	Rough ground or grassland, dry.	> 4m apart.	Some parts of the course can be wooded. Clumps of trees preferred to continuous forest.		

QUIREMENTS

Terrain and gradient	Natural water bodies	Minimum required facilities	Institutional, seasons etc.	Constraints		*Advantages of Forest Environment*
				Density, numbers taking part	Climatic	
All slopes acceptable.	Water and marsh may increase variety of species e.g. duck, snipe.	None.	Largest number of wildfowl present Oct.–Mar. Winter season.	Variable.	Fog.	Forests suitable where habitat favours each species.
Steeply undulating < 20° flatter land acceptable.	Not important.	None.	Season 1 Oct.– 1 Feb.	Variable < 30 present at a shoot.	Fog. Heavy snow.	Pheasants favour woodland habitats especially if layout is well planned.
All slopes acceptable.	Not important.	High seats for shooting and observation.	Seasons: *Does* Oct.–Feb. *Bucks* No season but Apr.–Oct. proposed.	Stalking usually in very small parties or singly.	None.	Roe deer prefer woodland habitat with cover and good food supply.
Undulating –4°. Short steep slopes acceptable.	As hazards and for landscaping.	Club-house facilities inc. electricity, water, phone, car park, sewerage.	Most golf clubs own their own courses.	Maximum approx. 72 on 18-hole layout.	Fog, Heavy rain, Snow, High wind. Also during thaw.	Trees may increase quietness, seclusion and visual appearance of course.
	Avoided.	Storage of equipment.				
Wide range of slopes.	Not important.	Water supply, Car parking.	Permission for use of land.	Variable.	None.	Restricted visibility emphasis on map reading.
Undulating + several short steep slopes –18°.	Shallow streams add interest to course.	Toilets. Water supply. Changing facilities.	Winter season. Permission for use of land.	Average number of competitors = 40–50 + spectators.	None.	None.

TABLE 8 *(continued)*

RECREATION US

Activity	Minimum space requirements	Distance from roads	Ground surface texture	Tree spacing	Stand layout	Stand penetrability	Tree preferen
CYCLING (Informal)	Track >1m width. As extensive as possible.	On roads or tracks.	Tarmac, concrete or any other smooth surface.	Cycle route should be clear of trees although it could lead through a forested area.			
HORSERIDING Hacking Long Distance Riding	2–3m wide up to 30km long.	Any distance from road.	Firm, dry ground— turf, paths, etc.	1m apart.	Not important.		Yew and rhododendrons poisonc Variety preferre
Cross country training area	1–6m Flexible shape.	Access road.	Short vegetation, dry.	Area should be clear of trees.			
RAMBLING	Variable. Some extensive paths desirable.	Any distance from roads. Access. road convenient.	Any penetrable ground. Not marshy.	Wide spacing.	Some wooded preferred to continuous forest.	Penetrability through stands desirable.	Variety preferre Trees > may blc views.
PICNICKING	Variable. Small areas suitable e.g. 20m²	Any distance.	Soil dry, not stony. Fertile sites withstand use better.	Variety of tree characteristics important. Broadleaves can be used for coppicing or screening. Open canopy will encourage vegetation regeneration.			
WILDLIFE STUDY	Variable.	Access road convenient.	Of any type.	Tree characteristics are elements of the habitat and influence flora and fauna. Mixtures of tree species will produce diversity of wildlife.			
ANGLING	*Coarse fishing* water area ½m Width 9–10m *Game fishing* uninterrupted access to stretch of water	Any distance. Access road convenient.	Banks should be firm short vegtn. sandy etc.	Casting area must be clear of trees. Trees should be at least 5–6m from the edge of the water.			

After Goodall and Whittow, 1973.

REQUIREMENTS

Terrain and gradient	Natural water bodies	Minimum required facilities	Institutional, seasons etc.	Density, numbers taking part	Climatic	Advantages of Forest Environment
				Constraints		
Difficult to cycle up prolonged slopes of > 6°.	Add to interest of route.	None.		Variable. Usually in twos and threes.	Snow on ground.	Forest roads can be used where good surface. Quiet and may be extensive.
Maximum prolonged slope is 8°.	Adds to scenic attraction. Shallow streams can be crossed.	Way-marking.	Permission for use of land unless public road or bridleway	Heavy use of paths may cause damage in wet weather	Fog, Frost.	Visual appearance may be attractive. Quiet areas are suitable
Flat or undulating < 6°.	Water avoided.	None.				
All slopes acceptable.	Adds to interest of route.	Way-marking on paths.	May use public rights of way.	Variable. Heavy use will damage vegtn. on path.	None.	Ramblers may appreciate quietness and seclusion. Other advantages depend on visual attraction and interest of forest.
Gentle slopes preferred < 14°.	Attraction for picnickers	None.	Mainly in summer.	Variable.	Unpleasant weather. Low temps. Fog etc.	Shelter and seclusion. Trees may enhance visual appearance of site.
All slopes acceptable.	Add to the range of habitat.	None.	Permits for some areas.	Large number of people may trample vegtn. & other disturbance.	None.	Forest may be quiet for observation and listening. Characteristic habitats in forest areas.
Fairly flat area for casting < 14°.	Any water well stocked with fish.	Car parking.	*Game* 16/1–14/3 *Trout* 1/4–1/10 *Salmon* Jan.–Nov. No licences or seasons for sea angling.	Coarse & Sea Angling: spacing can be only a few m. apart. Much more for game fishing.	None.	Seclusion. Trees may increase visual attraction.

development cost and benefit, and avoid errors which would be likely to arise if development were on an *ad hoc* basis and might have to be rectified later.

A careful survey of the estate must first be made to determine, and to map, the features of interest, and their location in respect of areas important to other objectives of the estate. In this survey should be noted the best sites for development and the fragile areas to be avoided. Possible communications, public rights of way, information systems, and other facilities should be considered. The base map, generally best drawn up at a scale of 1:25,000 ($2\frac{1}{2}$ ins to the mile), can be used with overlays to contrast development options. The recreational opportunities, with an assessment of capacity, can then be compared with the anticipated demand, and a financial appraisal made to determine the most attractive option available.

In appraising the likely demand, the planning authority will be of great help, and must be consulted early for development approval. It is known from national surveys that people visit rural destinations for recreational purposes mainly by car, though a significant number still walk. Only a few travel by public transport. It has also been established that the vast majority of visits are made within a 30-mile radius of home. The planning authorities might be able to help by computing the statistics appropriate to the location, and relating them to population levels, car ownership, traffic flow patterns, and existing provision elsewhere in the area. Guidance on predicted trends of participation might also be available.

A schematic presentation of planning considerations is given in Table 9.

Facility design is best done on a plan of scale 1:500 (with detail on 1:200), on which is shown all significant features of the site. The design should take advantage of existing natural features to provide a facility which blends with the landscape, has visual interest, and is pleasant to use. The constructed facility should be subject to routine inspection by management to ensure that a good standard is maintained.

TABLE 9

PLANNING CONSIDERATIONS

Scheme	Objective
1. Prepare a base map.	Survey the estate and note features of recreational interest.
2. Relate the fragile areas and constraints with the base map using overlays.	Identify the most suitable development options and account for acceptable capacities. Consider visitor movement patterns and access points and decide on a visitor flow strategy.

TABLE 9 *(continued)*

PLANNING CONSIDERATIONS

Scheme	Objective
3. Assess the demand.	Consider: Population characteristics within day-trip range both for residents and tourists; traffic flow patterns; public transport routes; existing provision of participation levels within a radius of 30 miles; prediction of future trends.
4. Review recreational potential.	Compare demand data and the attractiveness of the woodland for recreation. Decide also whether, due to its situation and size, the estate offers a particularly good site for overnight facilities.
5. Calculate the car park capacity requirement for the next 20 years based on the anticipated length of stay of visitors and the style of recreation to be offered.	To control the level of use and to economise on development costs.
6. Carry out a financial appraisal.	To determine the financial viability and the acceptable level of investment.
7. Design facilities on 1:500 scale with detail at 1:200 scale.	To create a facility which is pleasant and efficient and which does not intrude on the general landscape.
8. Submit plans to the planning authority.	To obtain development permission. Revise plan if necessary. (Consultation with the planning authority will have started at an early date in the planning process).
9. Progress development.	Carefully brief and supervise the construction work. Use the minimum structures consistent with efficiency. The form, materials and location of structures should be chosen with care in harmony with good principles of design.
10. Achieve a high standard of maintenance.	To ensure visitor satisfaction.
11. Monitor usage and compare with predictions.	Adjust management plans if necessary.

Conclusion

Though multiple land use is no stranger to the private estate, in which good integration of different land use objectives is often achieved, there are very few public recreation facilities in private woodlands. This is sometimes due to understandable pride of ownership, and reluctance to open private woodlands to the public. Difficulty of access may also play a part, and the need sometimes for considerable capital investment. However, some financial assistance is now available through the grant aid schemes of the Countryside Commissions.

There is no doubt that the increasing pressure for recreation in the countryside has brought a real public awareness of the social benefits of the forest. The owner of private woodland is encouraged to welcome the public on his land, and so make a worthwhile contribution towards satisfying the recreational needs of society.

BIBLIOGRAPHY:
THE FOREST AND RECREATION

Forestry Commission Publications. (See also Bibliography on Wildlife, Chapter 5.)

BULLETIN

No. 46   *Forest of Dean day visitor survey.* 1973.

BOOKLETS

No. 6   *Forest Parks.* 1975.
No. 15   *Know your conifers.* 1976.
No. 20   *Know your broadleaves.* 1971.
No. 21   *Public recreation in national forests.* 1967.
No. 33   *Conifers in the British Isles.* 1972.
No. 38   *Common trees.* 1974.
No. 42   *Field recognition of British elms.* 1974.
No. 44   *The Landscape of Forests and Woods.* 1978.

FOREST RECORDS

No. 102   *Three forest climbers, ivy, old man's beard, and honeysuckle.* 1975.
No. 106   *Mushrooms and toadstools of broadleaved forests.* 1975.
No. 107   *Mushrooms and toadstools of coniferous forests.* 1976.
No. 112   *Monitoring Day Visitor Use of Recreational Areas.* 1977.

RESEARCH AND DEVELOPMENT PAPERS

No. 81   *Forest management for conservation, landscaping, access and sport.* 1971.

No. 93   *Valuation of non-wood benefits.* 1972.
No. 104   *Public demands on forests in relation to forest wildlife.* 1973.
No. 107   *Organisation of outdoor recreation research in the Netherlands.* 1974.

GUIDES

Argyll Forest Park, 1976.
Bedgebury Pinetum and Forest Plots. 1972.
Bedgebury, Kent (National Pinetum and Forest Plots). Short Guide. 1974.
Cambrian Forests. 1975.
Forests of Central and Southern Scotland (Booklet No. 25). 1969.
The New Forests of Dartmoor. 1972.
Dean Forest and Wye Valley (Forest Park). 1974.
Border Forests
Drumtochty (Kincardine). 1953.
East Anglian Forests, 1975.
Glamorgan Forests. 1961.
Glen More Forest Park (Cairngorms). 1975.
Galloway Forest Park (previously Glen Trool). 1974.
Gwydyr Forest in Snowdonia. A History. (Booklet No. 28). 1971.
Kilmun Arboretum and Forest Plots (near Dunoon, Argyll). 1969.
New Forest
Explore the New Forest. 1975.
Forests of North-East Scotland. 1977.
North Yorkshire Forests. 1972.
Queen Elizabeth Forest Park (Ben Lomond, Loch Ard and the Trossachs). 1973.
Snowdonia Forest Park. 1973.
Westonbirt Arboretum. 1969.
Westonbirt in Colour. 1976.

POSTERS—*Forest Trees of Britain.*

MISCELLANEOUS

Forestry Commission potential for permanent tourist accommodation. Planning and policy report.

Other Publications

British Tourist Authority (1972/1973). *British national travel survey.* London.
Forestry policy: June 1972. HMSO.
Goodall, B., and Whittow, J. B. (1973). The recreational potential of Forestry Commission holdings. *Forestry Commission Report on Forest Research 1973, 161–162.*
Goodall, B., and Whittow, J. B. (1975). *Recreational Requirements and forest opportunities.* Geographical Paper No. 6, University of Reading.

Parliament (1973). Ministerial statement on forestry policy. *Hansard (House of Commons)* vol. 861 (163), 24.10.73, cols 517–519.

Stewart, G. G. (1975). The impact in Great Britain of increasing demand for recreation and tourist facilities on forests, forest management and policies. *Symposium on forests and wood: their role in the environment.* Economic Commission for Europe.

Tourism and Recreation Research Unit (1975). *Scottish tourism and recreation study (STARS), series No. 2: summary report.* Edinburgh University.

LEGISLATION

Countryside (Scotland) Act 1967
Countryside Act 1968.

Chapter 8

PLANNING, ORGANISING AND CONTROLLING PRODUCTION

The material dealing with the assessment of Yield Class, thinning control and production forecasting mentioned in this Chapter is covered comprehensively in Booklet 34, *Forest management tables (metric)*, published by the Forestry Commission.

A plantation of trees, once established, may be left untended until it has reached the stage of development when the timber can be harvested in one clear felling operation. More usually, however, a sizeable proportion of the produce would be removed in a series of thinnings carried out at intervals of a few years, prior to clear felling. There are countless possible variations in the nature, timing and frequency of thinnings and in the timing of clear felling. These various factors, comprising the **cutting regime**, can have a considerable impact on the financial return from any plantation. Furthermore, these factors can have an important influence on marketing strategy.

Any single intervention in a stand should not be considered in isolation but, since it influences the development of a crop over a long period of time, must be considered as an integral part of a complete cutting regime. This means that decisions affecting an individual thinning, such as the volume to be removed, the types of trees to be removed, can only be properly assessed by considering their longer-term effects, e.g. the timing, amount and size classes of future produce, all of which are important both to market planning and profitability generally.

Before a forest manager can decide on appropriate cutting regimes for the various crops comprising his forest, he requires certain basic information. Clearly, the **area** and **species** composition of the crops are parts of this necessary information. Also fundamental is the **rate of growth**, both current and future, of each stand. Rates of growth are important in that they affect the way in which the stand may be treated. It is also important to be able to predict growth rates for planning purposes. In Forestry Commission practice, rates of growth are identified through **yield classes**. A yield class is a specific growth rate category to which a crop can be assigned relatively easily. The growth rate of any even-aged stand is not constant, but varies throughout the life of the crop in a characteristic and predictable pattern. These patterns are an integral feature of the yield class system, and to use these to advantage one further item of information is required—the **age** of the crop.

Knowing the species, area, yield class and age, the manager is in a good position to decide on the cutting regime which will produce maximum benefits according to the particular management objectives for the forest. He is also able to implement and control the regime and to forecast the long-term implications for timber supply, and thus to adopt an appropriate marketing strategy.

The following paragraphs explain the yield class system and give guidance on the choice of cutting regime, including consideration of the factors which contribute to its preparation and control, together with methods for collecting the necessary information.

THE YIELD CLASS SYSTEM OF CLASSIFYING GROWTH POTENTIAL

The growth of trees is conventionally quantified in terms of stem-wood volume over 7 cm diameter overbark.

The pattern of volume growth in even-aged stands is typically depicted in Figure 6. Some years after planting the volume increment of the stand increases, reaches a peak and falls off at the rates shown by the curve labelled CAI (Current Annual Increment).

This curve represents the annual rate of increase in volume at any point in time. The average annual rate of increase in volume from planting to any point in time is shown by the second curve labelled MAI (Mean Annual Increment). For example, at 'n' years the annual volume increment *at that time* is 'x', whilst the average annual volume increment over the period from planting to 'n' years is 'y'. The MAI curve reaches a maximum level where the two curves meet. This point defines the maximum average rate of volume increment which a particular species can achieve on a particular site. This general pattern of growth is typical of all even-aged stands, although differences in rates of growth occur within any one species on different sites. For any species the faster growing stands have higher maximum mean annual increments, which also reach a maximum earlier. Although the same general pattern of growth is true for all species, there may be important differences between them. For example, while maximum mean annual increments of different species may be the same, they may reach a maximum at totally different ages.

A wide range of maximum mean annual increments is commonly encountered in British conditions. It can be as low as 4 m³/ha for many broadleaves, larches and pines, and as high as 30 m³/ha in the case of Grand fir. **Yield classes** are created simply by dividing this range into steps of 2 m³/ha and numbering them (even numbers) accordingly. Thus a stand of yield class 14 has a maximum mean annual increment of *about* 14 m³/ha, *i.e.* greater than 13 m³/ha but less than 15 m³/ha.

It is important that the maximum benefit of the system be available to management. The most accurate way of doing this is to assess the mean annual increment of the crop and, using the age, refer to a series of MAI curves for different yield classes of the species

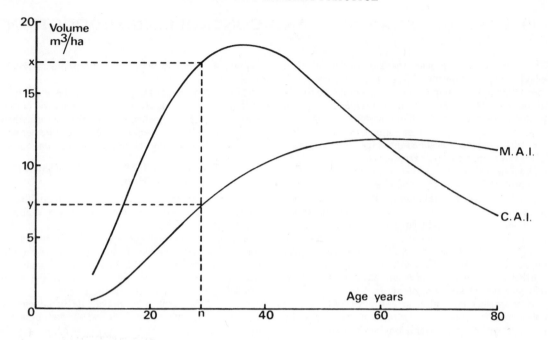

Figure 6   Patterns of volume increment in an even-aged stand.

to find out which curve most accurately represents its growth pattern. It is not always practicable, however, to assess total volume production, nor is it justified in view of the expense involved. Fortunately, a good relationship exists between top height (the mean height of the 100 trees of largest diameter at breast height per hectare) and total volume production of the stand, and this can be used to avoid the necessity of actually measuring or recording total volume production. Top height/age curves from which yield class can be read directly have been prepared (Forestry Commission Booklet 34). By using the top height and age of the stand, the **general yield class** can be identified from these curves.

An improved estimate can be obtained by assessing **production class**. Production classes embrace differences in the relationship between volume production and top height. General yield classes which are modified by production class are termed local yield classes, and imply a more accurate assessment of yield class.

The assessment of local yield class is considered in Booklet 34.

CUTTING REGIMES

Standard yield tables are available in Booklet 34. These trace the development of various crops by showing the values of some of the crop characteristics at regular intervals in time.

The crops are assumed to have been established at conventional spacings and thinned according to the recommended thinning practice for Forestry Commission plantations. Non-standard yield tables are available in Bulletin 52. These deal with different initial spacings and with non-thinning treatments. Further non-standard tables will be published from time to time. Minor modifications to thinning treatments, for example changes in the thinning cycle of a year or two, will make little difference to either total volume production or mean diameter of the crop, but treatments varying more radically from those outlined above require knowledge of their effect on both volume production and diameter growth, which may not be readily available to the private owner.

Economic Appraisal of Alternative Regimes

The essential components of the yield table or model for the purposes of economic analysis, are the thinning and main crop volumes and their respective diameters at breast height. The revenue of each thinning can be calculated from the product of the thinning volume, and the prices indicated according to an appropriate price-size curve. The final crop revenue can be calculated in the same way. In order to make a valid comparison it is, however, necessary to discount these revenues, which occur at various ages, to one common date, usually the year of planting, or, alternatively, the year in which the various treatments are first implemented. Adding the discounted revenues of thinnings and final felling will produce a total discounted revenue. Total discounted revenues will vary according to the thinning treatment and to the timing of final felling, such that an optimum regime may be chosen.

The economic criteria used by the Forestry Commission in determining optimal treatments may not necessarily be appropriate to private estates. However, in general, it is unlikely that the optimal treatments will be very far removed from those adopted by the Forestry Commission. In the following paragraph it is therefore assumed that the Commission treatment will, in fact, generally be appropriate.

THINNING

Basic Considerations

Conventional practice is to plant some 2000 to 3000 trees per hectare in establishing a plantation. When the crop has developed to the point at which a complete canopy is formed, competition between individual plants will have begun. Trees which are suppressed and over-topped by their dominating neighbours will ultimately die. If the stand is left untended, this process will continue to occur throughout the remaining life of the crop. In the course of a normal rotation such mortality would represent a very considerable loss of merchantable volume. By removing these trees in thinnings before death occurs, this loss of merchantable volume could be prevented. The realisation of this fact probably accounts for the origins of thinning practice. Nowadays, the approach to thinning is rather more purposeful than simply anticipating the death of

suppressed trees. The ultimate objective in current thinning practice is usually to obtain the largest financial return from the crop. The financial result of one particular thinning, however, cannot be judged in isolation. One thinning may yield very little profit immediately, although its effect on the ultimate profitability of a crop may be quite considerable. As a general rule, the most profitable way to thin a crop is to remove as much volume as possible in the form of thinnings, without any appreciable reduction in total volume production. Quite a large proportion of the total production, something like 50–60 per cent by volume or 80–90 per cent by numbers of trees, can be removed as thinnings during the life of the crop without reducing total volume production. If at any stage excessive volume is removed in thinnings, the productive capacity of the remaining crop will be reduced. The volume removed in a thinning quite obviously has an important impact on the profitability of a particular thinning regime, but there are a number of other factors which are also quite critical to the financial return from the crop. The various factors which together constitute a thinning regime are considered separately below.

Thinning intensity is the rate at which volume is removed from a stand in thinnings, i.e. the annual thinning yield or the volume removed in a particular thinning divided by the intended cycle. Over a wide range of thinning intensities the total production remains unaffected. Higher thinning intensities have the effect of creating more growing space for the main crop trees, which are able to respond with increases in diameter and average volume. But as intensity increases, the situation ultimately arises where the main crop cannot respond sufficiently to make full use of the

TABLE 10

AGES AT NORMAL TIME OF FIRST THINNING

Species	Yield Class													
	30	28	26	24	22	20	18	16	14	12	10	8	6	4
Scots pine									21	23	25	29	33	40
Corsican pine						18	19	20	21	23	25	28	33	
Lodgepole pine									19	21	23	26	31	40
Sitka spruce				18	18	19	20	21	22	24	26	29	33	
Norway spruce						20	21	22	23	24	28	29	31	35
European larch										18	20	22	26	32
Japanese larch/Hybrid larch									14	15	17	19	22	26
Douglas fir				16	17	17	18	19	21	23	25			
Western hemlock				19	20	21	22	24	26	28				
Western red cedar/Lawson cypress				21	22	23	24	26	28	30				
Grand fir	19	20	20	21	21	22	23	24	25					
Noble fir					22	23	25	27	29	31				
Oak												24	28	35
Beech											26	29	32	37
Sycamore/Ash/Birch										14	15	17	20	24
Poplar														

growing space created by the thinnings, and the result is a loss in total volume production. The maximum intensity which can be maintained without loss of volume production is termed the **marginal thinning intensity.** In normal circumstances the value per unit of volume increases as the mean diameter increases. In addition, greater thinning yields per hectare tend to produce greater revenues per unit volume. Taken together, these features tend to make higher thinning intensities more profitable, but a maximum occurs where these gains are offset by loss of revenue resulting from losses in total volume production. Maximum profitability coincides roughly with the marginal thinning intensity which can conveniently be quantified in terms of a percentage of the yield class of the crop. For a specified age of first thinning, an annual thinning yield of 70 per cent of the yield class, i.e. 70 per cent of the maximum mean annual increment, is approximately the marginal thinning intensity. Thus a stand of yield class 10 thinned at marginal intensity would have an annual thinning yield of 70 per cent of 10, i.e. 7 cubic metres per hectare per annum, over the life of the crop. In defining the marginal thinning intensity in this way it is equally important to define the age of first thinning. Table 10 indicates the age of the first thinning for various yield classes of the major commercial species.

The **thinning cycle** is the interval in years between successive thinnings. It has an influence on profitability in that the net value of any single thinning depends, in part, on the scale of the operation. Long cycles entailing heavier single thinnings are thus usually more profitable, but may increase the risk of windblow, and in extreme cases may result in loss of volume production. The usual range of thinning cycles is from four to six years in young or fast growing crops, to about 10 years for older or slow growing crops.

The **thinning type** refers to the type or dominance class of trees which are removed in thinning. For example, a **low** thinning is the term used to describe that in which trees are removed predominantly from the lower canopy, i.e. sub-dominants and suppressed trees, whilst in a **crown** thinning the accent is on the removal of upper canopy trees, i.e. dominants and co-dominants. Trees of the upper canopy tend to be more efficient producers, so that, in general, predominantly low thinning is preferred. This is not to say that the removal of some upper canopy trees is undesirable. On the contrary, some thinning in the upper canopy is usually inevitable in order to release the better dominants, which will form the ultimate main crop of a stand. One should remove very coarse, spreading trees, leaning trees (which produce compression or tension wood), forked trees, trees with spiral bark (this often indicates spiral grain in the stem wood), and trees with thin, unhealthy-looking crowns. Provided they justify the cost of cutting, small suppressed trees should be removed.

Other Considerations

LINE THINNING

There are basically two approaches to line thinning. Where the trees are arranged in clearly identifiable and reasonably straight rows following the planting pattern, and where ground conditions are reasonably level, the removal of some of these complete rows is a convenient method of thinning. On the other hand, where ground conditions are difficult or where the trees do not follow easily identifiable lines, a chevron pattern of line thinning can be used. In general, line thinning should be confined to the first and, exceptionally, the second thinnings. Although, in many cases, the volume removed in line thinning will be approximately the same as for selective thinnings, there are some unique features of line thinning which may influence the volume removed per hectare. In the first place, the non-selectivity of the system means that some of the better individuals, the more efficient producers, inevitably have to be sacrificed, which leads to a loss in volume production. This restricts the choice of trees which will ultimately form the final crop. Even more important, however, is the fact that the benefits resulting from thinning are confined to those trees immediately adjacent to those removed.

To be fully effective, a row thinning must involve the removal of not less than one in three rows. Similarly, with chevron thinning patterns (Figure 7), spacing between the arms of the chevron should be such as to leave ideally no more than two adjacent rows of trees. The major advantage of line thinnings is to assist extraction and thereby to raise net revenues. The pattern of line thinning will consequently depend to some extent on the machinery employed. Depending on the spacing of the original plantation, the removal of one row may not be adequate to allow sufficient access. In these situations, two adjacent rows must inevitably be removed, but it should be noted that this will lead to a greater loss in total volume production of the stand (Bulletin 55).

THINNING OF MIXTURES

It is impossible to give very precise guidance on the thinning of mixtures, because there are an infinite number of combinations of species in different proportions and arrangements. The relative rates of growth of different species may vary at different periods during their lives and on different sites. It frequently happens that one constituent of a mixture which appears to be more promising at a certain point of time, is favoured in thinning at the expense of the other constituents. At the time of a subsequent thinning the situation may be reversed. It is important, therefore, not to plant mixtures haphazardly, but to have a clear idea of the intended role of each species from the beginning.

RISK OF WINDBLOW

Windblow is likely to be a serious risk, especially for

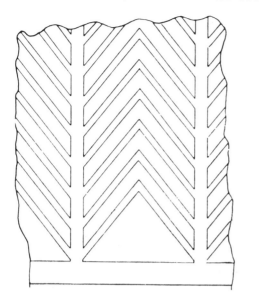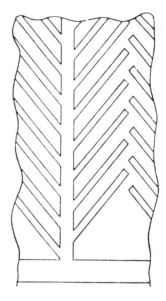

Figure 7   Chevron and staggered chevron patterns of line-thinning.

spruces, Douglas fir and the larches, on shallow rooting clay soils, and for most species on shallow peat soils, particularly on high exposed ground. The most serious risk occurs after thinning and when the ground is waterlogged. The risk of windblow is greatly increased when thinning has started after a long period of delay. It is therefore advisable, in these situations, to thin early and selectively, or not at all.

It is undoubtedly true that line thinning attracts a greater risk of windblow than conventional selective thinnings. Broadly speaking, the heavier the thinning, i.e. the greater the proportion of the crop removed, and similarly the greater 'width' of a gap created by line thinning, the greater will be the risk of windblow. In areas where the general risk of windblow is high, the adoption of selective thinning methods will reduce the risk relative to that of line thinning.

Field Procedures

PREPARATORY MEASURES

It is advisable to cut inspection racks through the plantation, in order to assess the need for thinning or other treatments. These racks are best made by sawing off the lower branches of two adjacent rows of trees with a pruning saw. Enough racks should be cut to enable one to form a good idea of the state of the plantation as a whole. These should be sited where they will best serve the extraction of produce, or ease of access in the case of fire. With selective thinnings proposed it will usually be necessary to undertake a measure of brashing, that is, the removal of the lower branches to head height. The branches should be cut cleanly and close to the stem, using a curved pruning saw in preference to a bill-hook. Brashing enables a forester to move about freely to view the individual trees, and to mark those to be cut. However, it is an expensive operation, and even in selective thinning it is rarely justifiable to brash every tree. It should, therefore, be confined to achieving the specific object of freedom of access for marking. Where row thinning is proposed, brashing can largely be dispensed with, since it is only necessary to mark the end trees in each row to be removed. With chevron patterns, however, an element of brashing may be necessary along the proposed main racks.

METHOD OF MARKING

Marking can be done either by one man or in teams of two or three. With selective thinnings, it is desirable to look at the crop from more than one direction. This means that every tree selected must be marked on at least two sides, otherwise it is impossible to see from every angle which trees have already been chosen for removal and which have not. Marking may be done with paint, with a timber scribe, or, more conventionally, by cutting a blaze on the side of the tree with a slasher. The last named method is of course only suitable for indicating those trees which have to come out. If it is decided to mark trees that are to be retained, paint should be used. White paints with a titanium base are found to last the longest.

THINNING CONTROL

Having decided on the thinning treatment which will yield the maximum benefit, e.g. maximum volume

TABLE 11

Yield class	4	6	8	10	12	14	16	18	20	22	24	26	28	30
Annual thinning yields (m3/ha)	2·8	4·2	5·6	7·0	8·4	9·8	11·2	12·6	14·0	15·4	16·8	18·2	19·6	21·0

production, maximum diameter increment of the main crop, maximum profitability etc, it is essential to exercise some measure of control in order that these aims and long-term plans may be realised. Thinning control is best exercised through the volume of thinnings removed. This is used in preference to controlling the level of the remaining growing stock, for three main reasons. First, since the thinning volume is some one-third to one-twentieth that of the residual growing stock volume, the effect of errors in assessing thinning volume are much less serious than errors of the same proportion in assessing the residual growing stock. Where errors are made in the assessment of yield class, here again the effects are less serious where control is exercised through the thinning yield. Secondly, control through thinnings discourages drastic reduction in the level of the growing stock of overstocked stands, which leads to volume production losses and which might result in windblow. Thirdly,

since thinnings usually provide a large proportion of the total yield of the stand in the course of a normal rotation, there are clearly many advantages to management in having a regular thinning yield. Booklet 32, *Thinning control in British woodlands*, provides more comprehensive information.

Assuming that the thinning intensity adopted is the marginal thinning intensity as described above, the annual thinning yields in cubic metres per hectare may be determined according to the yield class from the Table above.

From the time of first thinning, which is outlined in Table 10 p. 71, the yield which is removed in one thinning will be the product of the annual thinning yield and the proposed cycle. Table 12 gives thinning yields for different yield classes and cycles.

Stands may be judged as ready for thinning by visual inspection and by reference to the table of threshold basal areas given in Table 13. (Basal area is the cross-

TABLE 12

TABLE OF NORMAL THINNING YIELDS

(Applicable to fully stocked crops of all species for the duration of their normal thinning life)

Yield Class	Volume per net hectare (cubic metres overbark to 7 cm top diameter or 7 cm dbh) Thinning cycles (Number of years before the next thinning, not since the last)							Yield Class
	3	4	5	6	8	9	10	
2	4·2	5·6	7·0	8·4	11·2	12·6	14	2
4	8·4	11·2	14·0	16·8	22·4	25·2	28	4
6	12·6	16·8	21·0	25·2	33·6	37·8	42	6
8	16·8	22·4	28·0	33·6	44·8	50·4	56	8
10	21·0	28·0	35·0	42·0	56·0	63·0	70	10
12	25·2	33·6	42·0	50·4	67·2	75·6		12
14	29·4	39·2	49·0	58·8	78·4			14
16	33·6	44·8	56·0	67·2	89·6			16
18	37·8	50·4	63·0	75·6				18
20	42·0	56·0	70·0	84·0				20
22	46·2	61·6	77·0	92·4				22
24	50·4	67·2	84·0					24
26	54·6	72·8	91·0					26
28	58·8	78·4						28
30	63·0	84·0						30

TABLE 13

THRESHOLD BASAL AREAS FOR FULLY-STOCKED STANDS

Basal areas in square metres per hectare

Species	Top Height (Metres)										
	10	12	14	16	18	20	22	24	26	28	30
Scots pine	26	26	27	30	32	35	38	40	43	46	
Corsican pine	34	34	33	33	33	34	35	36	37	39	
Lodgepole pine	33	31	31	30	30	31	31	32	33	34	
Sitka spruce	33	34	34	35	35	36	37	38	39	40	42
Norway spruce	33	33	34	35	36	38	40	42	44	46	49
European larch	23	22	22	22	23	24	25	27	28	30	
Japanese and Hybrid larch	22	22	23	23	24	24	25	27	28	29	
Douglas fir	28	28	28	29	30	31	32	34	35	37	40
Western hemlock	32	34	35	36	36	36	37	38	38	39	40
Red cedar		49	50	51	53	55	57	60	63	66	70
Grand fir		39	39	39	39	39	39	40	41	43	45
Noble fir		45	46	46	47	48	49	51	52	54	
Oak		24	23	23	23	23	24	24	25	26	
Beech		20	20	22	23	25	27	29	31	33	35	37
Sycamore, Ash, Birch		16	15	17	19	22	26	30	34		

NOTE: Stands with a yield class which is relatively high for the species, or which are thinned on a long cycle, ought to have basal areas which are up to 10 per cent greater than those quoted in the table.

sectional area of the tree measured overbark at the breast height point.) Thinning will normally be deferred if the basal area of a stand is less than that specified in the Table for a given top height. Basal area may be assessed with a relascope, or by measuring the breast height diameters of all trees in several plots of 0·01 ha, and deriving the basal area per hectare. (See Booklet 39.) If it is considered necessary to thin an understocked stand, the thinning yield should be reduced. Where a stand is clearly overstocked yield can, if desired, be raised by one year's cut, and if need be this can be repeated in succeeding thinnings.

There are basically two methods of controlling the intensity of thinning. Both are applied at the time of marking. The preferred method is for the marker to lay down plots from time to time while marking, and to check the *volume* per hectare of the trees marked in each plot. As he progresses he can adjust his marking so that the specified volume is marked. This is essentially a skill acquired with practice, and the frequency of checking will consequently diminish. Plots should be such a size as to include 5 to 10 marked trees. The diameter at breast height (dbh) of each tree is measured, and its volume may be estimated by using the top height volume table given in Table 14. The volume per plot has been converted to a volume per hectare in order to make comparisons with the target figure. The alternative is to check the total basal area of marked trees against a target figure given in Booklet 34.

TABLE 14

TOP HEIGHT VOLUME TABLE FOR THINNINGS

Volumes in cubic metres to 7 centimetres top diameter

BH DIAM cm	10	11	12	13	14	15	16	17	18	19	20	21	22	23	24	25	BH DIAM cm
10	0·028	0·029	0·031	0·032	0·034	0·035	0·037	0·038	0·040	0·041	0·042	0·044	0·045	0·047	0·048	0·050	10
11	0·037	0·039	0·042	0·044	0·046	0·048	0·050	0·052	0·054	0·056	0·058	0·060	0·062	0·064	0·066	0·068	11
12	0·048	0·050	0·053	0·056	0·059	0·061	0·064	0·067	0·069	0·072	0·075	0·077	0·080	0·083	0·085	0·088	12
13	0·059	0·062	0·066	0·069	0·073	0·076	0·079	0·083	0·086	0·090	0·093	0·096	0·100	0·103	0·107	0·110	13
14	0·071	0·075	0·079	0·084	0·088	0·092	0·096	0·100	0·104	0·109	0·113	0·117	0·121	0·125	0·129	0·133	14
15	0·084	0·089	0·094	0·099	0·104	0·109	0·114	0·119	0·124	0·129	0·134	0·139	0·144	0·149	0·154	0·159	15
16	0·098	0·104	0·110	0·116	0·122	0·127	0·133	0·139	0·145	0·151	0·157	0·163	0·168	0·174	0·180	0·186	16
17	0·113	0·120	0·127	0·133	0·140	0·147	0·154	0·160	0·167	0·174	0·181	0·188	0·194	0·201	0·208	0·215	17
18	0·129	0·137	0·144	0·152	0·160	0·168	0·175	0·183	0·191	0·199	0·206	0·214	0·222	0·230	0·238	0·245	18
19	0·145	0·154	0·163	0·172	0·181	0·189	0·198	0·207	0·216	0·225	0·234	0·242	0·251	0·260	0·269	0·278	19
20	0·163	0·173	0·183	0·193	0·203	0·213	0·222	0·232	0·242	0·252	0·262	0·272	0·282	0·292	0·302	0·312	20
21	0·18	0·19	0·20	0·21	0·23	0·24	0·25	0·26	0·27	0·28	0·29	0·30	0·31	0·33	0·34	0·35	21
22	0·20	0·21	0·23	0·24	0·25	0·26	0·27	0·29	0·30	0·31	0·32	0·34	0·35	0·36	0·37	0·39	22
23	0·22	0·23	0·25	0·26	0·28	0·29	0·30	0·32	0·33	0·34	0·36	0·37	0·38	0·40	0·41	0·42	23
24	0·24	0·26	0·27	0·29	0·30	0·32	0·33	0·35	0·36	0·38	0·39	0·41	0·42	0·44	0·45	0·47	24
25	0·26	0·28	0·30	0·31	0·33	0·35	0·36	0·38	0·39	0·41	0·43	0·44	0·46	0·48	0·49	0·51	25
26	0·29	0·30	0·32	0·34	0·36	0·38	0·39	0·41	0·43	0·45	0·46	0·48	0·50	0·52	0·54	0·55	26
27	0·31	0·33	0·35	0·37	0·39	0·41	0·43	0·45	0·46	0·48	0·50	0·52	0·54	0·56	0·58	0·60	27
28	0·34	0·36	0·38	0·40	0·42	0·44	0·46	0·48	0·50	0·52	0·54	0·56	0·58	0·61	0·63	0·65	28
29	0·36	0·38	0·41	0·43	0·45	0·47	0·50	0·52	0·54	0·56	0·59	0·61	0·63	0·65	0·67	0·70	29
30	0·39	0·41	0·44	0·46	0·48	0·51	0·53	0·56	0·58	0·60	0·63	0·65	0·68	0·70	0·72	0·75	30
31	0·42	0·44	0·47	0·49	0·52	0·54	0·57	0·60	0·62	0·65	0·67	0·70	0·72	0·75	0·78	0·80	31
32	0·44	0·47	0·50	0·53	0·55	0·58	0·61	0·64	0·66	0·69	0·72	0·75	0·77	0·80	0·83	0·86	32
33	0·47	0·50	0·53	0·56	0·59	0·62	0·65	0·68	0·71	0·74	0·77	0·80	0·83	0·85	0·88	0·91	33
34	0·50	0·53	0·57	0·60	0·63	0·66	0·69	0·72	0·75	0·78	0·82	0·85	0·88	0·91	0·94	0·97	34
35	0·53	0·57	0·60	0·63	0·67	0·70	0·73	0·77	0·80	0·83	0·87	0·90	0·93	0·97	1·00	1·03	35
36	0·57	0·60	0·64	0·67	0·71	0·74	0·78	0·81	0·85	0·88	0·92	0·95	0·99	1·02	1·06	1·09	36
37	0·60	0·64	0·67	0·71	0·75	0·79	0·82	0·86	0·90	0·93	0·97	1·01	1·05	1·08	1·12	1·16	37
38	0·63	0·67	0·71	0·75	0·79	0·83	0·87	0·91	0·95	0·99	1·03	1·07	1·11	1·15	1·18	1·22	38
39	0·67	0·71	0·75	0·79	0·83	0·88	0·92	0·96	1·00	1·04	1·08	1·12	1·17	1·21	1·25	1·29	39
40	0·70	0·75	0·79	0·83	0·88	0·92	0·97	1·01	1·05	1·10	1·14	1·18	1·23	1·27	1·32	1·36	40
Approx. Tariff No.	18	19	20	22	23	24	25	26	27	28	30	31	32	33	34	35	*Approx. Tariff No.*

TABLE 15

FELLING AGES

Thinned Crops

Yield Class	Scots Pine	Corsican Pine	Lodgepole Pine	European Larch	Japanese Larch	Douglas Fir	Norway Spruce	Sitka Spruce	Western Hemlock
4	75		60	55	50				
6	65	60	55	50	50		70	60	
8	65	55	55	50	45		65	55	
10	60	55	50	45	45	55	60	55	
12	55	50	50	45	45	50	60	55	55
14	55	50	50		45	50	55	50	55
16		50				50	55	50	50
18		45				45	55	50	50
20		45				45	50	45	50
22						45	50	45	50
24						45	50	45	45
26									45
28									45
30									45

CLEAR FELLING

Table 15 above shows the ages of clear felling, for different coniferous species and yield classes, adopted by the Forestry Commission.

DATA COLLECTION (SURVEYS)

Objectives

While forest surveys and inventories are undertaken for many purposes, for production planning it is necessary to know about:
—distribution and classification of the forest estate;
—species composition and age classes;
—stocking and yield class;
—roading layout.

Earlier Data

Data from earlier surveys, planting and felling records, compartment schedules and forest histories, will provide a useful guide to the survey intensity required. Such data normally concern land utilisation, species planted, area statements, and thinning and felling records. They should not, however, be accepted without reservation. Their value is generally inversely proportional to age, since adoption of new definitions and descriptive conventions may have occurred in the meantime.

Terrain and Crops

A preliminary reconnaisance enables the forester to make an assessment of the character of the terrain and the broad crop classification, and will give an indication of the value of such records as may be at his disposal.

He will then be able to decide how much work will be needed to carry out the inventory survey.

Resource Requirements

Having decided what further information is needed, the resources required to obtain it must be estimated. Here it should be noted that it is frequently better value to seek results of a lower order of accuracy quickly, than it is to spend much time in the pursuit of perfection. Paretos' Law states that 80 per cent of information can be obtained in 20 per cent of the time required to collect it all. Decide standards beforehand and plan the survey with these in mind.

Maps

In the Forestry Commission, the basic planning and record maps are based upon the latest 1:10000 or 1:10560 scale (6 inch to one mile) Ordnance Survey sheets. Every private woodlands dedication or approved woods plan of operations has to be accompanied by a map at one or other of these scales. It is the largest at which the whole of Great Britain is covered.

1:25000 ($2\frac{1}{2}$ inch to one mile) scale OS maps are a convenient and complementary base for production planning in large forests, and in particular, when drawing up sales contracts to show access routes in relation to the public road system, loading bays, and stacking and conversion sites.

Aerial Photography

The rapid extension of aerial photography, with the consequent increasing availability of up-to-date good quality photo cover, has radically altered the approach to forest survey and crop inventory. Time saving through their use can be as high as 75 per cent, although 45 per cent is probably a truer general indication of their value, without loss of accuracy, over ground survey methods. Survey and inventory design should therefore combine air photo interpretation with ground checks requiring the use of only fairly simple equipment.

Central registries of aerial photography have been established from which information may be obtained concerning the availability of photographs for any area. Addresses are given in List A on p. 81. All enquiries of a register or to an air survey company should be accompanied by a tracing taken from the appropriate 1:50000 or 1 in to the mile OS sheet, quoting the sheet number, outlining the area of interest, and with national grid lines drawn in and labelled. If complete cover for stereoscopic examination is not required, then 'once-over cover' should be requested.

Vertical photographs are essential for basic mapping and for normal crop interpretation, Panchromatic black and white film is normally adequate for general inventory work. Black and white, infra red, true colour and false colour (infra red), do give consistently better identification of species but the additional cost, especially of infra red, is seldom justified in Great Britain. Vertical photographs, currently available at a scale of 1:7000 to 1:10000, provide adequate resolution of forest detail at reasonable cost and are generally recommended for map and crop classification work. It is inadvisable to use photos which are appreciably smaller in scale than the map to which the information will be transferred. Enlargements can usually be obtained at a small additional cost. The size of contact prints, not including marginal notes, is usually 230 mm × 230 mm (9 in × 9 in).

Where suitable photographs are not available, 35 mm photography, taken from a light aircraft by hand held or fixed mounted camera, can be quite cheap provided the pilot and photographer have had some experience. Such aircraft are available for hire from many air taxi firms and aero clubs. The photography will probably be unsuitable for basic mapping, but can be invaluable for sketching in sub-compartments within reliably mapped compartmentation.

Basic Survey and Mapping

For production planning it is essential to have stock and road maps for the identification of felling blocks, for the preparation of sales plans, and for the planning of harvesting and road systems. The map must be sufficiently accurate to measure areas of individual stands to at least the nearest 0·5 hectares. It is often convenient to prepare a basic map of the forest, based on Ordnance Survey sheets, showing permanent features such as streams and rivers, rides, roads and boundaries, from which transparencies may be prepared to provide the basis for stock, road and other management maps. In this connection, it must be noted that the Ordnance Survey hold the copyright to all their maps, and permission must be obtained before copies are taken from any of them.

Complicated maps with complex legends must be avoided. For example, while the stock map will show road lines which form compartment or sub-compartment boundaries, it will certainly be more convenient to show road classification, bridges, culverts and proposed road lines on a separate roads map.

Figures 8 and 9 show respectively examples of Forestry Commission stock and road maps. Suggested legends for maps are given in List B on p. 82.

The main features to be checked or surveyed are external boundaries, road lines and forest rides. Depending upon the density of existing OS detail, additional features in the forest can be surveyed using air photos and ground survey. A two-man team is ideal for this work.

Where up-to-date air photography is available, features can often be transferred directly onto the base map within a framework of at least two known ground control points per photograph. When scale differences between plots and basic map are small, this task can be done by means of a scale rule, proportional dividers, direct tracing, or by means of a transparent grid.

A recommended list of instruments and equipment for forest survey and crop inventory is given in List C on p. 83.

Stock Mapping

The basic management unit of a forest is the stand or sub-compartment. This is described as being an area comprising a more or less homogenous crop in terms of age, species, composition, and condition. It is a sub-division of the permanent compartment as delineated on the basic forest map. They are not necessarily permanent units of management since they will probably change with the development of the forest through felling, fire, restocking etc.

The boundaries should be identified and mapped wherever possible direct from air photos, when a minimum of ground check will be necessary to confirm their validity.

Boundaries of crops less than two metres in height are, however, difficult to identify from air photos at 1:10000 or smaller scale. Where air photos are not available, it is seldom worth conducting detailed ground surveys to measure them on the ground. Adequate sub-compartmentation can be achieved by pacing, combined where possible with sketch mapping from adjacent hillsides.

Where there are considerable height variations, and for stocking densities between adjacent groups too small to map individually, arbitrary grouping may be

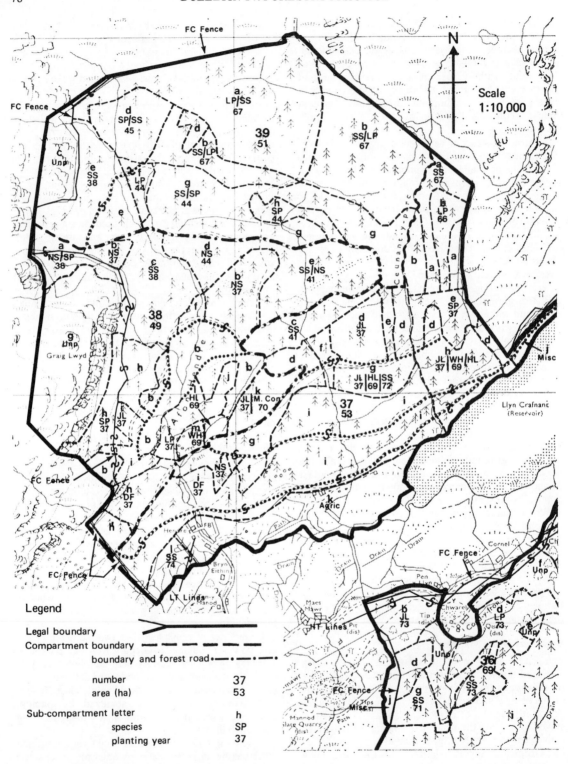

Figure 8 Part of a Forestry Commission stock map.

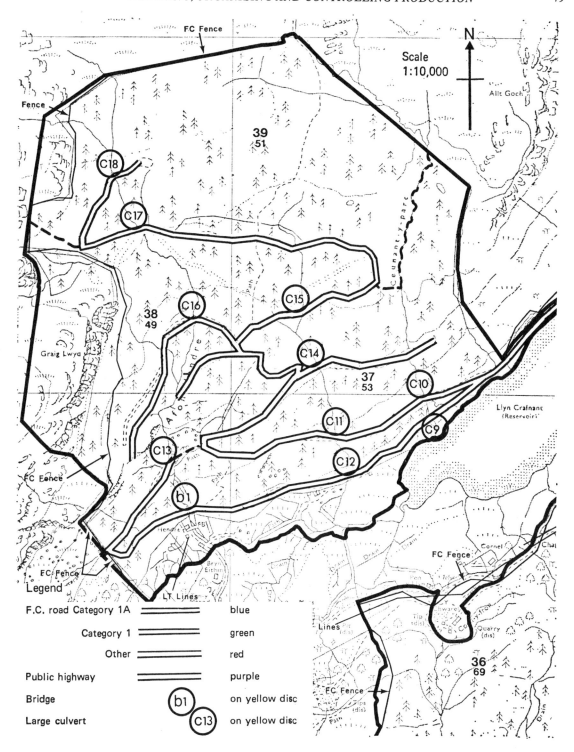

Figure 9 Part of a Forestry Commission roads map.

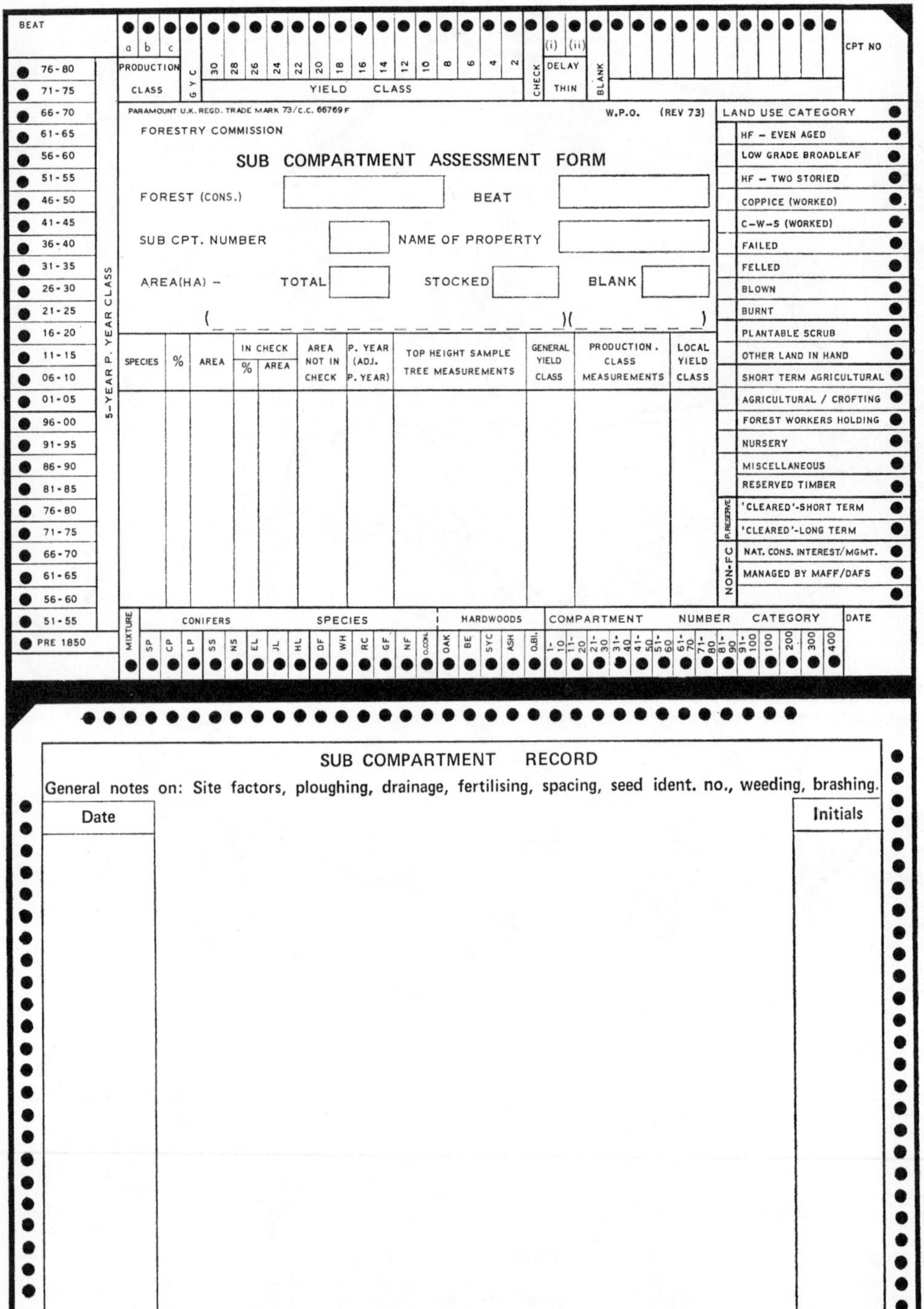

SUB COMPARTMENT ASSESSMENT FORM

BEAT

CPT NO

a	b	c	
PRODUCTION	G Y C		
CLASS			

30 28 26 24 22 20 18 16 14 12 10 8 6 4 2

YIELD CLASS

CHECK · DELAY THIN · BLANK

(i) (ii)

5-YEAR P. YEAR CLASS

76-80
71-75
66-70
61-65
56-60
51-55
46-50
41-45
36-40
31-35
26-30
21-25
16-20
11-15
06-10
01-05
96-00
91-95
86-90
81-85
76-80
71-75
66-70
61-65
56-60
51-55
PRE 1850

PARAMOUNT U.K. REGD. TRADE MARK 73/C.C. 66769 F　　W.P.O.　(REV 73)

FORESTRY COMMISSION

FOREST (CONS.)　　　　　BEAT

SUB CPT. NUMBER　　　NAME OF PROPERTY

AREA(HA) –　　TOTAL　　　STOCKED　　　BLANK

(　　　　　　　)(　　　　　　　)

SPECIES	%	AREA	IN CHECK %	IN CHECK AREA	AREA NOT IN CHECK	P. YEAR (ADJ. P. YEAR)	TOP HEIGHT SAMPLE TREE MEASUREMENTS	GENERAL YIELD CLASS	PRODUCTION. CLASS MEASUREMENTS	LOCAL YIELD CLASS

LAND USE CATEGORY

HF – EVEN AGED
LOW GRADE BROADLEAF
HF – TWO STORIED
COPPICE (WORKED)
C–W–S (WORKED)
FAILED
FELLED
BLOWN
BURNT
PLANTABLE SCRUB
OTHER LAND IN HAND
SHORT TERM AGRICULTURAL
AGRICULTURAL / CROFTING
FOREST WORKERS HOLDING
NURSERY
MISCELLANEOUS
RESERVED TIMBER
'CLEARED'-SHORT TERM
'CLEARED'-LONG TERM
NAT. CONS. INTEREST/MGMT.
MANAGED BY MAFF/DAFS

P. RESERVE / NON-FC

MIXTURE

CONIFERS　　SPECIES　　HARDWOODS　　COMPARTMENT　NUMBER　CATEGORY　DATE

SP CP LP SS NS EL JL HL DF WH RC GF NF O.CON. OAK BE SYC ASH O.BI. 1-10 11-20 21-30 31-40 41-50 51-60 61-70 71-80 81-90 91-100 100 200 300 400

SUB COMPARTMENT RECORD

General notes on: Site factors, ploughing, drainage, fertilising, spacing, seed ident. no., weeding, brashing.

Date		Initials

Figure 10　Front (top) and reverse side of the Forestry Commission sub-compartment assessment form.

resorted to when the average crop features will be applied to the whole sub-compartment.

Crop Inventory—Description of the Crop

With practice and some elementary training, relatively inexperienced surveyors can readily learn to use stereoscopes to identify tree crops in air photos. The major tree genera, if not the species, can be seen on good quality air photographs at 1:10000 or larger scale. These instruments enable the surveyor to construct a three-dimensional image from a pair of adjacent overlapping photographs. Cheap pocket stereoscopes can be used in the forest with a pair of photographs mounted on a clip board. The more expensive table or mirror stereoscopes give a fuller view of the stereoscopic model, thus speeding up interpretation work, but they cannot be used in the field.

At 1:10000 or larger scale the proportions of species in mixtures, stocking densities, blank areas and canopy cover in two-storied crops are more readily and accurately measured from aerial photos than from ground survey. The significance and absolute value of these features for production forecasting and harvesting planning can be determined from later ground inspection. The ages of crops are generally obtained from records, but may be estimated by whorl or ring counts where they are not otherwise available, or where extensive and late beating up has taken place. Where crops have suffered a period of check, an adjusted age should be used if production forecasts are to be made using the yield class system.

PRODUCTION FORECASTING

Reliable production forecasts can be achieved provided the growth predictions are accurate, the thinning and felling policy is carried out as planned, and the growing stock data is accurate. Obviously the task of preparing a production forecast can prove a complex matter according to the nature of the forest area concerned, and the thinning and felling policy adopted. For example, one of the advantages of using the cutting regime outlined at the beginning of the chapter is the constant annual thinning yield which makes for simplification in forecasting thinning yields.

Further guidance on the subject of production forecasting is given in Part III of Booklet 34.

DATA RECORDING

There are no generally accepted standard forms for data recording. The design of forms or schedules depends upon the information to be collected, and on the way it is to be summarised and presented. Ease of retrieval is equally important. If automatic data processing machines are to be used for calculations and summarisation, then it is essential that this also be taken into account from the outset.

An example of the sub-compartment record form used in the Forestry Commission is shown in Figure 10. These are Paramount edge punched cards for manual needle sorting as a first step in data retrieval. Items in various combinations can also be readily extracted for summarisation for operational programmes and forecasts. The summary of growing stock suggested for production forecasts is an example.

Even where the quantity of data to be handled justifies complete automatic data processing, it is usually desirable to retain some form of manual data retrieval system, since access to the computer is unlikely to be sufficiently fast for local operational use.

LIST A

REGISTERS OF AIR PHOTOGRAPHY

Central Register of Air Photography
Department of the Environment
2 Marsham Street
London, SW1P 3EB

Scottish Register of Air Photographs
Scottish Development Department
New St Andrew's House
St James Centre
Edinburgh, EH1 3DG

Welsh Register of Air Photographs
Welsh Office
Cathays Park
Cardiff CF1 3NQ

Commercial Sources of Air Photographs

Aerofilms Ltd
4 Albermarle Street
London W1X 4H3

B.K.S. Surveys Ltd
Cleeve Road
Leatherhead
Surrey

Cartographical Services Ltd
Landford Manor
Salisbury
Wilts

G

LIST A *(continued)*
REGISTERS OF AIR PHOTOGRAPHY
Commercial Sources of Air Photographs *(continued)*

Fairey Surveys Ltd
Reform Road
Maidenhead
Berks

Hunting Surveys Ltd
6 Elstree Way
Boreham Wood
Herts

Meridian Airmaps Ltd
Commerce Way
Lancing
Sussex

A J Storey & Partners
92 Church Road
Mitcham
Surrey

LIST B
LEGENDS FOR BASIC FIELD SURVEY DOCUMENTS

Stage I
Information Put on Maps in the Office

Legal boundary	External yellow verge to existing map detail or to a broken black line if legal boundary does not follow map detail.
Right of Way granted to the owner	Brown line (brush line).

Stage II
Information Put on Maps in the Field

Forest boundary not coinciding with legal boundary	Orange line
Road	Brown line (pen)
Right of Way available to owner and not already shown on map	Brown line (pen)
Ride	Broken brown line
Compartment boundary	Broken red line
Compartment boundary coinciding with road	Red line
Fire tower	$\frac{1}{8}$ inch red circle enclosing a St. George's cross.
Detail which no longer exists either within or immediately adjacent to external boundary	Small blue or green crosses.

Stage III
Information Put on Maps in the Office

Compartment number	Block numerals (transfer or pen) placed within compartment.
Compartment area	Black numerals (transfer or pen) placed centrally immediately below compartment number
Name of Forest or Survey Area	Black pen or transfer
Date of Survey	Black pen or transfer

LEGENDS FOR STOCK MAP

Sub-compartment boundary	Black pecked line (pen)
Sub-compartment letter	Black pen or transfer
Species and other word or letter symbols	Black pen or transfer
Unplantable land	U/P
Bare/unplanted	Bare
Electricity or telephone transmission lines	HT LT
Experimental plots	Expt
Loading bays	(LB)

Tree species should be indicated by the abbreviations listed in Chapter 15 p. 133.

LIST C

SUGGESTED LIST OF SURVEY EQUIPMENT FOR A FIELD TEAM

Field Survey

Prismatic, Silva or Suunto compass	1	Steel straight edge (24 in)	1
Artillery director with tripod	1	Circular protractor	1
20-metre engineer's chain	1	Drawing set (compass, pen, parallel rule)	1
30-metre fibron tape	1	Drawing pen or rapidograph	1
Surveying arrows	10	Set square	1
Banderoles	10	Lead weights	6
300 mm Blundell scale rules	1	Light table	1
(1:1,250, 1:2,500, 1:10,000, 1:10,560)		Planimeter	1
Mirror stereoscope	1	Haversack	1

Crop Assessment (2-man team)

Pocket stereoscope	2	Slide rule and /or	1
Binoculars	2	Pocket calculator	1
Hypsometer	2	Stand data case	2
Hectare grid	2	1- or 2-metre girthing tapes	2
(1:10,560 or 1:10,000 scale)		Air photo grid	2
20-metre fibron tape	4	Random dot grid	2
150 mm Blundell scale rule	2		
(1:1,250, 1:2,500, 1:10,000, 1:10,560)			

Suppliers include:

Stanton Hope Ltd
422 Westborough Road
Westcliff-on-Sea
Essex

J. H. Steward Ltd
154a Church Road
Hove, Sussex

Stobart & Sons Ltd
67/73 Worship Street
London, EC2A 2EL

BIBLIOGRAPHY: PLANNING, ORGANISING AND CONTROLLING PRODUCTION

Forestry Commission Publications

BULLETINS

No. 52 *Influence of spacing on crop characteristics and yield.* 1974.
No. 55 *Aspects of thinning.* 1976.

BOOKLETS

No. 26 *Volume ready reckoner for round timber.* 1978.
No. 30 *Metric conversion tables and factors for forestry.* 1971.
No. 31 *Metric top diameter saw log tables.* 1970.

No. 32 *Thinning control in British woodlands (metric).* 1970.
No. 34 *Forest management tables (metric).* 1971.
No. 36 *Timber measurement for standing sales, using tariff tables.* 1973.
No. 37 *Volume tables for smailwood and round pitwood.* 1973.
No. 39 *Forest mensuration handbook.* 1975. £4. (embraces Booklets 26, 31, 36 and 37).
No. 44 *Forest Road Planning.* 1976.
No. 45 *Standard Timetables and Output Guides.* 1978.

FOREST RECORDS

No. 97 *Forest Site Field Guide to Upland Britain.* 1974.
No. 114 *Terrain Classification.* 1977.

RESEARCH AND DEVELOPMENT PAPERS

No. 56 *The formulation of production goals in forestry.* 1967.

No. 60 *Inventories and production forecasts in British forestry.* 1967.

No. 102 *Production planning in the Forestry Commission.* 1973.

No. 106 *Nothofagus yield tables.* 1974.

No. 110 *Initial spacing in relation to establishment and early growth of conifer plantations.* 1974.

Other Publications

Johnston, D. R., Grayson, A. J., and Bradley, R. T. (1967). *Forest planning.* London: Faber & Faber.

Chapter 9

HARVESTING

Timber harvesting can be carried out by timber merchants to whom the standing trees have been sold; by specialist firms who do some or all harvesting operations on contract; or by workers employed directly by the forest owner. Modern timber harvesting requires competent planning and a high degree of operator skill: **it is not a job for amateurs.** Machines such as power saws are highly dangerous in untrained hands. Inadequately planned and poorly executed logging is a certain way to waste money.

Harvesting by direct labour must be on a large enough scale to make it worthwhile training operators, providing adequate equipment, and keeping production teams employed all the year round. Few owners of small woodland properties can do this, and they are strongly recommended to use merchants or contractors instead.

On some small estates, woodmen are employed on small-scale harvesting operations at times when no other work is possible. This may be worth doing, as a means of keeping men usefully employed, but adequate

training in safe working techniques is still essential. Part-time harvesting work seldom allows operators to develop a satisfactory degree of skill, and it must be accepted that the financial results may be disappointing.

PLANNING

Harvesting is basically transportation. Careful planning is necessary to select the methods best suited to the circumstances of the operation. The most important factors are:
—Terrain
—The forest crop: in particular, tree size, and type of felling (i.e. thinning, felling)
—Markets: these determine specification of produce
—Machinery available
Other factors, such as the availability of labour, may also be important.

Terrain

The term 'terrain' is used here to mean land as a working surface. Good knowledge of the forest terrain

TABLE 16

CLASSIFICATION OF TERRAIN

		Class		
1	2	3	4	5
Ground conditions				
Very good	Good	Average	Poor	Very poor
e.g. Dry sands and gravels	Firm mineral soils	Soft mineral or ironpan soils in drier areas	Peaty gleys in drier areas; soft mineral soils in wetter areas	Peaty gleys in wetter areas: deep peats
Ground roughness				
Very even	Slightly uneven	Uneven	Rough	Very rough
e.g. obstacles (e.g. boulders, plough furrows) small or widely spaced	intermediate	obstacles of 40 cm at 1·5–5 m spacing	intermediate	Obstacles of 60 cm or more at 1·5–5 m
Slope				
Level	Gentle	Moderate	Steep	Very steep
0–10%	10–20%	20–33%	33–50%	50%+
0– 6°	6–11°	11–18°	18–27°	27°+

Sites are described by the class numbers. A 4.3.2 site means:
   4. Poor ground conditions.
   3. Uneven ground.
   2. Gentle slope.
The standard order of 'Ground conditions, Roughness, Slope,' must always be observed. The examples of ground conditions and ground roughness given above are to illustrate typical instances, and are not intended as precise definitions of the classes.

TABLE 17

APPROXIMATE TERRAIN LIMITS OF EXTRACTION MACHINERY

Machine type	*Worst terrain class on which machine can be expected to operate*			Remarks
	Ground conditions	*Ground roughness*	*Slope*	
Agricultural tractors 2-wheel drive				
Extraction				
uphill	3	3	2	Uphill extraction may require
downhill	4	3	3	reduced load
Agricultural tractors 4-wheel drive				
uphill	3	4	3	Uphill extraction may require
downhill	4	4	4	reduced load
Forwarders frame-steered				
uphill	3	4	3	Uphill extraction may require reduced load
downhill	4	4	4	Band-tracks essential in worst conditions
Skidders frame-steered				
uphill	3	4	3	Band-tracks essential in worst conditions
or	4	4	2	
downhill	4	4	4	
Crawler tractors				
uphill	4	4	3	
downhill	4	4	4	
Cablecranes	5	5	5	

Note 1. Each class covers a range, and it should never be assumed that a machine will operate at the extreme limit of the class. For example, frame-steered skidders extracting downhill will probably cope fairly well with poor ground conditions (4) and rough ground (4) if the slope is in the lower portion of class 4—say 33 to 38 per cent—but might find it difficult at the upper limit, 45–50 per cent. *Classes in the above table are borderline*; the table is a general guide only.
2. Most tractors can run on 'very poor' ground conditions (Class 5) if a carpet of brash can be provided and if slopes are no greater than the lower end of class 3. Flotation tyres or band-tracks are desirable, in addition to brash. Band-tracks are essential on soft or steep ground.

is the starting point for operational planning. The Forestry Commission uses a classification system based on the three factors of ground conditions, ground roughness and slope. These factors influence the use of machinery in the forest, and the classification system provides a convenient 'shorthand' method of describing working sites. The main features of the system are given in Table 16.

The type and method of use of forest machinery is determined very largely by terrain. Table 17 lists the approximate limits of machines in use at present.

The Forest Crop

In general, harvesting operations are easier and cheaper when trees are large and there is plenty of space to move (clearfelling of mature crops is a good example). First thinnings, in contrast, combine small trees and confined working space. They can present considerable difficulty, and in extreme cases the cost of the operations may be greater than the value of the timber produced.

Markets

These govern the specification of products, which in turn influence the harvesting operations. If one or two simple products, e.g. 3 m pulpwood, or pulpwood and random-length sawlogs, are required, it may be possible to prepare them at stump. Where more than two products are made, preparation at stump can result in sorting difficulties. Products which demand accurate dimension measurement, such as pitwood, are best prepared at roadside or in a depot, where working conditions are better.

Machinery Available

Developments in specialised forest machinery have been rapid in the past decade. Many of the more advanced extraction and processing machines are highly efficient, but their purchase price is so high that only the largest forest enterprises can operate them economically. Harvesting methods using such machines are out of reach of many forest owners, except through timber merchants and contractors.

Harvesting machinery in general use includes the following:

CHAINSAWS

Now used for all felling and delimbing, and practically all cross-cutting carried out in the forest. Lightweight models are most commonly used for conifers and smaller hardwoods. Important features of a good chainsaw are:

(1) The model and make should be reliable, and the manufacturer should give prompt treatment to warranty claims.
(2) Local supply of spares and servicing should be good.
(3) Power should be adequate for the work.
(4) The undersurface of the saw should be smooth, with minimal 'snagging' points for twigs or branches to catch. Saw width beyond the line of the guide bar on the right hand side should be minimal.
(5) Handles should be well shaped to take a gloved hand easily.
(6) External adjustment of the carburettor should be easy.
(7) Weight should be less than nine kg, complete with guide bar chain, fuel and oil, for all lightweight saws. Larger saws, for work on big hardwoods, should not greatly exceed this weight.
(8) Fuel tank capacity should be at least 0·5 litre and the oil tank should not run dry at maximum setting until fuel tank is empty.
(9) Fuel and oil filler caps must be accessible, and on the same side of the saw. A filter funnel should be provided.
(10) Guide bar length should be 30 to 40 centimetres for delimbing and felling trees of up to one metre in butt diameter. Delimbing takes half the total job time, and the risk of damage to the chain increases with length, so the shortest possible bar is recommended. A trained operator can fell trees of butt diameter up to $2\frac{1}{2}$ times the bar

length. When felling trees larger than one metre in butt diameter it is often worth having two saws; one with a long guide bar for felling only, and one with a short bar for delimbing and most cross-cutting.

(11) The guide bar should be a sprocket-nosed alloy steel type, used with two safety guard link chains and rim sprockets, all made by the same firm. Safety chains are specially designed to reduce the incidence of kick-back, and the two chains are used in rotation. Alloy bars are claimed to last as long as six chains. The clutch sprocket or sprocket rim should be replaced when the two chains are replaced. The grease gun supplied with the saw should be checked to ensure that it has a fine enough nozzle to fit the bar sprocket which should be greased each time the saw is refuelled. When purchasing a saw the dealer will change the bar, chain and sprocket for the recommended types, if not already fitted.
(12) An on-off ignition switch and a 'dead-hand' trigger control must be fitted. The latter prevents inadvertent activation of the chain by branches, etc.
(13) The front handle guard should incorporate a safety brake, which stops the chain when the guard is pushed. This gives positive protection against kick-back.
(14) The rear handle should have a chain catcher and chain break guard, to reduce the risk of injury from chain breakage.
(15) The saw must have anti-vibration damping, to minimise the cumulative effects of vibration exposure, caused by using a chainsaw regularly for several years. The engine unit is isolated from the handles and fuel tank by rubber bushes or springs.
(16) Noise when cutting could not exceed 105 dBA at the operator's ear. Chainsaw noise levels are so high that there is a long-term risk of injury to operator's hearing. This is reduced by wearing ear muffs at all times when the saw is being used. Most ear muffs give adequate protection up to 105 dBA, but only a few can protect above this level. Many current saws have noise levels between 106 and 110 dBA.
(17) Exhaust fumes should not be directed towards the operator in any position of felling or delimbing. Position of silencer and direction of outlet should be checked to ensure this.

For occasional saw users, anti-vibration damping is less essential, but because the job has to be relearned on each occasion, the other safety features are particularly necessary.

SKIDDERS

These are tractors which extract by lifting one end of

the load clear of the ground and pulling it out with the other end dragging on the ground. Timber pieces, poles or whole trees can be extracted in this way. Skidders can be of several types.

(1) Two-wheel drive farm tractors with engines of around 50 bhp; fitted with safety cab and extra guarding on sump, radiator and wheel valves, and with some form of butt plate at the rear. Load attachment can be by a small rear-mounted winch, single or double-drum, or by a simple hydraulic grapple (Leaflet 55).

(2) Larger farm/industrial tractors with engines in the range of 60 to 80 bhp; nearly always with four-wheel drive, and safety cab, extra guarding and butt plate. Usually equipped with a double-drum three or four-tonne winch, and often with a front-mounted stacking blade as well.

(3) Specially designed forest tractors with frame steering, and engine sizes generally from 80 bhp to 150 bhp and above. They have all the features of type (2), and can have winches of up to 10 tonne pull. They are also available with rear-mounted hydraulic grapples in addition to the winch.

Because a skidder suspends its load behind the rear wheels, weight distribution is important. Most farm tractors carry a greater proportion of weight on their rear wheels in the unladen state, and when used as skidders are grossly unbalanced. All type (1) skidders above require front weight to correct this. Type (2) skidders also require front ballast, though the front stacking blade may assist. The frame-steered skidders, in contrast, start with a front:rear weight ratio of 60:40, which becomes a near-ideal 50:50 when the load is attached.

Rough forest terrain requires good ground clearance. Farm tractors, particularly the smaller ones, may have only 330 mm clearance, which limits their use on rough ground. The best of the type (2) skidders have about 450 mm, which is generally adequate; frame-steered skidders normally have 470–500 mm or more.

The size of skidder required is largely determined by the average load size. A rough guide is that 30 flywheel bhp are required for each cubic metre of load. This rule holds good up to 120 bhp or so: above this size, horsepower requirements are somewhat less, perhaps 20–25 bhp per cubic metre.

Small agricultural tractors can be highly manoeuvrable with turning radius of about 3·0 m. Many of the type (2) skidders can achieve 6·0 m turning radius, but in both cases brakes have to be used. Frame-steered skidders generally have smaller turning radii than conventional tractors of equivalent size, and do not require brakes for tight turns. In rough, boulder-strewn conditions the frame-steered skidders are far superior, because of more precise steering and better axle oscillation. In soft ground, the performance of

types (1) and (2) can be improved by the use of demountable band tracks ('half-tracks'), but conventional front-wheel steering becomes progressively less effective as conditions deteriorate.

Specially-designed wheel chains will greatly improve tractor performance in rough and moderately soft conditions. On the poorest bearing surfaces, large flotation tyres are a help, together with the use of branches and tops to form a 'mat' over which the machines can run.

The skidder winch is used with detachable sliding choker hooks, of 'EIA' pattern or similar, to which poles are fastened by detachable slings, called chokers. Chain chokers are common, but polypropylene rope chokers are better, being cheaper and lighter. A single winch rope (9 mm 6 × 19 is typical for work in smaller conifers) can carry 6 choker hooks comfortably, which allows perhaps 10 or 12 small poles to be attached. At, say, 0·07 m^3 per pole, this is not a full load. So double-drum winches should always be chosen for small timber work, thus allowing twice the number of chokers to be used. Only in this way can economic load sizes be obtained. Double-drum winches are better than single-drum for average tree sizes of up to 0·5 m^3. Above this size, single-drum winches are preferable.

Three-tonne winches, of which the Igland 'Kompakt" is a good example, are adequate for the general run of conifer and small hardwood logging. Larger winches may be necessary for large hardwoods, or where it is particularly desirable to have drums with the capacity to carry a long rope. Modern tractor extraction uses the winch as a means of load assembly only; it relies on getting the tractor as near the timber as possible, then pulling it out by tractor power, not by winching. Earlier techniques using a tractor as a means of transporting and powering a massive single-drum winch, which then moved the timber from stump to roadside by winching only, are now rarely employed, having been supplanted by more efficient skidders, forwarders or cablecranes.

Crawler tractors were formerly used as skidders, but their use in this country is now confined to a few large timber operations. High cost of track maintenance and inability to run on public roads are major disadvantages. There are very few cases where wheeled skidders are not more efficient.

FORWARDERS

These are tractors which extract timber lifted entirely clear of the ground. The timber is carried on a linked trailer or integral rear bunk. All use a fitted loading crane. As with skidders, there are several types, of which the most usual are:

(1) Forwarders consisting of an industrial or farm tractor of about 60–80 bhp, equipped with safety cab and extra guarding. Drive can be two-wheel, usually with additional band tracks, or four-

wheel. The loading crane is hydraulic on all but the simplest forwarders. The trailers are usually detachable, two or twin-bogie wheeled, with load capacities of 6 to 10 tonnes. Some Scandinavian firms produce a trailer with the crane pillar-mounted on the drawbar, so that a suitable farm tractor, or a skidder, can be converted to a forwarder by simply coupling on the trailer unit and the hydraulic connections.

The distinguishing feature of this type of forwarder is the absence of any drive to the trailer wheels.

(2) Forwarders essentially the same as type (1), but with power drive to the trailer wheels. This can be a mechanical drive from the tractor PTO shaft, or hydraulic drive. A variation of the latter is hydraulic drive to a ribbed wheel mounted centrally above each pair of rear bogie wheels, and which can be brought to drive directly onto the bogie wheel tyres when traction is required.

(3) Frame-steered forwarders, with engine, cab and crane mounted over the front axle and load carried over the rear wheels. Engine size generally 80 bhp and above, though a few smaller models have been produced. Load capacity is 6–8 tonnes for large forwarders. Medium and large machines usually have the rear axle with twin bogie wheels. All wheels are driven mechanically or hydraulically.

The engine-power requirements for forwarders per tonne of load are less than for skidders, because the fully-supported load makes for more efficient traction. Ten to twelve bhp per tonne of load is usual. The cross-country ability of forwarders is less than the corresponding type of skidder on rough or steep ground because of their higher centre of gravity, though the most modern frame-steered forwarders can cope with very rugged terrain because of improved axle design.

All larger forwarders use twin-bogie rear wheels to reduce rear-wheel ground pressure. Even with this, a forwarder such as the Volvo SM868 has a laden ground pressure of approximately 100 kN/m^2 on its rear bogie wheels, but this is still greater than the $45–50 \text{ kN/m}^2$ of most skidder rear wheels. Wheel chains assist in certain circumstances, and the use of logging waste to improve the bearing surface is essential on really soft conditions.

Forwarder ground clearance is about the same as for the equivalent type of skidder, but some type (1) forwarders are limited by the low position of the trailer drawbar connection: this creates difficulties on undulating ground. Forwarders, particularly the frame-steered models, are much more manoeuvrable than is generally realised: the Volvo SM 868, for example, has a turning radius of $6 \cdot 0$ m, as good as many skidders. The better forwarders have a rotating seat which allows the driver to operate the loader easily, and there are

usually dual controls which enable the machine to be moved with the driver facing rearwards.

All but the simplest forwarders are usually fitted with a single-drum winch, to pull in timber lying out of reach of the hydraulic crane. This winch is sometimes powerful enough to assist in de-bogging, and it may be remotely controlled by extendable electric cable.

Choice of loader for a forwarder is important, because crane work usually takes up the bulk of working time. Most hydraulic cranes are of the 'knuckleboom' type, consisting of an inner and an outer boom, with a rotatable grapple at the end of the latter. Reach should be at least $4 \cdot 7$ m, and a telescopic extension to the outer boom is an advantage. The size of log to be loaded will determine the lifting torque required: $2 \cdot 5$ tonne-metres is a minimum. Lifting and slewing should be quick and smooth. Good operator training is essential, and in addition, it is worth equipping forwarder cranes with two-lever controls in place of the normal six-lever controls. The grapple should be of the horizontal-cylinder type, preferably fully rotating. For general work, a grapple of $0 \cdot 35 \text{ m}^2$ jaw area is required, but if loading is nearly all in pulpwood, a special $1 \cdot 0 \text{ m}^2$ grapple allows faster work.

The loader can be pillar-mounted behind the cab or on the trailer drawbar. This blocks vision, and a better mounting position is on top of a specially strengthened safety cab. Loaders should not be mounted in front of the cab.

Practically all the hydraulic loaders used on forwarders in Britain are of Swedish or Finnish manufacture.

Because of their larger load-carrying capacity, the cost of the actual **movement** of timber is less per m^3 for forwarders than for skidders. This affects requirements for forest roads, as forwarders can extract over longer distances than skidders for the same cost, and so roads can be spaced further apart. This aspect is discussed in Chapter 11.

The ability to carry timber economically over fairly long distances, entirely on wheels, makes forwarders particularly attractive for work on estate woodlands. They can travel over intervening fields with minimum damage to grass, in contrast to the ploughing effect of skidders. The amount of stacking space required at roadside is usually less, because the crane can make fewer, higher stacks, and timber is generally cleaner.

CABLECRANES

These are ropeway systems where timber is extracted by means of moving cables, powered by a stationary winch. The timber load is usually carried wholly, or partially, clear of the ground.

Two types of cablecrane are in general use:

(1) High lead cablecranes: these are double-drum winches, generally mounted on a tractor. One drum hauls in the 'main line' with load attached,

the other pulls in the 'haul-back line', which passes round a pulley block on a spar tree at the far end of the cableway and so to the main line, drawing it out again. A 6 or 7 m tower mounted on the tractor, and the height of the 'tail block' on the spar tree, help to raise the cables and load off the ground. The lifting effect is increased by suspending the load from a block, running on the haul-back line: each winch drum has a clutch and brake, and by applying the haul-back drum brake when the haul-in drum pulls in the load, the line system tightens and lifts the load. Loads can be picked up 10–12 metres or more from the line of the cablecrane.

(2) Skyline cablecranes: these also have two main rope drums, but the load is supported by a block running on a tensioned fixed cable, the 'skyline'. This burden cable may be supported by fixed supports at intervals along its length.

Cablecranes used in this country are those based on the Norwegian Igland and Jobu-Isachsen double-drum winches, or the 'Timbermaster' models manufactured by G. & R. Smith, Aberfeldy. The former can be tractor- or trailer-mounted, while the Timbermaster is now only trailer-mounted. Skylines require additional drums to carry the skyline cable and a light cable, the 'straw line', which the riggers lay out first of all, and which is then used to pull out the heavier ropes.

High-lead cablecranes are the more efficient over short distances, up to 120 m maximum extraction distance, depending on site. Distances beyond this become difficult to extract by high lead, and 180 m represents the limit for this type of machine. Skyline cablecranes can operate at ranges of up to 600 m with equipment on the lines described above. Ranges greater than this are possible with special cablecranes of Norwegian or Austrian manufacture, but there are few instances where extraction distance is so great as to require their use.

In almost every case, it is preferable to use tractors for extraction, if at all possible. Cablecranes need a crew of at least two men, and their outputs are generally well below efficient tractor operations. Cablecranes can, though, extract timber on the most difficult sites, where all other methods fail.

LOADERS

Timber handling, stacking and loading by hand is extremely hard and should be replaced by mechanical handling wherever possible. The maximum size of billet for manual handling should not exceed 30 kg. The main types of loader are:

(1) Hydraulic 'knuckleboom' loaders. These can be lorry-mounted or tractor-mounted, and their use on forwarders is described above. Lorry-mounted loaders are usually mounted behind the cab, though mid-body or tail mounting are

sometimes used. A demountable lorry crane is also obtainable, so that the crane is left behind in the forest and the lorry can carry its full payload, undiminished by weight of the crane.

Knuckleboom loaders are available in a wide range of sizes, with maximum reaches of 4 m to 14 m, and lifting torque of from 2 to 10 tonne-metres or more. Loaders with maximum reach of 5–6 m and lifting torque of 3 tonne-metres are commonest in this country at present.

(2) Front-mounted loaders. These are purpose-built, high-capacity loaders, which are very efficient if there is a sufficiently high volume to keep them fully employed. Maximum lift height is about 3·8 m, and lifting capacity is in the range of 4 to 7 tonnes as a rule.

(3) Tractor foreloaders. Basically farm tractors with foreloader attachments, log grapples are available which convert these for timber handling. Maximum lifting capacity is about one tonne.

The tractor foreloaders are the cheapest, but are limited to relatively simple operations; front-mounted loaders are the most efficient, but require high-volume operation. Both these types need a certain amount of space to move around. The knuckleboom loaders are the most versatile, and most used. The use of tractor-mounted knuckleboom cranes as lorry loaders and roadside timber handlers is increasing. The choice of loader depends on type of produce handled and frequency of use. The range of choice is described in two publications—Forest Record 78, *Loading and unloading timber lorries*, and Forest Record 87, *Hydraulic grapple cranes for forest use*. Both publications contain useful charts to assist in the selection of a loader.

Harvesting Systems

TREE-LENGTH SYSTEM

Most of the timber cut in Britain is harvested by this system. The tree is felled, and delimbed at stump; extracted, by tractor or cablecrane, to roadside; crosscut into sawlogs and other products (pulpwood, stakes, etc.), and these products are then sorted and stacked for collection by lorries.

The principal variation of this system is when the sawlog part of the stem is cut off at stump, and extracted separately from the rest of the stem. This is usually done to make sorting at roadside easier, so that sawlogs can be stacked separately from other products. However, the shorter pieces may reduce the load size, and so the efficiency, of the extraction. This variation is common in hardwood logging, where the main stem may be extracted entire, and branches made into short cordwood pieces at stump.

Tree-length harvesting needs careful supervision to get the three phases of felling, extraction and crosscutting in step with each other. It allows a number of different products to be cut from the stems and sorted at roadside. The concentration of crosscutting means that this can be done by a skilled operator, trained to select the cutting points that will give maximum value of products cut. This is particularly important with valuable timber.

Forwarders can extract in this system if the poles are not too long, but nearly always skidders are used. Cablecranes can also carry out tree-length extraction, though roadside space for cross-cutting is necessary.

SHORTWOOD SYSTEM

Here the feller combines delimbing with crosscutting at stump, so that all subsequent extraction handles only saleable products and all waste is left in the forest. This system can be highly efficient if one or two products are cut. More than two products presents difficulties of sorting, both at stump and roadside.

Conditions within the stand are seldom favourable for accurate, high-value crosscutting. As every feller crosscuts, not just the most skilled, this system works best where product specification allows some latitude.

Shortwood is relatively easy to organise and control, with only two phases of felling/delimbing/crosscutting and extraction to keep in balance.

Winch skidders are unsuitable for shortwood work; either the chokering of many short pieces is too time-consuming, or the preparation of large enough piles of billets (perhaps with pre-set wire slings) requires too much work by fellers. Grapple skidders can extract billets, but the short pieces mean inefficiently small loads. Forwarders are the ideal extraction method for shortwood, exactly suited to the bulk-handling concept of this system. Cablecranes can also operate shortwood efficiently, and the elimination of roadside crosscutting makes the system particularly suitable for mountain forests where roadside space is limited or non-existent.

Ordinary road lorries are sometimes used on flat, dry sites, particularly on clearfelling, for extraction from stump to depot or customer. This can be very efficient, particularly on short haulage distances, but the number of sites where this method can be used is very limited.

OTHER SYSTEMS

These have little place in this country as yet, but technical developments are rapid and they may have a wider use in years to come. The **whole-tree** system involves felling the tree, extracting it complete with branches, then delimbing and crosscutting at roadside or depot or industry. It has no advantage over the tree-length system if manual delimbing is done, but if delimbing and crosscutting are mechanised it has the benefit of removing as much work as possible from within the stand.

There are a number of possible harvesting systems incorporating the process of chipping. The whole tree can be chipped, or only part of the stem and branches, and the chipping can be done at stump, rack, roadside or depot. Chip systems have not yet been developed as harvesting systems to any extent in this country.

Choice of System

Shortwood has an important advantage in small-size crops, i.e. where average tree cut is 0.1 m^3 or less. The small trees are cut into logs or billets at an early stage, and thereafter the timber is handled not as small trees but large bundles. Tree-length work retains the tree as the unit of load until a late stage. This is less efficient with small stems, but advantageous with large trees. The main advantages and disadvantages of the two systems are summarised below:

It is not possible to give a single set of rules for selecting a harvesting system because different factors affect particular situations. For example, a forest where the principal product is pitwood is almost bound to use a tree-length system, even if other factors favour

TABLE 18

Tree-length System	Shortwood System
Less efficient on trees smaller than 0.1 m^3 average	Efficient with small and large trees.
Three-phase system needs good co-ordination.	Two-phase system, easier to supervise.
Several products can be cut.	Preferably not more than two products.
Suitable for accurately-cut or high-value products.	Less suited for accurate cutting.
Working space necessary at roadside	Stacking space only required at roadside.
Sorting and stacking required at roadside. This can be mechanised.	Fellers pile smaller billets in wood. Difficult to mechanise.
Timber dirty in wet conditions.	Timber clean.
Higher density of roads required for skidder extraction.	Lower density of roads required for forwarder extraction.

shortwood. Similarly, an owner of a large forest might decide that the savings on road investment associated with a shortwood-forwarder system outweigh all other factors.

Apart from road investment, the operating costs of the two types of working are not greatly dissimilar, and it will often be best to use the techniques for which the operators are best trained and equipped.

HARVESTING TECHNIQUES

Felling

ORGANISATION

The underlying principle is that felling should facilitate later operations, particularly extraction. If no rack system exists the racks should be marked out to suit the particular extraction system. An existing rack system should be checked, and improved if necessary. Racks required for particular extraction methods are described later.

The felling area should be divided into sections. Each section is felled by one, or at most two, fellers. It is essential to keep a safe working distance between fellers. This should be not less than twice the height of the tallest tree to be cut. If possible the felling sections should be sufficiently uniform to allow a single piecework price to be set for the whole section.

Felling should be done along a 'face', arranged so that the wind does not blow the trees being felled into the standing trees. An alternative felling face must be provided, so that work is not held up if wind changes direction.

Felling direction is governed by the type of extraction. In principle, felling should move timber in the desired extraction direction, but the possible felling direction may be limited by strong winds, or a consistent lean on all trees. When this happens it is better to fell trees in the easiest direction and fell them as nearly parallel as possible. Above all, avoid felling in a criss-cross manner.

Felling should be done in the racks first, then in the stand. The extraction rate is the key factor in harvesting organisation, and the number of fellers is varied to suit the extraction: if the skidders, for example, average 4 m³ per hour and each feller can cut 1 m³ per hour, then four fellers are required for each skidder.

EQUIPMENT

In addition to a chainsaw and spare chains, the operator requires maintenance equipment, fuel and oil containers, safety helmet, ear protectors and gloves. A loggers belt, to carry measuring tape, pulp hook or other equipment is an advantage. The operator will also require magnesium wedges, breaking bar, and some type of turning tool such as a cant hook, or lever and turning cable. A pulling device is necessary for dealing with hung-up trees, such as a Tirfor T7 hand winch.

METHODS

First decide the direction of fall of the tree, then clear away any branches, undergrowth, debris, etc. around the base of the stem. An 'escape route' should be cleared of obstacles, so that it is possible to get clear if the tree should fall the wrong way. Check that there is no one within two tree lengths of the tree being felled, and no hung-up trees within one tree length.

Felling starts by cutting a 'sink', a vee-shaped piece at the base of the stem. The alignment of the sink determines the line of fall in normal trees (Figure 11). The main felling cut is then made, level with the bottom of the sink or slightly above. This does not go into the sink, but stops short, leaving a 'hinge'. It is most important that the hinge is not cut through otherwise control of direction is lost.

The felling technique varies with the size of tree. This is shown in Figures 12, 13 and 14 for small, medium and large trees respectively.

The breaking bar is of great assistance in felling smaller trees. A skilled feller knows exactly when to insert the wedge-plate, before the saw is pinched, and uses the bar to guide the start of the fall of the tree when the felling cut is complete (Figure 15).

Even the best fellers occasionally get a tree hung up in adjacent crowns, though they minimise this by correct assessment of felling direction and accurate sawing. Small trees may be pulled down using long-handled felling tongs. Larger trees can sometimes be turned, using a cant-hook or turning cable and lever, so that the tree rolls out of the crown in which it is lodged (Figure 16). The cant-hook or lever must always be pushed **away** from the feller, never pulled towards him—if he slips, the tree may continue turning and fall on top of him. Alternatively, the butt may be moved backwards using a lever, or lever-plus-rail (Figures 17 and 18). A Tirfor hand winch, or similar, may be used to pull the tree down, using a pulley block on an adjacent tree for safety (Figure 19). Really well-jammed trees need a larger winch, i.e. on a skidder, to pull them down.

Hung-up trees **must** be handled with care. If a hung-up tree has to be left temporarily, other workers in the vicinity must be warned. Operators should **never**

—go under a hung-up tree,

—climb the stem to bring it down by jumping,

—try to fell the tree in which it is lodged, to bring both down together,

—fell another tree across the lodged one, or

—try to cut sections off the butt.

It is always better to spend a few minutes fetching help than to take unnecessary risks.

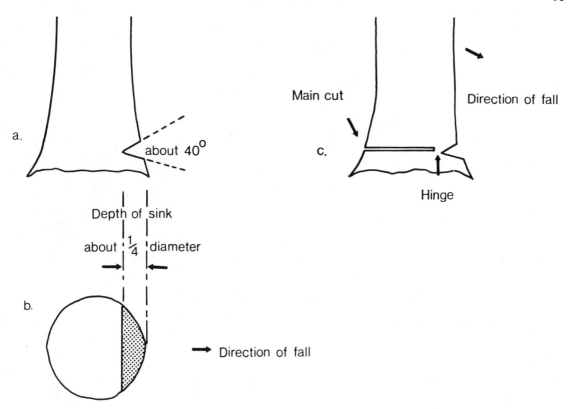

Figure 11 Felling trees. The alignment of the 'sink' determines the line of fall.

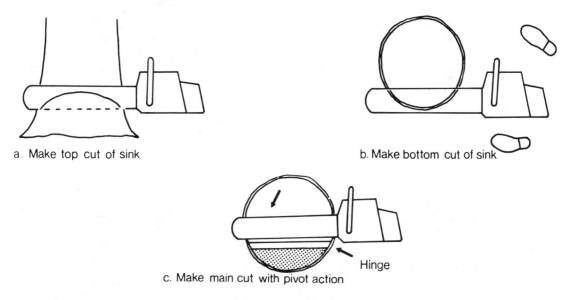

Figure 12 Felling small trees, i.e. diameter is less than guide bar length.

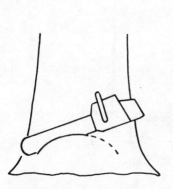

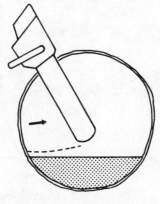

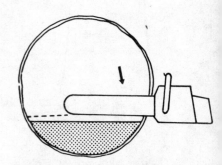

a. Make top cut of sink, starting with tip of saw at far side

b. Start main cut with tip of bar pivoting across behind hinge. Try to keep hinge thickness equal

c. Complete main cut with saw engine swinging round, finishing behind hinge parallel to sink

Figure 13   Felling medium sized trees, i.e. diameter is $1-1\frac{1}{2}$ times guide bar length.

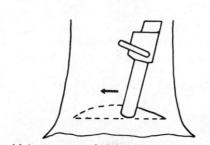

a. Make top cut of sink with pushing chain

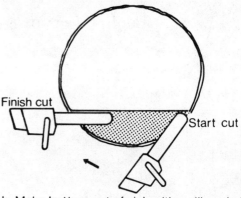

b. Make bottom cut of sink with pulling chain

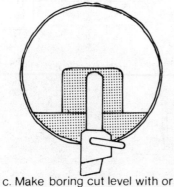

c. Make boring cut level with or slightly above centre of sink

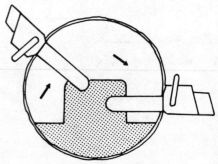

d. Complete cut as in fig 13 (b. c.) pivoting saw behind hinge

Figure 14   Felling large trees, i.e. diameter is $1\frac{1}{2}-2\frac{1}{2}$ times guide bar length.

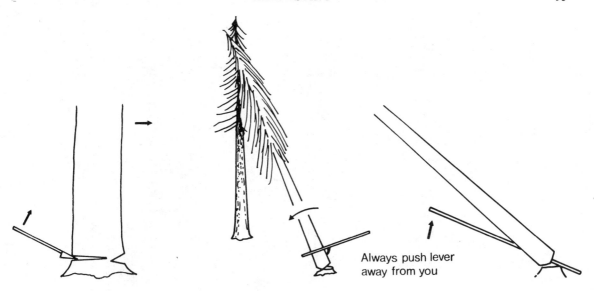

Figure 15 (left) Using the breaking bar to guide the start of fall.

Figure 16 (centre) Turning a lodged tree with cant-hook or turning cable and lever.

Figure 17 (right) Using a lever to move a jammed butt backwards.

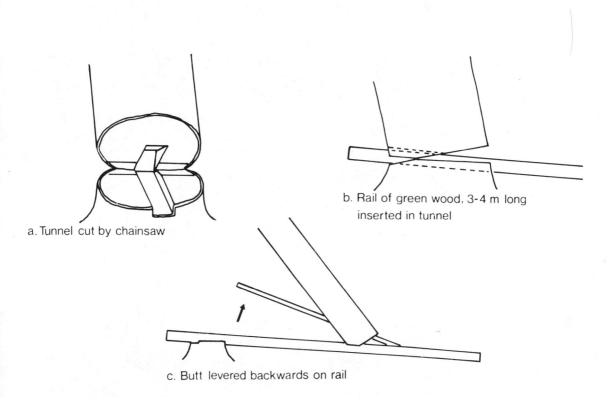

Figure 18 Using a rail and lever to move butt backwards over soft ground.

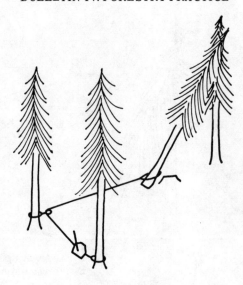

Figure 19 Using a hand winch to pull down a lodged tree.

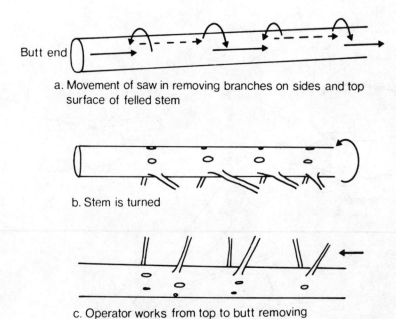

Butt end

a. Movement of saw in removing branches on sides and top surface of felled stem

b. Stem is turned

c. Operator works from top to butt removing remaining branches

Figure 20 Sequence of operations when delimbing a felled tree.

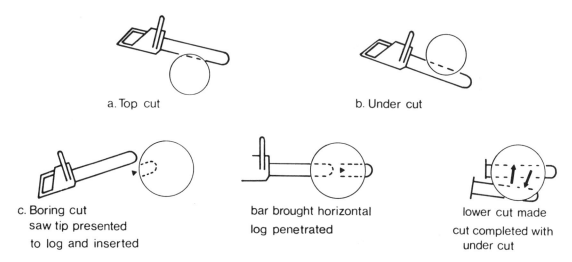

a. Top cut

b. Under cut

c. Boring cut
  saw tip presented
  to log and inserted

bar brought horizontal
log penetrated

lower cut made
cut completed with
under cut

Figure 21 Crosscutting techniques.

Delimbing

This is done with light-weight chainsaws immediately after felling. Proper training in correct technique is essential.

During delimbing, the weight of the saw is taken on the trunk where possible: branches are cut with pivoting strokes with the top of the bar, normally one whorl at a time. The sequence of branch removal is shown in Figure 20.

Crosscutting

In pre-chainsaw days, crosscutting was usually done on mobile self-powered sawbenches. These are still used for accurate cutting of small poles, such as preparation of round pitwood. They can also rip (i.e. saw along the length) and point stakes, which make them particularly useful for estate work.

Chainsaws do the great bulk of forest crosscutting. This needs a chainsaw with a 33 or 38 cm bar. The operation is usually combined with the measuring of billet or log lengths, using a graduated measuring rod or a springloaded logger's tape, usually attached to the waist belt. Light measuring rods of up to 1 m in length can be attached to the chain-saw: the 'Vidler bar' is an example of such a device.

METHODS

The **top cut** is normally used when the tree or billet length is so supported that the cut will open at the top. When the support is such that the cut will open underneath, the **under cut** is used. If the cut is going to open underneath, but there is not enough room to start the cut from the bottom of the tree, the **boring cut** is used. This allows the saw to enter the log, which then cuts the lower portion, completing the cut by cutting upwards with an undercut. Figure 21 shows these cuts in use.

Particular attention is required as the cut opens, to take the weight of the saw immediately prior to completing the cut, and to watch for the log settling.

Extraction with Skidders

ORGANISATION

The extraction routes, or 'racks', must be planned and clearly marked on the ground before felling starts. The selection of routes should not be left to fellers or tractor drivers. The best direction is generally straight up and down hill, with as few bends as possible. In thinnings they should be at least 1·0–1·25 m wider than the maximum width of the tractors, and preferably wider on soft or rocky ground. Spacing should be close enough for the felled trees to be easily accessible from the rack: 25 m centre-to-centre spacing is common in thinning, and on clear felling this can be reduced to 15 m. Racks should be curved at junctions and main road exits to avoid damage by the load to standing trees. Stretches of firm, even ground should be utilised for main racks, which are cut wider than normal, and on which fast driving is possible. Figure 22 shows a typical layout.

Skidder extraction requires normal felling techniques. Rack trees are felled first, then trees between racks are felled, with particular attention to correct direction. The felled stems should lie at an angle of not more than 45° to the rack, pointing in the direction of extraction. Felling should proceed in

H

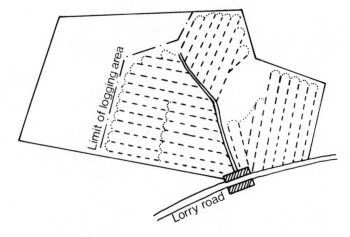

a. Layout for forwarder extraction · racks as long as possible
   alignment up and down slope

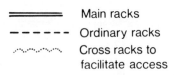

═══════════ Main racks
– – – – –   Ordinary racks
⌒⌒⌒⌒   Cross racks to
             facilitate access

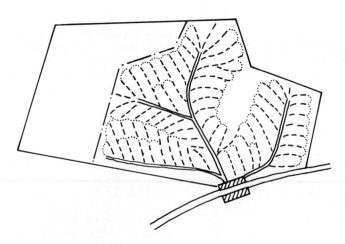

b. Layout for skidder extraction · shorter racks
   more main racks for fast driving · alignment not so critical
   but mainly up and down slope

Figure 22   Typical rack layout.

several racks simultaneously, so that timber is available to the skidder from a whole range of extraction distances; this allows loads to be taken in from near and far alternately, which evens the rate of flow of timber to the roadside, or conversion point or 'landing'.

Tip-first extraction gives higher outputs than butt-first when winch skidders are used, particularly with small trees. Fellers should leave two cm branch projections on the last whorl, to give a good grip for the choker slings. Butt-first extraction is easier for grapple-skidders, and is often desirable with larger stems, because the butt log suffers less damage, particularly in rocky terrain. On steeper, firm ground, butt-first extraction gives better traction than tip-first.

EQUIPMENT

In addition to the skidder equipment, the operator requires: safety helmet, safety boots, ear defenders, protection gloves for handling wire ropes, pulp hook or tongs for moving timber, snatch block for debogging by winch. A chainsaw, while not essential, is a great advantage.

METHODS

The skidder operator assembles the load with the winch, each drum of which usually carries up to 100 m of wire rope. The skidder is backed up to the poles, which are attached to the winch rope by chokers. Detachable chokers, such as the 'EIA' spring choker hook, or the 'Kockum' choker hook, are the most efficient. The choker slings may be of chain, wire rope, or polypropylene rope, of which the last is preferable. It is available as 3-strand rope, of which 10 mm diameter is suitable for small thinnings, and 14 mm for larger poles. The extreme end of each winch rope is formed into a soft loop, 30–50 cm long, through which a detachable pin, about 25 cm long, is placed, so retaining the sliding choker hooks in place. The winch rope is pulled out, the choker hooks and chokers attached, and each drum winched in, in turn. The load should be winched up tight against the butt plate. At the unloading point at roadside or landing, the detachable pin is removed and the winch rope is pulled free of the load very quickly. The skidder operator collects a fresh set of chokers from the poles. This operation requires at least three full sets of chokers.

Load assembly with a grapple skidder requires the skidder to back up as near to the pole butts as possible. Single poles are gripped and moved alongside others, building up full loads which are then picked up and extracted. Unloading is by opening the grapple and dropping the load. Grapple skidders may have to use an auxiliary winch (normally a single-drum) to bring in poles which cannot be reached by grapple.

Good skidder productivity is largely a matter of taking full loads, every trip; travelling at as high a speed as terrain will allow; and avoiding delays in chokering

and unloading. Good presentation of poles by the fellers greatly assists chokering. In certain circumstances (short extraction distances and small poles, usually) it *may* be economic to have a chokerman, to pre-choker the poles so that the time the skidder spends in load assembly is minimised. It is very difficult to get the work of the chokerman and skidder operator in balance, and the general use of chokerman is not recommended. Much skidder time can be wasted at roadside or landing by poor timber-handling arrangements. If no loader is available to sort or stack timber after crosscutting, the skidder may be required to move pieces too heavy for men to move: alternative solutions should be sought, as this work severely depresses the skidder output.

SAFETY

Good training provides a basis for safe working, when the operator is thoroughly familiar with the capabilities of the skidder. Points to note are:
—Correct driving technique, particularly for uphill turns and selection of proper gears for descents.
—No passengers.
—Front blade held high while travelling; lowered fully to ground when parked, especially at end of day.
—Winch ropes wound in when travelling empty; not trailing behind.
—Loads winched tight up to butt plate; not dangling.
—Winching-in always done in line with the long axis of the skidder; not angled from the side.

Extraction with Forwarders

ORGANISATION

As with skidders, the racks must be planned and marked beforehand. They should be straight, up and downhill if possible, avoiding side slopes. Width is normally 3·5 m, and wider on bends, soft or rough terrain. Minimum width is 1·25 m wider than the forwarders. Rack spacing should be 20–30 m in thinnings. 15 m or less on clearfelling. Spacing should be such that sawlogs from the trees felled midway between the racks can be reached by the knuckleboom loader of the forwarder. Figure 22 shows a typical forwarder rack layout.

EQUIPMENT

This is similar to skidder operator's equipment.

METHODS

Fellers fell trees in the racks, delimb, and crosscut into sawlogs, pulpwood billets, etc. Sawlogs are rolled to the side of rack: smaller pieces are piled. Trees between racks are then felled towards the rack, and crosscut. Sawlogs are not moved, but smaller billets are piled at rackside.

Piles should lie parallel to the rack, and be clear of obstructions such as standing trees, rocks and stumps at the pile centre when it will be gripped by the grapple.

Billet ends should be flush at one end. No bearers should be used, and there should be no brash below the pile centre. Optimum pile size is about 0·5 m³, and it is important to avoid small piles.

The racks should, if possible, be long enough for the forwarder to obtain a full load from a single rack: short 'herring-bone' racks should be avoided. Ideally, the forwarder should be able to travel empty up a just-extracted rack, move into a 'full' rack by way of a cross rack, and load up as it comes out.

Unloading at the roadside stacking space is straightforward. Stacks may need careful positioning of billets to build up a firm base to start with, on uneven ground, and should not be placed more than 5 m from the point where lorries will later be loaded. Timber which is required earliest should be placed nearest the road, and there should be space left for lorries to turn, if possible. If the forwarders can be unloaded onto waiting road trailers, a subsequent loading operation can be avoided.

SAFETY

Points mentioned under skidders apply equally to forwarders. The higher centre of gravity of a loaded forwarder makes it more sensitive to adverse terrain, particularly side slopes.

Extraction with Cablecrane

This is a specialised subject, of which only a general outline can be given here. A full description of all aspects of cablecrane work is given in Booklet 12, *Cablecrane technique*.

ORGANISATION

The choice of high-lead or skyline cablecrane depends on the road system at the forest. If the existing road system is dense, at 270–300 m spacing, high-lead cablecranes will be the more economic. If road spacing is wider, up to 900 m, skylines should be chosen. If the forest area is unroaded, the road network should be laid out for cablecranes with a maximum range of 600 m. Cablecranes with this range are not yet common in this country, but can be obtained without difficulty.

Good planning of the extraction racks is more essential for cablecranes than for any other means of extraction. In mountain forests when this method is used, stacking space on roadsides is usually limited, and this often determines the position of racks in thinning operations. Clearfellings usually allow more effective use of available stacking space. Stacking on sloping ground requires care in building up a secure base for the stack. 'Offset' working allows stacking on the road carriageway, but this blocks the road (Figure 25 p. 103). As well as starting an acceptable stacking space, racks should:
—be straight—this is essential;
—be 3·0–3·5 m wide;

—be spaced at 20–27 m;
—have adequate spar and anchor trees; and
—if possible, be parallel, all the same length, at right angles to the road.
If possible, avoid convex slopes for high lead rack alignment. Racks for skylines can be laid out on convex slopes, particularly where knolls etc. provide higher points on which intermediate supports can be erected. In both cases racks on side slopes should be avoided.

The best solution to the problem of restricted stacking space is regular clearance of produce by lorries. Other solutions rely on moving the produce from the rack mouth to an adjacent or distant stacking site by trailers, forwarders, Hydratong-grapple skidders, etc., or by special rigging techniques which allow the cablecrane to move timber laterally along the road.

EQUIPMENT

In addtition to the standard equipment of the cablecrane, the operators should be equipped with safety helmets, safety boots and protective gloves for handling wire ropes. They also require pulp hooks or tongs for handling timber, and a chainsaw.

Communication equipment is essential for all but the shortest ranges, when hand signals can be used. But hand signals can be missed, or the chokerman may not be able to get into a signalling position visible to the winch operator quickly enough. Field telephones can be laid out and used to convey a sequence of bell rings (e.g. one ring for STOP, two rings for HAUL IN, etc.). Radio communication suits all types of conditions, and is much quicker to use. It is recommended for all types of cablecrane work. The chokerman should have a light hand set carried on a harness with remote control microphone/speaker, while the winch operator should have a mobile set and loudspeaker mounted on the winch tractor. Radio sets need protection from shock, vibration, damp, frost and excessive heat.

METHOD

The normal crew size is two men. Their work is summarised as follows:

High lead
(a) Set-up: Chokerman walks to spar tree and rigs tail block. Winch operator aligns tractor, guys tower, and takes haul-back line out to tail block. Both men take end of haul-back line back to tractor, fix it to travelling block, and prepare to extract.

(b) Extraction: Winch operator winds in haul-back line, so pulling travelling block out to chokerman. Latter signals 'STOP' when block reaches correct position, then takes main line out to load. Load is connected by means of

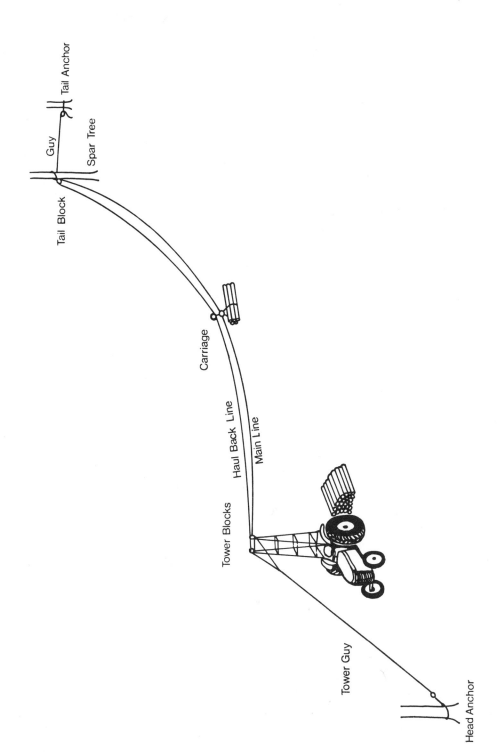

Figure 23 High lead cable crane.

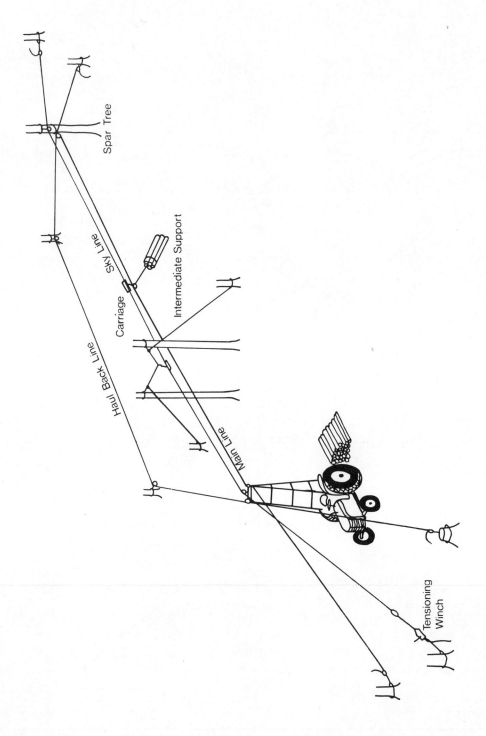

Figure 24   **Skyline cable crane.**

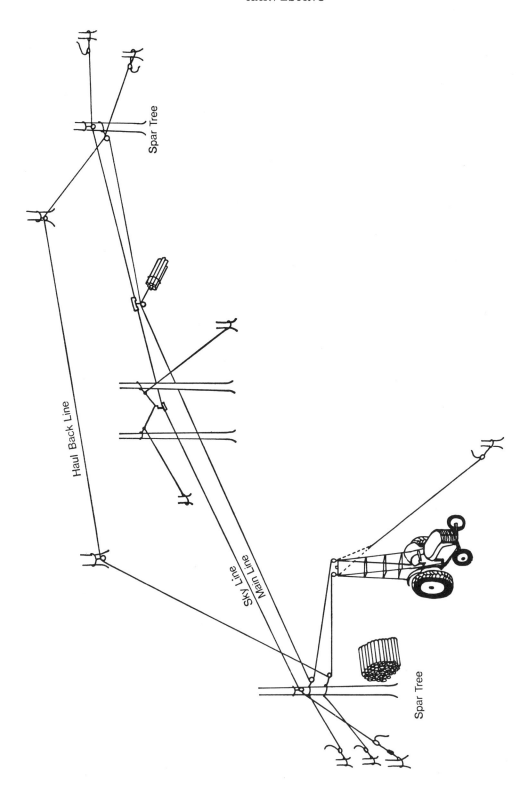

Spar Tree

Haul Back Line

Sky Line

Main Line

Spar Tree

Figure 25   Skyline cable crane: offset working.

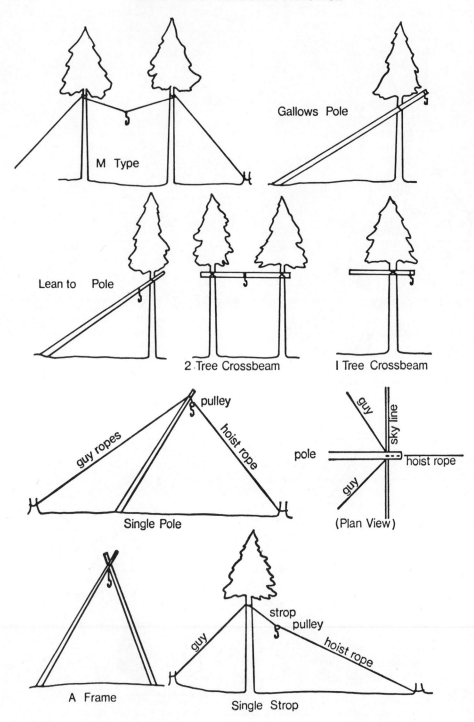

Figure 26   Some methods of constructing cable supports.

sliding chokers, similar in principle to those used by skidders, then chokerman signals 'HAUL IN'. Winch operator uses haul-back brake to tighten the line system, lifting load as it moves sideways to the cables, then brings load in to roadside. He drops the load on the stack, unchokers load, then returns the travelling block into the wood for another load; this cycle is repeated until all timber within reach of the rack is extracted.

(c) Take down: Operator detaches haul-back line from travelling block and winds it in. He then removes tractor guy ropes and moves to next rack to set up. Chokerman is near spar tree when extraction finishes, so he takes down tailblock assembly, carries it to next rack, and sets up tail-block on new spar tree, as in set-up described above.

Skyline

(a) Set-up: Here both men carry the spar tree equipment (ladder, guy ropes, tail block, etc.) to the far end of the rack. Chokerman also takes out a light rope, usually polypropylene, called the 'strawline', which is rigged through the tail block and back to the tractor. The chokerman rigs the tail block on spar tree, also the block to carry the skyline cable, and anchoring guy ropes. Winch operator meanwhile guys the tractor and prepares the anchoring point for the skyline cable.

The strawline (often carried on an auxiliary drum, mounted on the tractor wheel; the tractor is jacked up while this is driven) is wound in. The haul-back line is connected to it and is thus taken out and replaces the strawline in the blocks. The haul-back line is then used to pull out the skyline cable, together with the strawline; the latter is then pulled in, returning the end of the haul-back line to the winch. Use of the strawline means that the men do not have to pull out long, heavy cables manually.

Any intermediate supports are then rigged, and the carriage put on the skyline with the main line through the carriage block. Skyline is then finally tightened, having been anchored securely at each end.

(b) Extraction: Basically the same as for high-lead.

(c) Take down: On similar lines to high-lead. The operators dismantle skyline, and main line and skyline are wound in. Winch operator removes tractor guy ropes and moves to next rack. The chokerman takes down tail block assembly on spar tree and moves to next rack. Supports are also dismantled and moved to next rack as required. It is not always necessary to wind in the haul-back line at each move. The return portion of this line, with supporting blocks, can often be left in place for several moves.

Ground-skidding

It is possible to use a double-drum winch on a tractor as a pure ground-skidding device. Here no attempt is made to lift the load by means of a tower or spar trees: the haul-back line is used with a low-set tail-block solely to take the main line into the stand. The system is efficient over short distances, of 40–50 m, but over 70 m a proper cablecrane is more efficient. Ground-skidding over very short distances can be done with a single operator (when it becomes a useful technique for skidder operators, enabling them to reach inaccessible timber in gullies, etc.), but a chokerman is usually desirable for distances over 30 m.

SAFETY

The key to safe cablecrane work is good training in correct methods. **This cannot be self-taught.** Basic safety rules are:

—Operators must wear safety helmet and safety boots.
—No loose clothing.
—Never use non-standard, damaged or faulty equipment.
—Maintain equipment as scheduled.
—Use a safety belt when rigging up a tree.
Operator:
   —must never operate machine if anyone enters working zone of the cables;
   —must never operate in the bight of the rope;
   —must keep landing tidy and 'exit line' clear;
   —obey chokerman's signals: if in doubt, stop, and ask for repeat;
   —must use correct safety strop;
   —must have tractor on secure axle stands before operating wheel-mounted drums;
   —must operate wheel-mounted drums only from driving seat;
   —must check that skyline anchorage cannot slip;
   —must check that tower is correctly stayed.
Choker man:
   —must give clear, concise signals;
   —must never work under moving ropes;
   —must always signal from safe position: keep out of load path, either standing behind load or with a tree between himself and load;
   —must never cross a static rope without having previously given a stop signal.

Cablecrane units in use at the present time normally use a safety strop, designed as a weak link in the cable system which will break under excess load. This forms the connection between the carriage and the haul-back line, and protects operators and cables from damage caused by over-loading.

Minimum rope sizes in current use are as follows:

TABLE 19

Rope	Maximum safe working load of timber	
	1 tonne	*1·5 tonnes*
Main line, diam mm	8	9
Haul back line, diam mm	7	9
Skyline, diam mm	11	13
Safety strop failure ± 15%	2 tonnes	3·5 tonnes
Guy ropes: General use, diam mm	10	10
Single tower guy and tower slings, diam mm	12	12
Strawline: polypropylene, diam mm	16	16
Intermediate support ropes. M-type, nylon, diam mm	13	Not recommended
Steel support ropes, diam mm	8	8

Roadside and Depot Conversion

Shortwood harvesting requires only stacking space at roadside, which makes it well suited to cablecrane extraction on narrow mountain roads. All tree-length extraction requires greater stacking space. Occasionally the timber can be delivered to the customer in long lengths, but in most cases conversion must be done in the forest.

Roadside crosscutting and processing (i.e. peeling, splitting, ripping, pointing stakes, etc.) is a form of depot working, where the works is spread out in a linear fashion. With adequate road width it is possible to accommodate the full range of conversion operations, but it is normal to find considerable interference between operations, causing delays. This can often be accepted and there are no hard and fast rules as to when roadside conversion (giving shorter extraction distances but greater conversion difficulties) should be replaced by conversion depots (with longer extraction distances but more efficient conversion). Whichever is chosen, the principles of efficient working are the same.

SIZE

Depots should be 40 × 50 m as a minimum. Space is required for skidders to come in, unload, and go out; for storage of poles waiting to be crosscut; for crosscutting to take place and other processing operations similarly; for prepared produce to be stacked; for delivery lorries to come in, load, and go out; and, if independent loaders are used, room for them to operate.

LAYOUT

The above requirements demand careful layout. Figure 27 shows some possibilities. In every case the aim should be to have an orderly inflow of poles, with the products moving towards the lorry loading point with the minimum of handling.

Figure 27 (opposite)

Conversion depot layout.
 (a) simple landing layout: no mechanical stacker.
  — skidder feeds one side regularly to bed A or B. If both full, skidder feeds buffer store beds.
  — crosscutters work regularly on beds A and B. If skidder is delayed, they work buffer beds.
  — skidder piles sawlogs with stacking blade. Pulpwood stacked manually by crosscutters.
 (b) Simple landing layout: mechanical stacker available.
  — skidder feeds two beds regularly, with third bed as buffer store.
  — loader moves sawlogs and pulpwood to roadside stacks, or to reserve storage area if collection by lorries is delayed.
 (c) Roadside conversion area: knuckleboom loader available.
  — skidder feeds beds on verge.
  — loader moves logs and pulpwood to stacks on other side of road, leaving roadway clear.
 (d) Roadside conversion area: restricted space, no loader.
  — skidder may only be able to feed two beds.
  — skidder exits may be restricted.
  — work may be interrupted by delivery lorries.
  — skidder stacks logs with front blade: pulpwood stacked by hand.

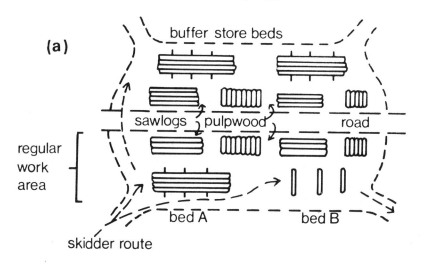

(a)

buffer store beds

sawlogs pulpwood road

regular work area

bed A bed B

skidder route

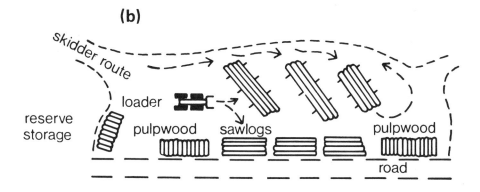

(b)

skidder route

loader

reserve storage

pulpwood sawlogs pulpwood

road

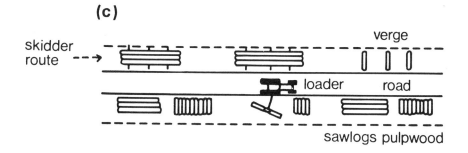

(c)

skidder route

verge

loader road

sawlogs pulpwood

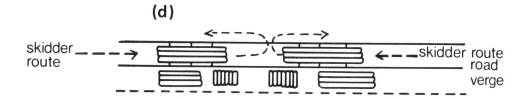

(d)

skidder route

skidder route
road
verge

INCOMING POLES

Skidders should have defined entrances and exit points. Poles are delivered to two working 'beds', one being filled up while the other is crosscut, so minimising interference between extraction and conversion.

CROSSCUTTING

Generally by chainsaw, the poles are crosscut on lateral bearers. These avoid damage to saw chains by keeping poles off the ground, and should be spaced so that the skidder can push heavy sawlogs into storage stacks with the front-mounted blade, or allow a loader to operate. Skidders bringing in loads should have no difficulty crossing these bearers.

LOADING

Small-scale operation does not justify the use of mechanical loaders. This is a good reason for organising harvesting on a big enough scale to allow the use of loaders, eliminating as much manual movement of timber as possible. Both front-end loaders and agricultural-type foreloaders are efficient, provided there is sufficient room for manoeuvre. In confined spaces a tractor with knuckleboom crane (preferably cab-mounted) can operate successfully.

Loaders should not work on a bed where crosscutting is in progress, if this can be avoided.

DESPATCH OF PRODUCE

Prompt collection by road lorries is highly desirable to avoid congestion and the temporary off-road storage of timber on reserve-storage areas. Roadside conversion in restricted space may entirely depend on products being cleared at the right time. As far as possible, lorries should be able to load without interfering with inflow of poles, or with crosscutting. The use of road trailers may be a solution, loading them 'out of hours', and moving them to a pick-up point, clear of the conversion operations.

Timber Transport

Road lorries do almost all the timber transport in this country. Road transport is a specialised business, and most growers (including the Forestry Commission) find it advantageous to use contract haulage firms for the major part of their timber deliveries. Timber merchants and sawmillers rely on their own road transport to a greater extent.

Certain haulage firms have considerable experience in timber work, and their drivers are familiar with loading and driving in forest conditions. In particular, they appreciate the need for regular removal of timber to avoid congestion of roads and depots. Hauliers who can arrange for return loads are able to quote competitive rates. Forest owners are recommended to seek the advice of their Growers' Organisation before arranging haulage contracts.

Most timber haulage is done by lorries of 20 tonnes Gross Vehicle Weight or more, and there is a tendency towards the use of the largest legally-permitted lorries of 30–32 tonnes GVW. Many roads to and within forests are not designed to carry this class of vehicle. It should be made unmistakably clear to haulage firms **and their drivers** which roads can be used with any type of lorry, and which roads are restricted.

Legal limits also apply to load widths (max. 3 m) and vehicle lengths (maximum lengths are 11 m for rigid vehicles, 15 m for articulated, and 18 m for vehicles with trailers). Loads may project 3 m at the rear. While these limits may be exceeded in certain circumstances, they can affect the specification of the timber being carried. There are statutory requirements in respect of safety of loads. A useful guide is *Code of practice: Safety of loads on vehicles* (Department of the Environment, 1972). This includes sections on Round Timber and Whole Trees, and the code should be understood, and observed, by all concerned with timber transport.

Outputs

The figures on output given in Table 20 are very general, and there will be substantial variations above and below these figures for a particular work site, depending on crop and terrain conditions, and on the skill of the operators and harvesting managers. They are intended to give an indication of the relative outputs which can normally be expected. Note that felling and crosscutting outputs are in m^3 per man-hour, while extraction outputs are per machine-hour.

Personal Safety Equipment

In addition to the basic clothing recommended for forest work, harvesting workers should be equipped with the following:

Boots: Part of basic clothing, a safety toe cap is essential. Canadian lumber boots with a rubber foot and leather upper are best, and should be worn with 'Bootsox'.

Gloves: Left hand mitts and right hand mitts with index finger in waterproofed leather are required for chainsaw work. Leather palm gloves are essential for all work with wire ropes.

Hard hats: These are essential. Heavy duty standard BS 2826 with rain brim and back neck strap instead of a chin strap are required. Ventilation is important and the hat should be as light as possible, with a comfortable harness.

Eye nets: Wire gauze with a plastic surround, and designed to attach to the hard hat, these are essential for chainsaw work.

Ear muffs: Essential for work with chainsaws, saw benches, peeling machines and most tractors. Muffs should be designed to attach to the hard hat. Ear plugs are not recommended.

TABLE 20

APPROXIMATE RELATIVE OUTPUTS

Operation	Output, m³ per man-hour		
	Tree size m³		
	0·1	0·2	0·3
1. *Felling:*			
(a) felling and delimbing by chainsaw: tree-length system			
Thinning:			
SP, DF	1·4	2·0	2·4
CP	1·0	1·8	2·4
JL	1·3	1·8	2·2
NS	1·1	1·5	1·6
SS	0·9	1·2	1·6
Clearfelling:			
Pines, EL, DF	1·4	2·0	2·4
JL		2·8	3·3
(b) felling and delimbing by chainsaw, crosscutting at stump, piling pulpwood etc: shortwood system			
Thinning:			
Pines, larch, DF	0·7	1·0	1·2
spruces	0·6	0·9	1·1
Clearfelling:			
Spruces	0·7	0·9	1·1

These outputs relate to moderate to soft ground conditions, uneven ground (e.g. shallow ploughing) and slopes up to 33%; in the Terrain Classification System such sites are 3.3.3.

2. *Crosscutting:*			
Crosscutting by chainsaw at roadside or depot: all conifers.			
—1m pulpwood and sawlogs	2·4	3·0	3·5
—2m pulpwood and sawlogs	2·5	3·5	4·5
The operation includes hand stacking of pulpwood			

Operation	Output, m³ per m/c hour	
	Average extraction distance, m	
	100	200
3. *Extraction:*		
(a) MF 135/hydratongs skidders (47 bhp) on good sites, i.e. class 2.2.2. or better		
Thinning: Average tree size:		
0·1 m³	5·8	5·0
0·2 m³	6·0	5·2
0·3 m³	6·5	5·5
Clearfelling: Average tree size:		
0·1 m³	6·8	6·0
0·2 m³	7·0	6·2
0·3 m³	7·5	6·5
(b) County 754—type winch skidders (75 bhp) on moderately good sites, i.e. class 3.3.3.		
Thinning: Average tree size:		
0·1 m³: load 1·5 m³	2·6	2·4
0·2 m³: load 2·4 m³	5·0	4·4
0·3 m³: load 2·4 m³	6·8	5·8
Clearfelling: Average tree size:		
0·1 m³: load 1·5 m³	3·3	2·8
0·2 m³: load 2·4 m³	6·2	5·1
0·3 m³: load 2·4 m³	8·2	6·4

TABLE 20 *(continued)*

APPROXIMATE RELATIVE OUTPUTS

Operation	Output, m³ per m/c hour	
	Average extraction distance, m	
	100	200
3. *Extraction: (continued)*		
(c) 100 bhp frame-steered skidders. Clearfelling only: average load size 2·5 m³. Average tree size 0 2 m³ and over.		
Good sites: e.g. Class 2.2.1 or better	9	8
Moderate sites: e.g. Class 3.2.2.	7	5·5
Difficult sites: e.g. Class 4.3.3.	6	4
(d) Forwarders, tractor-trailer type, 70 bhp. 10 m³ load.		
Moderate sites: e.g. Class 2.2.2.		
Thinnings or clearfelling: pulpwood and sawlogs.		
Volume felled 100 m³/ha.	8·1	7·6
Volume felled 200 m³/ha.	8·7	8·1
(e) Forwarders, frame-steered 100 bhp, 10 m³ load.		
Moderate sites: e.g. Class 3.2.2.		
Clearfelling only: pulpwood and sawlogs.	13	11
(f) Cablecranes, Igland 4000 type.		
Thinnings only: pulpwood and sawlogs: two man crew.		
Average rack length, m	200 m	400 m
Average load size:		
0·4 m³	3·0	2·5
0·5 m³	3·5	3·0
0·6 m³	3·9	3·5

Face masks: May be necessary when dust is a problem in drought conditions, particularly in tractor cabs. A dust filter mask is practical and comfortable in these conditions.

Ballistic nylon material is available which will resist the cutting action of a chain saw until the chain stops. It should be specified for chainsaw gloves—on the back of the left hand and thumb. It is used on Canadian lumber boots and is a valuable leg protection when used as knee pads, in a pocket about 20 cm by 40 cm which can be sewn onto the inside of each trouser leg.

Spare items should be available on the work site: for example, a spare work shirt and spare Bootsox for change at mid-day. Three spare pairs of protective gloves for chainsaws or wire ropes are recommended.

Intending purchasers are recommended to consult the Growers' Organisations or the Forestry Commission about possible sources of supply.

BIBLIOGRAPHY: HARVESTING

Forestry Commission Publications:

BULLETINS

No. 41　*Forest management and the harvesting and marketing of wood in Sweden.* 1967.

No. 47　*Work study in forestry.* 1973.

BOOKLET

No. 19　*Timber extraction by light agricultural tractor.* 1967.

No. 43　*Forest Road Planning.* 1976.

No. 45　*Standard Time Tables and Output Guides.* 1978.

LEAFLETS

No. 55　*Hydratongs.* 1973.

No. 59　*Hydrostatic skidder.* 1974.

FOREST RECORDS

No. 78　*Loading and unloading timber lorries.* 1971.

No. 87　*Hydraulic grapple cranes for forest use.* 1974.

No. 93　*Cross country vehicles in forestry.* 1974.

No. 114　*Terrain Classification.* 1977.

RESEARCH AND DEVELOPMENT PAPERS

No. 52　*Norwegian timber extraction methods.* 1967.

No. 86 *Census of harvesting equipment and methods, 1969.* 1971.
No. 94 *Cablecrane design studies.* 1973.
No. 97 *Report of a working party on lorry transport of roundwood.* 1973.

Other Publication

Department of the Environment (1972). *Code of practice: Safety of loads on vehicles.* HMSO.
Forestry Safety Council—see Chapter 16.

Chapter 10

MARKETING AND UTILISATION

Good marketing requires a sound knowledge of what is to be sold and what the timber is worth. The first requirement means that a grower should have:

A long-term estimate of production from the woodland. This could be an estimate of annual production for the 5th, 10th and perhaps 15th year from now. This is calculated from the areas under each species and age-class, with the help of Management Tables. Such an estimate, even in broad terms, indicates the size of the marketing task in the years ahead, and allows the prospects for cooperative marketing to be assessed.

A short-term estimate of production, for each of the next five years. The estimates for the next two years will be in greater detail and should give information on volume to be cut by species, size-class, and whether from thinning, clearfelling, or selective cutting in mature stands.

Knowledge of timber value requires a study of local, regional and national markets, both of price levels and current demand. This is important, even where trees are sold standing, as the price the buyer can afford to pay is determined by the markets he can supply. The growers' organisations (Timber Growers' Organisation in England and Wales, and the Scottish Woodland Owners Association) can provide their members with extensive market information, in addition to services such as preparing production estimates, measuring timber, making valuations, advising on merchants and contractors for harvesting and haulage, etc. Similar services are provided by a number of Forestry Consultants in practically every part of the country.

LICENSING OF FELLING

The felling of growing trees is controlled by a licensing system under the Forestry Act 1967. There are exceptions to the need for a licence, the main examples being:

—dangerous trees;

—trees in orchards or gardens;

—small trees under 3 inches in diameter (4 inches for silvicultural thinnings), measured 5 feet from the ground; coppice or underwood below 6 inches in diameter, measured 5 feet from the ground;

—where the amount of timber felled in any calendar quarter, irrespective of the size of the trees, does not exceed 825 Hoppus cu ft, provided that not more than 150 H. cu ft of it is sold;

—where the trees are on land subject to a positive dedication covenant or agreement, and the felling is in accordance with the plan of operations;

—any elm tree which is so severely affected by Dutch elm disease that the greater part of its crown is dead.

As the licensing system applies only to the felling of growing trees, no licence is necessary to cut up trees that have blown over, even if a whole wood has blown down.

Most other fellings must first be licensed by the Forestry Commmission, and the appropriate regional Conservator (see addresses in the Appendix) will supply the necessary application form on request. Any owner who foresees problems in completing it is invited to seek the Conservator's advice when requesting the form.

Licences often bear conditions requiring the land to be replanted after felling, but the owner is always consulted before such conditions are imposed, and should he object to the proposed conditions he would be advised as to the course of appeal open to him. Replanting conditions are not imposed on land dedicated to forestry.

Except where trees are covered by a Tree Preservation Order, forestry work is not subject to control under the Town and Country Planning Acts. Nevertheless, as the felling of trees can conspicuously change the appearance of the countryside, the Forestry Commission consults local planning and other interested authorities about most applications for licences, particularly where the trees are in an area of high amenity value. Consultation sometimes results in the owner being asked to modify his felling proposals, thus averting any need for a Tree Preservation Order. However, in those instances where the felling proposed would severely impair the landscape, for example, by the removal of all hedgerow trees from a wide area, the consultation procedure enables the local authority to make a Tree Preservation Order.

METHODS OF SALE

The following methods are in general use:

Negotiation

Here the prices and other conditions of sale are agreed between buyer and seller, and a suitable contract drawn up between them. Some growers negotiate mutually advantageous sales with the same merchant for several years in succession, and this has the benefit of giving the merchant stability in his labour force, including the sub-contractors, who are often extensively employed by merchants. It also allows the merchant to invest in harvesting equipment, with greater assurance. Negotiated sales depend on the grower having a sound knowledge of timber value, i.e. the likely working costs of the merchant, the latter's probable markets and revenue, and the amount he can be expected to be able to pay for the timber in consequence. If the grower does not possess this knowledge, the services of a consultant or one of the growers' organisations are necessary.

Tender

Sales by tender are competitive and can generally be expected to give a true reflection of market prices. They can be invited from selected merchants or by advertising in the trade press. The precise terms of sale must be determined before advertising, and copies sent to interested potential buyers so that they know exactly what these conditions are, before tendering. This is necessary because acceptance of a tender automatically concludes a contract on the advertised or published conditions.

Auction

Auction sales avoid the drawback of the tendering system, whereby a merchant can lose a parcel of timber because his tender is only marginally lower than the highest offer received and he has no chance to revise his price. This could disrupt the merchant's working, resulting in possible inefficiency and lower prices being offered. Auctions also attract more interest and this can bring better prices.

There is the possibility that wealthy monopolist buyers can always outbid weaker competitors at auctions, which may not be to the grower's long-term benefit. One can only sell specific goods ('ascertained goods') at auction, and some types of produce may be difficult to describe with the accuracy an auction sale legally demands. Sawlogs arising from future felling, where the range of sizes may be difficult to estimate, are an example. On a falling market, merchants tend not to bid at auctions and this can accelerate the fall in prices.

Auction sale expenses make it uneconomic to sell isolated small timber parcels in this way. The Forestry Commission holds regular auction sales in various parts of the country, and private growers can often enter lots in these sales, so reducing sale costs.

No one method of sale is best for all circumstances, and even the most experienced growers will find it advantageous to consult their growers' organisation. This is particularly true of competitive sales, where careful timing and grouping of advertisements and advance warning of future sales is necessary to achieve maximum effect. There are also advantages to be gained by co-ordinating marketing efforts with neighbouring growers, so as to be able to offer larger and more concentrated volumes of timber in a locality. This enables growers, or merchants buying standing timber, to make the best use of harvesting resources, to negotiate better road haulage contracts, and be in a stronger selling position with regard to customers. Once again, the growers' organisations are the best means of achieving this co-ordination.

STANDING SALES

The sale of trees 'standing' to a timber merchant is simple, involving the grower in the least outlay, work and commercial risk. It also lets him know, at the outset, what his financial return will be. The trees to be sold are marked, tree by tree in the case of thinnings and other selective cutting, or by marking the boundaries of clearfelling areas.

It may be preferable to divide a large parcel of timber into two or more smaller lots, especially if the timber comprises widely different types, such as small conifer thinnings and mature hardwoods.

Each parcel should be described separately, giving estimated number of trees, estimated total volume, and estimated average volume per tree for each species. Recording the number of trees by breast-height diameter classes, and calculating the total volume estimate for each class, is often helpful to both sides in arriving at the price to be paid. Private growers, whose local supervisors are not skilled in estimating volumes of standing trees, should seek the services of a forestry consultant or their growers' organisation.

The conditions under which the timber is to be sold should be clearly defined, so that the growers' interests are safeguarded and contingencies catered for. Unnecessary restrictions will reduce the price a buyer is prepared to offer, and should be avoided. Conditions of sale should be notified to interested merchants before they inspect the timber.

Standing Sale Contracts

When a sale bargain has been made, the conditions of sale should be incorporated in a legally binding contract signed by both parties. It is not possible to list every detail which might be covered by an individual contract, but the following items are normally included:

(a) A general description of the timber included in the sale. A precise description of the boundaries of stands, of the methods used to identify trees to be cut, and details of estimated numbers of trees and volumes should all be given. Method and time of measurement (e.g., before or after felling) should be specified. Many growers find it preferable to sell a stated or estimated number of trees, rather than a volume of timber. The stated number of trees are 'believed to contain' so many cubic metres. In the event of any dispute over the quantities involved in a sale, it is comparatively simple to verify the number of trees cut, by counting stumps: verifying the volume of trees after removal is much more uncertain. It is, of course, up to the buyer to satisfy himself that the estimate of volume stated, but not guaranteed, in the sale particulars, is sufficiently accurate.

J

(b)   The purchase price; the method of payment (either by lump sum or per cubic metre or per tonne); the terms of payment, e.g., cash in advance or by instalments; the method of invoicing; and the point at which ownership of the timber passes from the grower to the purchaser.

Growers should note that sales by volume can either be by measured volume or by weight converted to volume by an agreed volume-weight conversion factor. This latter method, like sale by weight on a price-per-tonne basis, is easy to operate using the weight tickets of the delivery lorries as a control (provided the grower is satisfied that all timber has been weighed). Sales by weight operate in favour of the grower, if the material is despatched promptly and weighed in a green state, but against the grower and the road haulier if the produce loses weight by drying-out.

(c)   The period of the contract; the date of entry by the purchaser; the completion date for the whole contract, and dates for completion of specified parts; and the dates for removal of produce and purchaser's equipment.

Provided the starting dates are sufficiently far ahead to allow the buyer enough time to organise his harvesting operations, markets, etc., it is as well for the grower to insist that the completion dates agreed with the buyer be adhered to. Extensions to completion dates should be exceptional. If there are doubts about completion dates, at the time the sale is agreed, the contract might specify the circumstances under which extensions would be granted, the maximum length of extension, and the extra sums payable by the buyer in consideration of such extension. Time limits for produce removal, even if already paid for, should also be adhered to firmly. Merchants should not be allowed to use the forest as free storage space.

(d)   Logging requirements; the standard of workmanship required, e.g., height of stumps; disposal of lop and top; avoidance of damage to remaining trees, drains, ditches and streams, fences and walls, and extraction routes; any special requirements regarding spar, support and anchor trees necessary for cable-crane work; and the removal of processing waste such as sawdust, peelings, etc. from processing sites. Any logging methods not acceptable to the purchaser should be specified, e.g., use of crawler tractors or skidders on forest roads.

(e)   Access routes. A clear statement, supported by maps if necessary, of which access routes, belonging to the seller, may be used and under what conditions. Repairs to and maintenance of access routes.

(f)   Working sites. An indication of sites owned by the seller which may be used by the purchaser, and under what conditions, e.g., sites for processing, stacking, seasoning, loading, erection of sawmills and other buildings. Any provisos regarding entry on seller's land let to tenants.

(g)   Claims. The settlement of third party claims for damages caused by the purchaser or his employees, and claims for damages to the seller's property, including standing trees not in the sale; claims by the purchaser for improvements carried out by him; descriptions of the condition of seller's properties, e.g., fences, gates, roads, buildings, etc., will be required to facilitate subsequent settlement of claims, and such descriptions must be agreed by the purchaser.

(h)   Fire precautions. The precautions to be observed by the purchaser or his employees, including liability of the latter to assist in extinguishing fires.

(j)   Animals. The restrictions on use of, or keeping of, animals on the forest or estate by the purchaser or his employees.

(k)   Sub-contractors. The limitations on employment of sub-contractors by the purchaser, and the obligations by sub-contractors to observe general conditions of sale.

(l)   Penalties for non-compliance with contract.

(m)   Arbitration in the event of dispute.

SALES AFTER FELLING

Some growers may not wish to sell their timber standing, for various reasons. The timber may be required for conversion in the grower's own sawmill; it may be desirable to do the felling at a particular season, or to provide work for woodsmen in the worst months of winter. The trees for sale may be too scattered to attract a timber merchant, or may have to be felled with extreme care to avoid damage to remaining young or specially valuable trees.

Whole trees can be sold felled at stump or at the roadside or rideside. A purchaser should be found before the trees are felled, and the sale should be subject to a contract covering the same points as for a standing sale.

Where the felled trees are to be converted and sold as products, e.g., sawlogs, pulpwood, mining timber, etc., it is **essential** to find a purchaser for the produce before a tree is felled. It is also essential to have trained men and the right equipment available. Above all, the supervisor in charge of the operations must be competent and experienced. Failure to ensure this will lead to financial loss.

Sales of produce can be made through or to a timber merchant, who will often be willing to arrange collection and transport by road haulage vehicles. Other customers may require produce to be delivered, either on the grower's transport or through a road haulage firm. The latter is generally preferable, as road haulage is a specialised business. In negotiating or quoting prices, it should be made clear whether prices are 'at roadside', where the customer does his own haulage and loading; 'free on transport' (FOT), where the grower is responsible for loading the customer's vehicles; or 'delivered', where grower is responsible for loading and delivery.

PRICES

Because home produced timber accounts for only a small part of the country's total needs, the price levels for imported timber and wood-based products have a strong influence on the general level of home timber prices. Large timber users, such as the National Coal Board, and the major pulpwood and chipboard makers, negotiate contract prices with their suppliers, which reflect imported price levels, haulage distance to mill, species supplied, etc. Sawlogs and standing trees are usually sold to timber merchants whose prices may be affected by their particular needs. If a merchant has a full order book and his round timber stocks are low, he may be prepared to pay higher than normal prices: conversely, if trade is slack and a merchant's stocks are high, he is likely to consider only low prices for further purchases.

Timber quality affects price to a varying degree, according to the locality and markets. For example, high grade sycamore may command a good price if local millers can themselves obtain premium prices from their customers, but may fetch only low prices if the local users are interested only in conifer sawlogs and pulpwood. The cost of road haulage is such that small lots of high quality timber are seldom worth sending to far distant customers. The factors which also affect price are species, size of parcel, tree size, ease of harvesting and access by road haulage vehicles. These, together with local or regional demand, will have to be taken into account when deciding the market value of a parcel of timber. Each factor will carry varying weight in different circumstances.

It must be emphasised that the grower who sells only occasional lots is in a weak selling position. It is not uncommon to find parcels worth thousands of pounds being sold with no independent valuation. Professional advice is available, and its use is strongly recommended.

Statistics on prices paid for timber on private estates are collated by the Commonwealth Forestry Institute at Oxford, and by the Department of Forestry at Aberdeen University, as well as by the two timber growers' organisations. The Forestry Commission regularly publishes average prices paid for standing sales of conifers from its forests: these schedules appear in forestry journals and the trade press. *A guide to home-grown timber prices and forestry costings*, by Dr Cyril Hart, is a useful and frequently-revised reference book.

PRODUCTS

The market for particular products may vary considerably in different parts of the country, and from time to time, and the grower is strongly recommended to find out what markets are currently available **before** preparing produce. The following selection of the commoner items gives a guide to possible categories of produce.

Saw Timber

CONIFERS

Home-grown sawn softwoods compete with imported timber from Scandinavia and Canada in up to 7 or 8 m lengths, and home merchants require a comparable range. Some have a market for shorter lengths down to 2 m or so in some cases. All logs over 16 cm top diameter overbark can be regarded as sawlog material. Certain sawmills which use chipper headrigs, to prepare squared timber from the round log, converting the outside rounded portions to saleable chips, can take logs of top diameters down to 14 cm or so overbark.

HARDWOODS

The markets for hardwood sawlogs require good quality, accurately sawn and adequately seasoned timber. The bulk of the material is of similar dimension to conifer sawlogs but, because the requirements of merchants vary considerably, anyone proposing to sell hardwood sawlogs is advised to agree the lengths and diameters required with the buyer, before work starts.

Mining Timber

There is a large market for sawn hardwood mining timber which provides a useful outlet for lower quality material in a wide range of sizes. The National Coal Board prepares specifications for these and also for sawn softwood timber. The preparation of sawn timber of any sort is a job more suited to the commercial sawmiller than to the estate owner.

Pitwood

Round pitwood is almost entirely conifer and is generally supplied to the collieries peeled and seasoned. Some unpeeled pitwood is supplied to South Wales collieries. The National Coal Board's usual sizes are currently in the following ranges:

Softwood pitwood:	Length m	Top diam mm
Peeled	0·375–3·6	60–230
Split, peeled	0·9 –2·7	100–230
Unpeeled	0·65 –3·9	60–200
Split, unpeeled	1·05 –2·7	100–230

J *

Because the needs of individual collieries vary from time to time, growers should obtain information on sizes before preparing pitwood. This information is available from forestry consultants, the growers' organisations and from the National Coal Board.

Pulpwood, Fibreboard, Chipboard and Wood-wool Material

Pulp mills require spruces mainly, and will accept certain other species. Two hardwood pulp mills, in Gwent and Kent, accept ash, beech, birch, Sweet chestnut, sycamore, elm, alder and lime, and the former also accepts oak.

Fibreboard manufacturers take most conifers and certain hardwoods (oak may be excluded). The proportion of hardwoods may also be limited.

Chipboard makers prefer conifers and also use large quantities of industrial wood waste.

Wood-wool is used as a packing material or in the production of wood-wool concrete slabs. Makers usually prefer pine and timber must be straight, seasoned and free from large knots.

Some typical specifications are given below:

TABLE 21

ROUNDWOOD SPECIFICATIONS

Product	Specification	
	Length (m)	Diameter (cm)
Pulpwood	3·0 tolerance to 2·5	5–40 ob
	3·0 tolerance to 2·5	7·5–30 ob
	2·3 tolerance to 1·8	6·5 ub–40 ob at butt
	1·2 tolerance to 1·1	9–41 ub
Fibreboard	1·2 tolerance to 1·1	8–20 ob
Chipboard	2·0 tolerance ± 0·05	4 ub–20 ob
	2·0 tolerance to 2·3	4 ub–35 ob
Wood-wool	1·85 or 2·46	15–25 ub
	2·0	13–25 ub
		ob = over bark measure
		ub = under bark measure

It is important to obtain details of specifications and prices direct from the firms concerned, as these can vary. Method of payment, e.g. by weight or volume, and the condition of the timber at time of delivery (fresh-felled or seasoned, etc.) must also be agreed with the firm in advance.

Fencing Materials

The following are some typical specifications of fencing materials:

TABLE 22

FENCING TIMBER SPECIFICATIONS

Type	Material Specification
Posts and rail fences for road-sides, morticed, cattle-proof	Posts, sawn: 150 × 75 mm 2·1 m long Rails, sawn: 90 × 40 mm 2·7 m long Intermediate posts: 90 × 40 mm 1·8 m long
Motorway fences	Posts, sawn: 150 × 75 mm or 130 × 100 mm minimum. 2·3 m long Rails: 90 × 40 mm (hardwood) or 100 × 40 mm (softwood) All species to be pressure treated with preservative
Posts and rail fences nailed	Posts, sawn: 140 × 65 mm 2·0 m long Rails: 90 × 40 mm
Post and wire fences	Posts, sawn: 75 × 75 mm 1·7 m long or 90 × 90 mm 1·7 m long or quartered from 180–200 mm top diam or round, 75–90 mm top diam or half-round, 100 mm face at top Straining posts, sawn: 150 × 150 mm or 180 × 180 mm or round 180–200 mm top diam all 2·1–2·3 m length
Deer fences	Posts: 75 × 75 mm 2·6 m long, or equivalent in quartered material Straining posts: 230 mm top diam 3.2 m length

Sizes and specifications of fencing materials vary considerably. Oak, Sweet chestnut and larch are commonly used without preservation treatment, where they contain a high proportion of durable heartwood. Other species are generally preserved, with pressure treatment the most effective.

Telegraph Poles

The Post office purchases telegraph poles in lots of 100 or more poles. Scots pine is preferred, but certain other species are also accepted. Poles must be of a high standard. Growers wishing to supply this market should contact The Post Office, Telephone House, Temple Avenue, London EC4Y 0HL, for tender forms, conditions of tender and specifications.

Turnery Poles

Some turneries take hardwoods, notably birch, ash, sycamore, beech and hazel, in poles of 75 mm minimum top diameter, lengths of 2·0 m and upwards. Turnery squares, sawn from round logs, are also used in a variety of hardwoods.

Rustic Poles

This can be a useful market near towns, for conifers (especially larch) and sometimes hardwoods. Sizes range from 2·5 to 6·0 m length, with top diameter of 20 mm and butts of 40–100 mm.

Stakes

A wide range of stake sizes are in common use in farming areas. Sizes generally run from 1·2 m × 40 mm top diameter to 2·1 m × 65 mm top diameter.

Other Forest Produce

Christmas trees can be a profitable market, particularly when they can be suitably packaged in polythene sleeves for ease of handling. Needle-fall in Norway spruce can be reduced by immersing the freshly cut tree in a 0·5 per cent solution of sodium alginate.

Foliage of Western red cedar, Silver firs, Lawson cypress and holly can often be marketed to the florist trade for wreaths and decoration.

BIBLIOGRAPHY: MARKETING AND UTILISATION

Forestry Commission Publications

BULLETINS

No. 27   *Utilisation of hazel coppice.* 1956.
No. 41   *Forest management and the harvesting and marketing of wood in Sweden.* 1967.
No. 51   *Forest products in the United Kingdom economy.* 1974.

FOREST RECORDS

No. 29   *Use of forest produce in sea and river defence in England and Wales.* 1954.
No. 35   *Use of home-grown timber in packaging and materials handling.* 1957.
No. 42   *Use of home-grown softwood in house construction.* 1959.
No. 68   *Pulpwood supply and the paper industry.* 1969.
No. 70   *Imports and consumption of wood products in the United Kingdom, 1950-1967.* 1969.

No. 72   *Experiments on drying and scaling close-piled pine billets at Thetford.* 1970.
No. 95   *Wood resources and demands.* 1974.
No. 108   *Tests on round timber fence posts.* 1976.
No. 110   *Conifer bark—its properties and uses.* 1976.

RESEARCH AND DEVELOPMENT PAPERS

No. 32   *The utilisation of bark.* 1969.
No. 62   *Some problems of long-term marketing arrangements.* 1967.
No. 77   *Treatment of Christmas trees.* 1974.
No. 90   *Planning and development of markets for man-made forests.* 1972.

INFORMATION PAMPHLETS

Horticultural and equestrian uses for bark.
Some uses for wood residues.
The marketing of forest tree seed and plants within the European Economic Community.

Other Publications

Hart, C. E. (1975). *A guide to home-grown timber prices and forestry costings.* Coleford, Gloucestershire.

LEGISLATION

Under the Forestry Act 1967:

The Forestry (Felling of Trees) Regulations 1951 (SI 1951 no. 1726).
The Forestry (Exceptions from Restriction of Felling) Regulations 1951 (SI 1951 No. 1725).
The Forestry (Exception from Restriction of Felling) Regulations 1972 (SI 1972 No. 91).
The Forestry (Exception from Restriction of Felling) Regulations 1974 (SI 1974 No. 1817).

Under the Town and Country Planning Act 1971:

Town and Country Planning (Tree Preservation Order) Regulations 1969 (SI 1969 No. 17), as amended by SI 1975 No. 148.

Under the Town and Country Planning (Scotland) Act 1972:

Town and Country Planning (Tree Preservation Order and Trees in Conservation Areas) (Scotland) Regulations 1975 (SI 1975 No. 1204).

Chapter 11

FOREST ROADS

The function of forest roads is to provide access to the forest for general management purposes and for the transport of timber to the market. Roads are essential in all but the smallest woods, but they are costly to construct. It is important that they be planned and designed with care.

No more than a brief outline of the principles of road planning, design, construction and maintenance can be provided here. The reader can supplement this information by getting advice from staff at the nearest Forestry Commission Conservancy Office and from reference books some of which are listed in the bibliography.

FOREST ROAD PLANNING

Forest road building involves heavy capital expenditure, and continuing charges for road maintenance; but a good road system will reduce the amount of cross-country movement of timber in extraction operations, and may allow greater use of larger, more economical road transport vehicles for delivery to the customer. The purpose of road planning is to try to achieve the combination of road cost and extraction cost (and sometimes road haulage cost as well) which gives the lowest overall cost of moving timber.

Road costs which have a bearing on the optimum intensity of roading include all bridges, culverts, turning and passing places. The road cost per cubic metre is influenced by the productivity of the forest crops: highly productive forests can generally afford a greater level of investment in roads. The off-road costs which are important are those related to the actual movement of the timber, and which increase in direct proportion to increase in extraction distance.

The process of planning new forest roads usually consists of:

(1) Obtaining the best available estimate of road construction and maintenance costs on the area in question.
(2) Making an assessment (based on a careful survey of the terrain) of the best means of extraction, and the movement cost of timber which this involves.
(3) Calculating the road spacing at which the road cost per cubic metre to be extracted equals the off-road movement cost per cubic metre. This is the theoretical optimum road spacing.
(4) Selecting possible road alignments on the ground so as to achieve a practical lay-out with road spacings as near to the optimum spacing as is technically possible, within the limitations of topography and the need to link into existing forest or public roads.

The use of modern extraction equipment usually requires road systems at intensities between 10 and 20 m per ha; very difficult circumstances may require more than this. On the other hand, many small blocks of woodland can only justify a single road through or to them, and then only if road costs can be kept low.

An alternative to the construction of lorry roads to small or isolated blocks of woodland is the use of forwarders. Designed as off-road extraction tractors, these vehicles can move timber at relatively low cost over fields or on simple tracks which cost less than lorry roads. On difficult terrain it may be quite expensive to construct even tracks, and maintenance costs may be higher than for roads. Road planning should compare the alternatives of lorry roads (with higher construction cost and lower costs of lorry transport along the road) and forwarder tracks (lower construction cost and higher haulage cost for similar distance along the tracks) per cubic metre to be moved.

Road planning may also involve the possible up-grading of existing sub-standard roads, the timing of investment, and the extension of existing road systems. Forestry Commission Booklet No. 43 *Forest Road Planning* deals with the various aspects of this subject in detail, and is recommended for further reading.

EFFECT OF TERRAIN, SOIL AND OTHER FACTORS ON ROAD LOCATION

Road location is greatly affected by topography and ground conditions, both of which vary over a wide range in Britain. The normal procedure, on cross sloping ground, is to locate the road alignment in such a way that excavation is minimised, but the terrain may well introduce problems of both horizontal and vertical curvature. It is essential to avoid substantial outcrops of rock but excavation is less of a difficulty where the rock can be ripped by large angledozer fitted with a hydraulically operated ripper.

Forming roads on peat, other than shallow peat, in embankment form, is commonly practised especially when morainic, or other suitable, deposits occur nearby as sources of good construction material.

In high rainfall areas the existence of streams and rivers poses a special problem of road location, and it is not uncommon for a bridge or culvert crossing to dictate the position of the future road.

Harvesting systems, whether involving skidder, forwarder or cable-crane methods of timber extraction, as well as engineering design considerations influence road location and alignment. Consideration of the

TABLE 23

SUMMARY OF FOREST ROAD STANDARDS

Item	Feature	Dimension	Remarks
Tree Felling for forest road	Clearance width	Variable	Depends on site conditions but must accommodate all roadworks and associated drainage, with adequate clearance to avoid excessive shrouding of road.
Road formation	Formation width	min 4·7 m	Batters—upper as steep as possible. Lower batters normally 1 in 1¼.
Road formation	Formation width on peat	min 5·6 m	Road formation is constructed on top of deep peat but with shallow peat up to 500 mm the peat can be excavated.
Road formation	Formation camber	min 75 mm	On slack gradients road camber is increased to 90 mm.
Road formation	Crossfall	min 150 mm but not exceeding 190 mm	On roads located on steep cross slopes crossfall replaces camber.
Gradient	Longitudinal	max 10%	Except on horizontal curves where road pavement width has to be increased.
Gradient	Longitudinal	min 1%	On flat country for efficient drainage.
Road pavement	Width	3·2 m	Standard width but increased for sharp horizontal curves as necessary.
Forest road	Horizontal curves	Radius / Road pavement width — m / m: 60·0 / 3·2; 45·0 / 3·5; 30·0 / 4·0; 25·0 / 4·2; 20·0 / 4·5; 15·0 / 5·0	Road pavement is widened on sharp horizontal curves for vehicles up to 32 ton (articulated) and up to 28 ton (fixed platform). Road pavement widening is achieved on the inside of the curve with a straight transition, 15 m length, to the inner radius.
Forest road pavement	Thickness of (i) base course + surfacing course (ii) combined base and surfacing course	Varies 150 mm to more than 450 mm	Dry bound macadam construction.
Turning places	Width / Length	4 m / 21 m	Set out in the form of a T.
Passing places	Width / Length	4 m / 33 m	

incidence, size and positions of timber handling, stacking and conversion facilities, is also important.

FOREST ROAD STANDARDS

In the United Kingdom the Construction and Use Regulations 1969 permit vehicles of up to 30 tons gross vehicle weight of the 4-axled rigid type, and up to 32 tons gross vehicle weight of the 5-axled articulated type. Both these types of vehicles have maximum overall width of approximately 2 m, maximum overall length of 15 m, and a maximum axle load of 10 tons.

Due to the distance from the forest to the market it is normally good economic practice to use the largest vehicle available, provided that there is sustained utilisation. This could be a problem with smaller forests, and there may be a case for the use of vehicles less than maximum size, especially, too, if any existing forest roads, and/or the existing approach public highway, are sub-standard.

As a general rule, it is considered that forest roads should be designed to accommodate safely the largest timber vehicles, and the summary of forest road standards set out in Table 23 is designed to achieve this aim.

As far as road standards for smaller vehicles are concerned it should be possible, from the aspect of horizontal curvature, to reduce the standards referred to in the above summary. The appropriate geometrical requirement will depend on the wheelbase dimensions of the vehicle. The geometry and pavement strength of forest roads are often determined by the vehicles used in their construction, and even the smaller timber haulage vehicles are of the same width (and of equal or even greater axle loading) as the largest permitted, so that it is only in radius of curvature that reduced standards can be adopted.

The classification of roads as suitable and safe for the vehicles using them, needs to be considered. The simplest classification is the most effective, and need only indicate whether the road is capable of taking any type of normal vehicle, up to and including the maximum size of vehicles allowed, and which are in common use, on public highways. Roads having features which would characterise them as sub-standard would either require to be improved to ensure safety or, for example, in the case of sub-standard bridges, would be assessed in respect of the safe load that could be carried.

SURVEY METHODS

Let us assume that the planning of the road in terms of a broad corridor has been accepted, and the road survey is about to take place. If the ground conditions are difficult then a detailed survey will no doubt be warranted. This will involve the preparation of a longitudinal section, with cross sections, and a plan. These, when drawn, will permit the design of the road, taking into account such aspects as the specification data, water crossings, soil conditions, road construction methods, the type of plant to be used on construction, the availability of suitable materials and other items.

The instruments used in detailed survey usually include a suitable tripod level for longitudinal section levelling, and an Abney hand level for cross sectioning. For the alignment traverse a tacheometer is recommended, or alternatively a theodolite or prismatic compass and chain can be used. Easier ground conditions for road survey may allow a more simple procedure, and the survey operation can be completed using only an Abney level, prismatic compass and chain. In both cases the survey should be carried out carefully and the resultant road alignment should be one compatible with specification, safety and cost limitations.

CONSTRUCTION OF ROADS

In private forestry it is more than probable that most road construction works will be put out to contract. This involves the preparation of contract documents even if only in a simple form. The main items of the road specification recorded elsewhere in this chapter should be observed, in relation to the particular site, to achieve a forest road of efficient and sound design. It is not feasible to describe all the types of ground conditions here, but one of the most common is that of a cross slope in firm subsoils. Another type which is quite common occurs where peaty soils prevail, on fairly flat ground, and this includes both shallow and deep peat.

Road construction in the former situation takes the form of a shelf, excavated by a large angledozer (normally fitted with hydraulically operated ripper), or medium sized excavator, with face shovel equipment. The latter is used mainly where the ground tends to be wet, and sleeper mats may have to be used. Where hard conditions prevail a rock ripper can often be applied, to facilitate rock excavation, and this is of great benefit compared to the operations of drilling and blasting of rock which tend to be fairly slow, much more costly, and less safe.

Where the peat is shallow (up to 500 mm, or even unfavourable conditions up to 1300 mm in thickness) it is usually excavated, and the sub-grade thus exposed is shaped accordingly. Where deep peat is concerned the established method is to construct a road embankment on top of the peat, using suitable, locally won materials.

The importance of an efficient drainage system for the road, in the form of side drains, lateral water crossings and road camber or cross fall, cannot be over-emphasised. It is imperative for bridges and culverts to have waterway areas of adequate size and to be constructed of sound materials.

The road formations resulting from the various types of construction are compacted, if possible, using a smooth roller or vibratory roller as required. In wet and soft conditions the compaction of road formations is often difficult to achieve.

The next consideration is that of pavement construction. Materials from proved sources such as existing quarries can be used, but on many sites it is necessary to search for and identify materials such as gravels, morainic deposits, burnt shale, tunnel spoil etc. for use in road works. The plant required for the construction of the road pavement consists basically of the medium sized excavator with face shovel, either hydraulically or rope operated, working at the rock or gravel face or stock pile. The excavator loads the tipper lorries which transport the material to road head, where it is spread on the road formation by a small angle dozer (Plate 17) or similar equipment. However, where this is not available, spreading by hand is feasible. The pavement should be capable of being maintained by motor grader or towed grader, and compacted by roller. If the latter equipment is not available, compaction by traffic may have to suffice.

ROAD CONSTRUCTION AND MAINTENANCE PLANT

In view of the references to the types of construction plant used on roadworks it may be useful to set this down in tabulated form. Accordingly the schedule shown below should provide an indication of the type of machine and its recommended application.

Type of Machine and Equipment	*Recommended Application*
Crawler tractor/angle dozer (45 dbhp 65 dbhp)	Light angledozing work and spreading stone on road formation.
Large crawler tractor/angledozer (over 100 dbhp)	Excavating and side casting road formations in cross sloping ground. In addition, cutting and filling longitudinally on an undulating road alignment.
Large crawler tractor/angledozer (over 100 dbhp) fitted with ripper	Ripping of rock in quarries and on road alignments.
Tracked excavator fitted with face shovel ($\frac{1}{2}$–$\frac{3}{4}$ cu m bucket capacity)	Excavation of road formation in soft ground-using sleeper mats if necessary.
Tracked/wheeled excavators with face shovel ($\frac{1}{2}$–$\frac{3}{4}$ cu m bucket capacity)	Loading of stone at quarry.

Type of Machine and Equipment	*Recommended Application*
Digger/loader	Excavation of drains, culverting. Loading stone on minor works.
Compressors, tractor mounted or towed (with rock drilling equipment)	Drilling in rock
Tractor and trailer	Transporting stone from source to road head on minor works.
Dumpers/dumpwagon	Transporting stone from source to road head over short distances.
Medium to large tipping lorries	Transporting stone from source to road head on major works.
Motor grader	Maintenance of roads.
Roller (e.g. 8-ton smooth wheel)	Compaction of road stone.
Vibrating roller	Compaction of road stone.

BRIDGE DESIGN, CONSTRUCTION AND MAINTENANCE

The incidence of water crossings which are encountered on forest road alignments is a feature of many forests. This may not apply in significant measure to small forest blocks, but some estate owners do have this problem, and it is worthwhile describing the broad policy of the Forestry Commission in dealing with this subject. Normally the need is for permanent bridges, designed with adequate waterway area, and capable of taking Department of Environment HA loading. This covers the largest vehicle permitted under the Construction and Use Regulations. Both reinforced concrete, and mass concrete abutments, are suitable, although shortage of skilled labour would suggest that the latter design is more appropriate in small forest blocks. As far as the deck superstructure is concerned the design, for spans up to 5·5 m, is that of a simply supported reinforced concrete slab. A useful and more straightforward alternative for spans of 3·7 m or more is precast prestressed concrete hollow box units with in situ concrete topping acting compositely with the precast units, and with mild steel transverse distribution reinforcement. Precast prestressed concrete inverted tee beams, with in situ concrete infill and topping, acting compositely, and with mild steel distribution, are used for superstructure spans over about 7·5 m and 16 m. This type of design is both economical and requires little skilled labour. A different type of superstructure for spans in excess of 16 m is advocated, in the form of

RSJs, or large prestressed concrete hollow box units, with in situ concrete structural topping and transverse prestressing.

If there is a need for a temporary bridge, or a bridge for special purposes, a Bailey bridge of required span would satisfy the need. This type of bridge was designed for military use, is expensive to maintain, and should be used only as a temporary expedient. It is possible to design short span bridges in timber, and the development of more advanced designs in timber is currently being considered.

It is felt that on private forestry work, bridge design should be carried out by a consultant, and the bridge constructed under contract, following the usual civil engineering procedure.

A number of forest blocks on private estates have old existing road bridges. Experience has taught that some of these are unsafe for timber vehicles. It is essential that the existing bridges be examined in detail by a qualified engineer, and their load capacities assessed. Restriction notices should be erected, and reconstruction, or replacement, of the sub-standard bridge may be required.

Advice and guidance on this subject is available from the Engineering Division of the Forestry Commission at their Headquarters in Edinburgh.

MAINTENANCE OF ROADS

Generally, roads in small forest blocks tend to be only intermittently used, and consequently do not suffer the deterioration that is experienced by a main traffic route through a large forest. Forest roads are designed with mechanised maintenance in mind, and, where there are a lot of small blocks, it is feasible for a motor grader team to move from block to block on a pre-arranged system reinstating the road as required. This work may be necessary only at intervals of a few years. Where plant cannot be justified, the repair of the road surface should be done, by hand, on the road, using a tractor with tipping trailer or tipping lorry to supply the material from the source used for maintenance purposes. If compaction equipment is unavailable, compaction by traffic may be the answer, although not the ideal one. The reinstatement of the road surface is important, but another essential item is that of regular maintenance of road side drains and culverts, including the clearance of debris and silt. Among the other features is the need to maintain roadside bank batters at a safe angle, and generally to clear brash and timber waste from the vicinity of the road. There is little doubt that a forest road, especially in a small block, is used not only for vehicle passage but also as a platform for the working of timber. This throws an added burden on road maintenance.

BIBLIOGRAPHY: FOREST ROADS

Forestry Commission Publications

BOOKLET
No. 43   *Forest road planning.* 1976.

FOREST RECORD

No. 81   *Protection of small steel structures from corrosion.* 1972.
No. 114 *Terrain Classification.*1977.

Other Publications

Armco International Corporation (1958). *Handbook of drainage and construction products.* Middletown, Ohio, USA.

Armco International Corporation (1974). *Design manual.* Middletown, Ohio, USA.

Department of the Environment (1968). *Advisory manual on the layout of roads in rural areas.* London.

Department of the Environment (1969). *Specification for road and bridge works.* London.

Department of the Environment (1970). *A guide to the structural design of pavements for new roads.* Road Note 29, 3rd edn. London.

Department of Trade and Industry (1972). *The law relating to safety and health in mines: Part 4, Quarries.* London.

Dumbleton, M. J., and West, G. (1971). *Preliminary sources of information for site investigation in Britain.* Report LR403, Transport and Road Research Laboratory, Crowthorne, Berkshire.

Federation of Civil Engineering Contractors (1970). *Supervisors' safety booklet.* 2nd edn. London.

Granfield, E. F., and MacMahon, C. D. (1969). Civil engineering in the Forestry Commission. *Highways and traffic engineering* **37**, No. 1720, 28–32.

O'Reilly, M. P., and Millard, R. S. (1969). *Roadmaking materials and pavement design in tropical and subtropical countries.* Report LR279, Transport and Road Research Laboratory, Crowthorne, Berkshire.

Royal Society for the Prevention of Accidents (1970). *Construction Regulations handbook.* London.

Transport and Road Research Laboratory (1968). *Soil mechanics for road engineers.* Crowthorne, Berkshire.

Transport and Road Research Laboratory (1969). *Bituminous materials in road construction.* Crowthorne, Berkshire.

Transport and Road Research Laboratory (1970). *The Marshall Committee's recommendations for standards of highway maintenance and for a maintenance rating system.* Report LR367. Crowthorne, Berkshire.

Chapter 12

RADIO

Radio now has a place in three main forestry functions: general administration, fire protection and harvesting. While a radio system can be a great asset to a forestry enterprise, much depends on its nature and organisation, and a careful assessment should be made of its viability before it is embarked upon. This should consist of two parts: a technical survey and a general financial appreciation of costs and benefits. It is a good idea to prepare a map showing the local coverage to be expected, i.e. the number of blind spots. If the assessment proves favourable, the next step is to obtain an operating licence from The Post Office, which is also responsible for allotting frequency channels and call signs.

CHOICE OF EQUIPMENT

Systems of various sizes can be built up from:

Main Stations: These are powered from AC mains, or a self-starting generating set, the choice normally being a matter of relative costs. Transmission can be up to 40 miles if the aerial is mounted at the highest point in the service area. Receiving distance will depend on the transmitting power and location of the other transmitter.

Mobile Sets: These may be fitted in any vehicle without modification of its electrical system. Reliable range will depend on topography, but can be up to 40 miles. Drivers soon accustom themselves to their area radio coverage idiosyncrasies, and avoid the blind spots which give poor or no transmission or reception.

Handsets: Their reliable range is about half a mile, and they are therefore designed for communication at close quarters, as, for example, during the course of fire fighting operations. However, careful choice of topography, when sending, can extend the range and messages can be received from a distant station, even if the low power does not allow transmission.

RADIO SYSTEMS

Two systems are used by the Forestry Commission, single-frequency-simplex and talk-through. The first is the cheaper and less sophisticated system, in which all messages are passed to one controlling station. The talk through system on the other hand, allows communication between all sets, any one of which may be the controlling station. This clearly is the one to be preferred for the largest forests, especially those with harvesting operations to control.

RADIO AND FOREST ADMINISTRATION

The advantages of radio for administrative purposes are obvious enough. A mobile or pack set enables a manager to remain in touch with his office and therefore to be in control of operations, wherever he may be during the day. Direct savings can also be achieved by the notification of machinery breakdowns, last minute lorry diversions, the call-up of individuals or gangs to meet unexpected crises and so on.

RADIO AND FIRE PROTECTION

The use of a main radio system enables a Fire Control Centre to maintain an up-to-date picture of the fire situation in the area, by receiving reports from mobiles, patrols, or lookouts suitably equipped. Such an arrangement enables the response to an outbreak to be greatly speeded up as fire services and stand by teams may be contacted within a minute or two of a report coming in. Unfortunately the staffing required to make full use of the system is very costly nowadays, and only extreme situations are likely to justify the expense.

A further and cheaper function may be performed at fire fighting operations. Operating at short range, two or three handsets may be very valuable if the fire is of any size, or is distant from the nearest road or track. Directions can be received from the officer controlling the operations by the squads actually engaged, and progress can, of course, be relayed to the Control Centre, should that be manned. The fire services and police operate on different wavebands from the Forestry Commission, and from those allocated to estates and other private organisations. However, it has been found that a good working liaison can be maintained during a fire fighting operation if the main operators stay close beside one another. All personnel engaged can then be kept fully briefed throughout the operation.

RADIO AND HARVESTING

Apart from the administrative benefits that can be applied to harvesting, radio has a particular use in skyline and highlead operations. The chokerman is equipped with a small portable set strapped to the body in a suitable harness which incorporates a flexible wire aerial. A microphone/loudspeaker is also clipped to his clothing, thus leaving his hands free. At the operator's end a mobile radio, powered by the tractor battery, can give a high pitched signal, which will stand out against any noise generated by the tractor. Use of these techniques has been found to increase production, and modern methods, involving lengthy extraction distances, are becoming increasingly dependent on them.

Recent work has shown that radio controlled vehicles are feasible, and, if suitable working techniques can be developed, these are clearly prospects of considerable labour saving.

Chapter 13

CAREERS AND TRAINING IN FORESTRY

CAREERS

Those wishing to embark on forestry as a career may look to either the state or private sector of the industry. In each sector, the employment of individuals can, generally, be said to be at craft, supervisory or managerial level. Certain minimum qualifications are required for forestry supervisors or managers in the Forestry Commission and, by and large, similar qualifications for these levels of employment are looked for by the larger employing organisations in the private sector. Qualifications at craft or forest worker level are also available as described later. While the Forestry Commission is by far the largest forestry employer, there is a growing list of alternative sources of employment where forestry knowledge and skills are sought. In addition to private estates, there are, for example, the private forestry companies and co-operatives, Universities and Technical Colleges, Research Institutes, Local Government service, Development Corporations and National Parks Authorities and Timber Companies.

QUALIFICATIONS

National qualifications are available as follows;
—City and Guilds of London Institute Forestry Stage I and Stage II
—NEBSS Certificate in Supervisory Studies
—Ordinary National Diploma in Forestry
—National Diploma in Forestry and Membership of the Institute of Foresters
—University Degrees
Additionally, qualifications are provided by the Royal Forestry Societies.

COURSES LEADING TO QUALIFICATIONS

City and Guilds of London Institute's Certificates

FORESTRY STAGE I: This is at junior craft level and is intended to meet the needs of those gaining their first few years of practical forestry experience. The course is provided by the Cumbria College of Agriculture and Forestry, Newton Rigg, Penrith, and by the Inverness Technical College, Longman Road, Inverness, on a block-release basis covering two separate six-week periods within an overall period of two years. Emphasis is placed on the practical application of the knowledge taught.
FORESTRY STAGE II: This is at general craftsman level and students who undertake it should, normally, have completed the Stage I course (and certificate examination) or have obtained the Woodman's Certificate or the Junior Forester's Certificate provided by the Royal Forestry Societies. The course is on a block-release basis during a single six-week period, and is available at the Cumbria College of Agriculture and Forestry, and at the Inverness Technical College. Emphasis is placed on the practical application of the knowledge taught.

Details of the course syllabuses for both Stage I and Stage II, and of the certificate examinations, may be obtained from the City and Guilds of London Institute, 76 Portland Place, London, W1N 4AA, or from the respective Colleges.

Ordinary National Diploma in Forestry

This is a three-year sandwich course at technician level available at the Cumbria College of Agriculture and Forestry. The middle year is spent at an approved forest, either with the Forestry Commission or in private forestry, gaining experience of a suitable nature. Other than during the middle year, the course is residential at the College. Educational entry requirements are, currently, four O level passes, which must include two science or mathematics subjects, and one involving the use of English. Similar passes at Grade I level in the examination for the Certificate of Secondary Education are also acceptable. Applications for the limited number of places on the course should be made to the Principal of the College. Selected applicants require to obtain pre-course practical experience in forestry employment before commencing studies at the College. This pre-course experience must extend over at least one year and, preferably, will extend over two years. It should be noted that the OND (Forestry) is, currently, the minimum qualification for entry to the supervisory grade of Forester in the Forestry Commission.

National Diploma in Forestry

This qualification is granted by the Central Forestry Examination Board of the United Kingdom. The holder of the NDF is, in the opinion of the Examination Board, 'so qualified in forestry as practised in Great Britain and Northern Ireland as to take full charge of extensive woodlands of a private or other estate'. A revision course for candidates for this qualification is provided by the Cumbria College of Agriculture and Forestry, and is covered in two separate residential periods each of three weeks. The revision course requires to be supplemented by private study. Candidates for the examination, which is normally taken at the end of the second three-week period of the revision course, must be at least 25 years of age and have held, for at least three years, one of the following certificates:

—Senior Forester's Certificate of the Royal Scottish Forestry Society.

—Forester's Certificate of the Royal Forestry Society of England, Wales and Northern Ireland.

—Forester's Certificate of the Forestry Commission.

—Forester's Certificate of the Society of Irish Foresters.

Applications for places on the revision course should be made to the Principal of the Cumbria College of Agriculture and Forestry.

University Degrees

The Universities of Aberdeen, Edinburgh, Oxford and University College of North Wales, Bangor, provide degree courses in forestry. These are under continual review and are designed to provide education in the management and utilisation of renewable natural resources. At Aberdeen, courses are offered leading to the designated ordinary and honours degree of B.Sc in Forestry. Edinburgh provides an ordinary degree in Ecological Science with opportunity to take honours in forestry, wildlife and fisheries resource management and ecology. Oxford has an Honours School of Agriculture and Forest Science (three years) and also provides a postgraduate M.Sc course (one year) in Forestry and its relation to Land Management. At the University College of North Wales in Bangor, there are courses leading to a general degree in Forestry, Forest Zoology and Wood Science, and honours degrees in Forestry or Wood Science.

An honours degree in Forestry is the normal requirement for entry to the grade of Forest Officer in the Forestry Commission.

Certificates of the Royal Forestry Societies

These qualifications have been of considerable importance to private forestry in the past, but are expected to be phased out in favour of the nationally recognised City and Guilds Certificates. The Woodman's Certificate of the RFS, and the Junior Forester's Certificate of the RSFS, have been considered appropriate to workers who have spent two or more years in forestry. The Forester's Certificate of the RFS, and the Senior Forester's Certificate of the RSFS, which are similar to each other in scope and standard, are considered appropriate to the experienced men expected to take charge of woodland areas, to be able to plan and carry out forest operations, and to provide written reports for their employers.

TRAINING

In-service training through short up-dating courses is available to employees at all levels from workers to managers in both public and private sectors. Since 1971, when forestry training in the private sector was placed on a voluntary 'pay-as-you-train' system, the task of ensuring the availability of adequate sources of training has been the concern of the Forestry Training Council. This is a representative, advisory body set up by the Forestry Commission, and includes in its membership the Forestry Commission, the Timber Growers' Organisation, the Scottish Woodland Owners Association, the Association of Professional Foresters, the Forestry Societies, the Institute of Foresters of Great Britain, the Trade Unions and others representing education and training interests. Thus, there is a joint training effort between the Forestry Commission and the private sector, to ensure the availability of systematic training, particularly of workers and supervisors.

Training demands for the state sector are identified by the Forestry Commission. For the private sector, the Timber Growers' Organisation and the Scottish Woodland Owners Association collect, sift and co-ordinate, on a regional basis, all applications for training. Arrangements are then made for courses to meet private sector demands, to be provided, on a re-payment basis by the Forestry Commission, local education authorities or other agencies. The Inverness Forestry Industry Centre, based on Inverness Technical College, and the Cumbria College of Agriculture and Forestry each provide short courses in a variety of forest operations, and may be contacted for details of forthcoming courses.

The Forestry Training Council has recommended a scheme for the training of new-entrant forest workers, and this is in operation in both the state and private sectors of the industry. The scheme involves a two-year period of training at recognised estates or forests (details of private estates or companies operating the scheme obtainable from TGO and SWOA). During this time a trainee is released from work, with pay, to attend the two separate six-week block-release courses at the Cumbria College of Agriculture and Forestry, or at the Inverness Technical College, leading to the City and Guilds Forestry Stage I Certificate previously described. The college courses are designed to provide up-to-date technical knowledge and initial practical instruction essential to the modern forest worker. They also include general studies to stimulate the young worker's ability to absorb, interpret and communicate information in both speech and writing. Instruction received at College is complementary to work-site training and experience, provided by the employer. Applications to enter the scheme are received by TGO and SWOA where employment and training is sought in the private sector, and by the Forestry Commission where such is sought in the state sector.

Identification of Training Needs

The Health and Safety at Work etc. Act, 1974, requires all employers and self-employed persons to use safe work practices and to ensure that adequate training is given. The probable introduction of a national grading scheme for forest workers may be expected to involve some form of skills testing, comparable with that now in use in agriculture, in general, and in Forestry Commission training courses, in particular. There is thus a general need for realistic assessment of training needs among forest workers.

Those employers who work to an annual budget are advised to carry out a skills audit at the time of its preparation. That is, they should compare the skills held by their current labour force with that required to meet the budgeted programme of work, and having identified the shortfall should either seek training for current staff, or employ new workers possessing those skills. Considerable savings in training time can be made if this analytical approach is sufficiently detailed to indicate whether the worker requires some, or all, of the skills in the use and maintenance of any particular piece of equipment. There is little point in training men in the particular chainsaw techniques required to deal with windblow situations, if such damage is rarely suffered, or for short wood presentation if extraction is normally in pole lengths. Reductions in course length and investment can be achieved when the required level of skill after training is carefully specified. For men who

must work with a minimum of supervision immediately, long periods of training are clearly necessary, as can be seen from the course lengths in Scandinavian countries. In the Forestry Commission, workers generally reach 80–100 per cent of experienced worker standard within the training course, and skilled supervision is available to give further advice at the work site. It has to be recognised that course duration is primarily a function of entry and exit standards, and to a lesser extent dependent upon the number of trainees attending a given course. Any good trainer will be prepared to state the relationship which exists between the present skills of the worker and the level of skill which can be achieved in the course duration allowed by the permissible investment in time and money.

BIBLIOGRAPHY: CAREERS AND TRAINING IN FORESTRY

Department of Employment and Central Office of Information (1976). *Forestry*. Choice of Careers Series, 81.

The Health and Safety at Work etc. Act, 1974.

Chapter 14

ADVICE TO WOODLAND OWNERS

This chapter is largely a reproduction of the main text of the Forestry Commission pamphlet *Advice for woodland owners* (revised August 1977), which is available free of charge from any of the Forestry Commission addresses given in the Appendix.

INTRODUCTION

The Forestry Commission provides financial, professional and technical assistance to woodland owners in a number of ways, to help them in bringing their existing woods to full production and to plant new ones. The various forms which direct financial aid may take are set out in this chapter. The nature of the grants, the amounts payable, and the regulations covering payment are subject to revision from time to time.

PROFESSIONAL ADVICE

Before commencing any forestry work that is likely to attract a grant (which cannot be paid until a scheme has been approved), owners are strongly advised to consult their appropriate Conservator of Forests, whose address will be found in the Appendix. Advice on the general suitability of any scheme will gladly be given by the Conservator's staff.

The Commission cannot, however, undertake the detailed management of a scheme, or such tasks as the preparation of a Plan of Operations, the actual replanting of woodlands, or the sale of timber. An owner who requires help in these respects is recommended to consult either a co-operative forestry society, a forestry consultant, or a firm of land agents that undertake such tasks either directly or indirectly.

The two associations of woodland owners, the Timber Growers' Organisation covering England and Wales, and the Scottish Woodland Owners Association in Scotland, will advise woodland owners who are in membership how and where to obtain the services of consultants and contractors.

FORESTRY IN THE EUROPEAN ECONOMIC COMMUNITY

The Council of the European Economic Community (EEC) has adopted directives on the marketing of forest reproductive material and on standards for forest reproductive material marketed within the Community. As a member of the Community the United Kingdom has agreed to abide by these directives.

The directives, which are mainly concerned with ensuring that seed, cuttings and plants, used in forestry, are selected from vigorous high quality, healthy trees, stipulate two categories of forest reproductive material. These are Selected Reproductive Material—whose external characters indicate that it is of a certain quality, and Tested Reproductive Material—material which is shown by comparative tests to have improved value for use. (See Chapter 1 'Seed Sources', and Chapter 3 'Type of Plant'. The F.C. has produced an explanatory booklet, *The Marketing of Forest Tree Seed and Plants within the European Economic Community*.)

The benefits from using seed and plants of high genetic value are well recognised by foresters and nurserymen in this country. For many years a register of the best-known sources of forest seed in Great Britain and overseas has been maintained by the Forestry Commission with the help of private woodland owners. This has done much to encourage use of the finest seed available.

Under the Regulations, all nurserymen must produce a Suppliers Certificate (SI 1973 No. 944) when planting stock is marketed and, in future, the Forestry Commission will require this Certificate to be produced before a planting grant in any grant-aided scheme is paid.

Where an owner raises plants from his own collected seed, and in the case of natural regeneration, an owner is advised to have his stands certified as being of EEC standard at the time of preparation of his plan of operations. Otherwise, planting grants may be withheld if the planted material is not up to standard.

THE FORESTRY COMMISSION'S DEDICATION SCHEME

A consultative document *Forestry Policy* was published on 28th June, 1972 (HMSO), which suggested the future lines for Government policy and suspended entry to all Grant Aid Schemes for private forestry from that date. Following consultation with a wide variety of interested bodies on the proposals contained in the consultative document, announcements made in October 1973 and July 1974 gave the framework of future forestry policy. This was designed to ensure that forestry formed part of a really effective pattern of rural land use, in which it would harmonise to the best possible advantage with agriculture and the environment.

To this end, a new scheme of grant aid was introduced to succeed the schemes established after the Second World War, and commenced on 1st October, 1974.

Under this scheme (Dedication—Basis III) woodland owners receive an outright payment per hectare when approved planting or replanting has taken place. In return, they accept a continuing obligation (usually by Deed or Agreement of Covenant) to manage all their woodlands within the scheme in accordance with Plans of Operations designed to secure sound forestry practice, effective integration with agriculture, environmental safeguards, and such opportunities for public recreation as may be appropriate.

For land approved for planting with broadleaved* trees, and planted so as to establish a broadleaved crop and give a predominantly broadleaved appearance in the landscape over the greater part of the woodland's life, a supplementary grant per hectare will be payable in addition to the basic grant. The normal minimum area for a scheme will be one hectare; the Commission will, however, give consideration to small schemes of a reasonable shape and size.

To meet the requirements of skilled supervision it is normally desirable that a trained forester be employed; but this is not essential if the owner himself, or his agent, has the requisite silvicultural knowledge and time available. Inspections by Forestry Commission officers, as the need arises, are an integral part of the scheme; such visits have been found mutually valuable for the exchange of technical information and the discussion of problems.

In administering this grant aid the Forestry Commission ensures that the land is suitable for forestry use, and consults with the Agricultural Departments and local planning authorities on the land use and amenity aspects of woodland owners' proposals. Nature conservation and recreation requirements are also taken into account.

Under a Basis III Dedication Scheme, a Dedication Covenant or Agreement normally comes to an end when approved felling takes place, but there is provision for rededication. When a dedicated estate changes hands, the successor in title is invited to continue to manage the woods under the approved Plan of Operations; the woodlands do in any case remain dedicated to forestry by the terms of Covenant, unless released on considerations which may be agreed.

The grant arrangements, including the amount of grant, are reviewed at intervals of not more than three years. Fuller details of the scheme are contained in the Forestry Commission leaflet *The new dedication scheme (Basis III)*, which can be obtained, together with application forms, from Conservancy Offices.

In 1977 Management Grants were introduced to the Basis III scheme, in respect of all effectively managed woodland. Also approved planting of Caledonian pine of local origin in special areas to be agreed with the Nature Conservancy Council attracted the same grants as broadleaved trees.

---

* In Forestry Commission usage the word 'broadleaved' has now replaced 'hardwood' when referring to the living tree.

SMALL WOODS PLANTING SCHEME

A small woods planting grant for areas of 0.25 up to 10 hectares was re-introduced in 1977. A higher rate was paid for areas under 3 hectares than above, with 75 per cent of the grant payable on completion of satisfactory planting and the remainder 5 years later (subject to satisfactory establishment).

GRANTS FOR SHELTERBELTS UNDER AGRICULTURE AND HORTICULTURE CAPITAL GRANT SCHEMES

As an alternative to the Basis III Scheme, grants towards the cost of establishing shelterbelts on farm or horticultural holdings are available as follows:

Type of holding	Scheme	Rate of grant
Hill Farms	Farm Capital Grant Scheme 1970	50%
Horticultural holdings	Horticultural Capital Grant Scheme 1973	25%
Farms with development plans	Farm and Horticulture	10%
Horticultural holdings with development plans	Development Regulations 1973	30%

Detailed information on the schemes, explanatory leaflets and application forms are available, in England and Wales, from the Divisional officers of the Ministry of Agriculture, Fisheries and Food and, in Scotland, from the area offices of the Department of Agriculture and Fisheries.

In all cases written approval must be obtained from the Ministry or the Department before work is started.

OTHER GRANTS FOR TREE PLANTING

Promotion of amenity tree planting is the concern of the Countryside Commission (in England and Wales) and the Countryside Commission for Scotland. Local Authorities also have powers to give financial assistance for this purpose.

FELLING LICENCES

A licence is usually required for the felling, or sale for felling, of growing trees, under the Forestry Act, 1967. This Act (copies of which may be obtained from HMSO) should be consulted for the legal definitions of exceptions from licensing, but it may be noted here that the main exceptions listed are:

(a) Trees in gardens, and fruit trees.
(b) Any trees below 3 inches in diameter, measured 5 feet from the ground.
(c) Underwood below 6 inches in diameter, measured 5 feet from the ground.

(*d*) Thinnings below 4 inches in diameter, measured 5 feet from the ground.

(*e*) Dedicated Woodlands, provided the felling is in accordance with the agreed Plan of Operations, and the positive covenants of the Deed or Agreement are applicable.

In addition, an owner may fell up to 825 cubic feet of timber (hoppus measure) per quarter of a calendar year, for use on his own property, without a felling licence. Of this quantity he may, if he wishes, sell without licence or other formal permission up to 150 cubic feet.

In most other circumstances a Felling Licence is required, and application should be made to the appropriate Conservator of Forests, who will arrange for the trees to be inspected. Where, as is usually the case, it is in the national interest that the ground shall be restocked, the Commission is empowered to impose Replanting Conditions on the issue of a felling licence. Replanting to be carried out in accordance with such conditions may qualify for grant aid under the Dedication Scheme (Basis III) or other forms of grant aid.

If a Tree Preservation Order is in force for the trees concerned, it is usually necessary for the local planning authority that made the Order to be consulted, and exceptions (*a*) to (*d*) above may not apply. The consent of the Forestry Commission is required before a Tree Preservation Order may be made on woodlands that have received Grants from the Forestry Commission.

TAXATION OF WOODLANDS

Special arrangements apply to the assessment for income tax of woodlands managed on a commercial basis and with a view to the realisation of profits. Taxation may be under either Schedule B or by election under Schedule D. In the assessment of capital gains tax only the land is taxable.

The former estate duty provisions for forestry were repealed when Capital Transfer Tax was introduced in 1975. The general effect of this tax is that the person liable for CTT on a woodland transferred upon death may either have the trees included with the rest of the estate and charged with tax accordingly at that time, or opt to have their value excluded from the estate. In the latter case an eventual liability to tax remains, but its application is deferred until the later disposal of the trees or of the woodland. The net proceeds (after deducting harvesting and restocking costs if applicable) are then chargeable at rates applicable to a new slice on top of the deceased's estate. A liability deferred by these arrangements is cancelled by a subsequent death, after which both options are again open, so that there need be only one liability to the tax during the life of the crop.

Further information on all these points will be found in Forestry Commission Leaflet No. 12, *Taxation of woodlands*, which has been prepared under authority of HM Inland Revenue and is published by HMSO.

ADVICE ON FIRE PROTECTION

Under Section I of the Fire Services Act 1947 every fire authority is required to maintain efficient arrangements for dealing with calls for assistance in case of fire, and also to make efficient arrangements for giving, when requested, advice as to fire prevention on private property, including woodlands.

Chief Officers, or Firemasters of local Fire Brigades, are ready, on request, to survey woodlands and to furnish reports recommending how owners can best achieve efficiency in fire prevention and combat a fire should one occur. Advice normally deals with the layout and clearance of fire rides, supply of simple equipment, improvement of natural or artificial water supplies, rendezvous points, the signposting and maintenance of adequate access into and through the woods, and the quickest way of getting a fire call through to the Brigade. This service is free. Insurance of woodlands against fire can be arranged through the usual commercial channels; preferential rates are often quoted for Dedicated Woodlands.

PROTECTION OF ANCIENT MONUMENTS AND SITES

Woodland owners, in common with other landowners, have a statutory obligation under the Ancient Monuments Acts to protect any scheduled or ancient monuments, field monuments or historic buildings on their land. Compensatory payments may be made for the protection of these monuments.

Owners are advised, before they commence planting, that if there is any likelihood of an area being a site requiring protection they should ask the Inspector of Ancient Monuments to inspect the ground or give his clearance before planting commences.

Addresses of Inspectors of Ancient Monuments are:

ENGLAND—Inspectorate of Ancient Monuments
23 Savile Row
London W1X 2AA

SCOTLAND—Inspectorate of Ancient Monuments
Argyle House
3 Lady Lawson Street
Edinburgh EH3 9SD

WALES—Inspectorate of Ancient Monuments
Government Buildings
St. Agnes Road
Gabalfa
Cardiff CF4 4YF

BIBLIOGRAPHY: ADVICE TO WOODLAND OWNERS

Forestry Commission Publications

BOOKLET

No. 35 *The plan of operations (metric): A guide to the preparation of the plan of operations for dedicated and approved woodlands. 1974. Free of charge from Forestry Commission.*

No. 46 *Managing small woodlands. 1978.*

FOREST RECORDS

No. 116 *The EEC Plant Directive and British Forestry. 1978.*

LEAFLET

No. 12 *Taxation of woodlands. 1976.*

INFORMATION PAMPHLETS (free from Forestry Commission)

Advice to woodland owners.
The new dedication scheme (Basis III).
The marketing of Forest Tree Seed and Plants within the European Economic Community.

Other Publications

Forestry policy: June 1972. HMSO.
Trees and Forestry Department of the Environment Circular 30/78, Welsh Office Circular 64/78. 3 May 1978.

LEGISLATION

Fire Services Act 1947.
Forestry Act 1967.

Under the Plant Varieties and Seeds Act 1964:
The Forest Reproductive Material Regulations 1973 (SI 1973 No. 944), as amended by SI 1973 No. 1108 and SI 1974 No. 887.
Under the Forestry Act 1967:
The Forestry (felling of Trees) Regulations 1951 (SI 1951 No. 1726).
The Forestry (Exceptions from Restriction of Felling) Regulations 1951 (SI 1951 No. 1725).
The Forestry (Exception from Restriction of Felling) Regulations 1972 (SI 1972 No. 91).
The Forestry (Exception from Restriction of Felling) Regulations 1974 (SI 1974 No. 1817).
Under the Plant Health Act 1967:
The Importation of Forest Trees (Prohibition) (Great Britain) Order 1965 (SI 1965 No. 2121), as amended by SI 1974 No. 1.
The Importation of Wood (Prohibition) (Great Britain) Order 1974 (SI 1974 No. 2).
The Watermark Disease (Local Authorities) Order 1974 (SI 1974 No. 768).
The Dutch Elm Disease (Local Authorities) Order 1974 (SI 1974 No. 830), as amended by SI 1974 No. 1816 and SI 1975 Nos 55, 1163 and 1905.
The Dutch Elm Disease (Restriction on Movement of Elms) Order 1975 (SI 1975 No. 1904).
Under the Town and Country Planning Act 1971:
Town and Country Planning (Tree Preservation Order) Regulations 1969 (SI 1969 No. 17), as amended by SI 1975 No. 148.
Under the Town and Country Planning (Scotland) Act 1972:
Town and Country Planning (Tree Preservation Order and Trees in Conservation Areas) (Scotland) Regulations 1975 (SI 1975 No. 1204).

Chapter 15

MANAGEMENT AND ADMINISTRATION OF A WOODLAND ESTATE

INTRODUCTION

In order to qualify for grant aid under one of the Forestry Commission's schemes, a woodland owner must agree to manage his woods in accordance with a Plan of Operations approved by the Forestry Commission. The standard *Plan of Operations* is described in Forestry Commission Booklet 35 (Revised September 1974). The introduction to Booklet 35 makes it clear that the standard Plan of Operations is designed primarily to satisfy the statutory requirements of the Forestry Commission and enable the Commission's officers to fulfil their functions in respect of payment of grants. On most woodland estates there will be a need for the owner to gather more information than the minimum prescribed in Booklet 35, and to analyse and present it in greater details for his own use.

Leaving aside the forms required for administration of the grant schemes, the standard Forestry Commission Plan of Operations comprises the following:

(i)   A map on the scale of 1:10 000 or 1:10 560 (6 inches to 1 mile). The map indicates the boundaries of the area and the boundaries of the compartments and sub-compartments, into which the area is divided. It also gives compartment numbers and areas, and sub-compartment letters.

(ii) *a.* A brief written description of the existing woodlands and areas to be planted.
      b. A statement of objects of management.
      c. A description of the proposed methods of working to be adopted in order to achieve the objects of management, and a note of the actual programme of work for five years ahead.

(iii) A tabular statement for the whole woodland area giving, for each woodland and part thereof (compartments and sub-compartments), the area by species and year of planting; unstocked areas; thinning, felling and planting proposals; all for the ensuing five-year period. An optional control form is provided to enable the owner to keep a record, year by year, of the work done, since the main form in the Plan provides only for a record of the work done during the five-year period.

(iv) an annual record of the volume removed by thinning and by final felling.

The purpose of these notes is to give guidance on some of the general principles involved in the preparation and execution of management plans.

PREPARING THE BASIC MAP AND COMPARTMENT RECORDS

The first step in the preparation of any management plan for woodlands is to decide the extent of the area to be brought into the scheme. The external boundaries of the area are marked on the relevant Ordnance Survey sheets, Scale 1:10 000 or 1:10 560. A preliminary survey is then required so that the boundaries of the permanent administrative units (compartments) can be decided; these should follow streams, roads, paths or other well defined natural features. A record is made in a field notebook of the nature of the site and the type and condition of the tree crop or other ground cover. Where necessary, sub-compartments may be formed so that variations of crop within a compartment can be mapped. Sub-compartment divisions are not intended to be permanent and, since creating them complicates survey work and record keeping, often it will suffice to record an estimated area breakdown between two or more crop types within a compartment, without actually delineating the stand boundaries on the map by means of sub-compartment boundaries.

The following minimum information is recorded in a field notebook for each compartment or sub-compartment as appropriate:

a. Area to the nearest one-tenth of a hectare.
b. Type of crop and nature of vegetation and site; e.g. high forest (broadleaved, mixed or coniferous), coppice (with or without standards), scrub and felled areas, bare land, unplantable areas.
c. Species and yield class.
d. Year of planting (if not known an estimate is made).
e. Treatment required and its urgency.

The information from the field notebook is then transferred to some suitable register, often kept in the form of Compartment Notes.

The information given in the register or compartment notes can be used to complete an Age Class Analysis by Species which, when combined with yield class, presents the data in a form suitable for making forecasts of production, or for deciding on felling and planting programmes aimed at bringing about a more even spread of age classes.

The information from the register or compartment notes is normally recorded on either a Detailed Analysis form or a Compartment Record form, the latter being obligatory for grant aided schemes.

The owner also needs information, from estate records and the field examination, on such factors as situation of the woodlands, configuration and altitude, geology and soils, climate, management history, access, communications, rights of way, sporting interests, local authority plans, conservation areas, ancient monuments and any other relevant factors.

DESCRIPTION OF THE WOODLANDS

Before formulating objects of management, it is necessary to make a written description highlighting the main features of the woodlands as they now exist and of the areas to be planted. This statement makes use of the information on the maps and the various sources of data already referred to.

OBJECTS OF MANAGEMENT

Having recorded the basic data, a woodland owner should then consider and state the objects of management, which are of crucial importance to the enterprise because they define the main goal and the subsidiary purposes to which the whole management of the woods is directed. The number and scope of objects of management vary from one estate to another, depending upon local conditions and the owner's personal circumstances and intentions. But all owners wishing to participate in one of the Forestry Commission's dedication schemes must accept the following particular objects of management:

(i) To manage the woodland area in such a way as to produce a utilisable crop of timber by sound forest practice.

(ii) To protect any scheduled ancient monument in accordance with the relevant statute.

Owners participating in Dedication Basis III schemes must also accept, in accordance with the terms of the dedication deed or contract, the following objects:

(iii) To secure good land use (including effective integration with agriculture).

(iv) To secure environmental benefits.

(v) To provide such opportunities for recreation (including provision for public access) as may be appropriate.

The Forestry Commission consider that items (iii), (iv) and (v) are all worthy objectives which should be accepted by all owners, and Basis I and Basis II owners will be encouraged to include them when their Plans are renewed. Additional items should also be listed including, for example, sporting, policy woods and shelter.

Only when the objects of management have been clearly stated can the best method of achieving them be worked out; that is why careful precise formulation of the objects of management is so important.

PROGRAMMES AND WORKING METHODS

Having stated the objects of management it is necessary to decide how they will be achieved. Two main aspects need to be considered—the programme of work and the methods to be adopted to achieve it. For most estates the key programmes are those of thinning, clear felling, new planting and restocking. Restocking programmes will depend on the area of mature timber which is to be felled annually as well as on the availability of labour and of funds. It is recommended that the owner first decides on the general level of planting (new and restocking) the estate can sustain, before drawing up detailed planting and restocking programmes by compartments for the ensuing five years.

A thinning programme for five years ahead is probably best set by first calculating an annual programme, based on the total area of coniferous woodlands and broadleaved woodlands in the thinning stages, divided by an approximate thinning cycle for the coniferous and the broadleaved woods respectively. The next step is to draw up the detailed thinning plan for the next five years.

All areas in, or likely to enter into, the thinning stage during the five-year period are listed to show the order of priority of thinning of the individual compartments or sub-compartments. Because of the implications for the restocking element of the planting programme, an examination of the stands nearing maturity and decisions on the areas to be clear felled may well have been made when the planting programmes were being drawn up. A Felling Proposals and Control Form is useful in drawing up felling plans. The form should detail, in the proposals section, the order of priority of dealing with specific compartments or sub-compartments.

It is now necessary to indicate the methods by which it is proposed to achieve the programmes, and to comment on and record some of the criteria which have been used in decision making during the formulation of the plan. Notes should be made on felling proposals, including comments on the rotation ages adopted in the plan; on thinning regimes; and on the species and planting distances to be used in new planting and restocking. This part of the plan answers the question—how is the plan to be achieved in terms of broad job specification?

MANAGEMENT AND RECORD KEEPING

The completion of each operation should be recorded. The standard Forestry Commission Plan of Operations only requires each programme to be shown as a single entry for a five-year period and records of new planting, restocking, thinning and felling actually carried out, to be kept in the same way. However, most owners will wish to keep an annual record of work proposed and carried out.

REVISIONS OF PLANS

Early in the fifth year of plan the owner should start to reassess the programme of work for the next five years and to review his plan as a whole. If the owner has dedicated his woodland, he is advised to consult his local Forestry Commission District Officer at this stage.

DEFINITIONS, TERMS AND ABBREVIATIONS

The definitions, terms and abbreviations used in the standard Forestry Commission Plan of Operations are given in the following paragraphs.

(i) *High forest* includes all stands, irrespective of age, that carry a reasonable crop of timber trees. Coppice growth, if suitable, and intended for conversion to high forest (i.e. without replanting), should also be classed as high forest, and so should crops in which a reasonable stocking of standards occurs among unworked coppice. Conditions may vary, and consequently to try to give a precise definition based on percentage stocking or 'productivity' is undesirable.

(ii) *Coppice.* This is coppice growth averaging more than two stems per stool which is suitable for, and in the process of, being worked or about to be worked on proper coppice rotation. If the coppice not being worked is to be converted into high forest by replanting, it should be classified as scrub.

(iii) *Scrub* is woody growth too inferior to be classed as high forest or coppice.

(iv) *Felled areas* are those unstocked areas which have not been converted to agricultural or other land use and still bear evidence of having been woodland.

(v) *Bare land* in this context is land which shows no signs of having been woodland.

(vi) *Unplantable areas* can include, for example, rocky outcrops and areas under power lines.

(vii) *Restocking* is the planting of felled woodland areas as defined in (iv) above, and the planting after felling of high forest, coppice and scrub as defined in (i), (ii) and (iii) above.

(viii) *New planting* is planting on land not previously used for forestry, i.e. bare land as defined in (v) above.

Crop Classification

(i) *Abbreviations*

CONIFERS

Scots pine	– SP
Corsican pine	– CP
Lodgepole pine (*Pinus contorta*)	– LP
Sitka spruce	– SS
Norway spruce	– NS
European larch	– EL
Japanese larch	– JL
Hybrid larch	– HL
Douglas fir	– DF
Western hemlock (*Tsuga heterophylla*)	– WH
Wellingtonia (*Sequoiadendron giganteum*)	– We
Californian redwood (*Sequoia sempervirens*)	– RW
Western red cedar (*Thuja plicata*)	– RC
Lawson cypress	– LC
Grand fir (*Abies grandis*)	– GF
Noble fir (*Abies procera*)	– NF
Other Conifers	– O Cf

BROADLEAVES

Pedunculate oak	– Oak, P
Sessile oak	– Oak, S
Red Oak	– Oak, R
Beech	– Be
Sycamore	– Syc
Ash	– Ash
Birch	– Bi
Spanish chestnut	– S Ch
Poplar	– Pop
Alder	– Al
Lime	– Lime
Elm	– Elm
Other broadleaves	– O Bl

(ii) A stand will be recognised as pure when one species occupies 80 per cent or more of the area by canopy or number of stems, whichever is appropriate.

(iii) For mixtures, (a) each individual species in a mixture may be credited with an area based on the proportion of the stand it occupies by canopy or number of stems, whichever is appropriate, e.g. a four-hectare stand of 50 per cent Norway spruce and 50 per cent oak could be recorded as two hectares pure NS and two hectares pure oak; (b) if recorded as a mixture, use the classification and abbreviations:

Mixed but mainly conifers	= M Cf
Mixed but mainly broadleaved	= M Bl
Conifers and broadleaved in similar quantities	= Mxd

(iv) Uneven-aged stands are those in which at least 20 per cent of the stocking by canopy is distributed through an age range of greater than 10 years.

Partial Planting

When an existing forest crop is underplanted or enriched—operations sometimes referred to as 'partial planting'—the net area treated is shown on the relevant forms. An acceptable method of assessing the net area is by calculating the area which the number of plants actually used would have occupied had they been planted at an ordinary spacing suitable to the species.

Partial Felling

This term is used to denote fellings which leave some trees standing but are sufficiently heavy to call for partial replanting. With partial felling the net area is that proportion occupied by the trees actually felled.

Direct Sowing and Natural Regeneration

Suitable direct sowing and natural regeneration are entered on the forms in the same way as planting and, if successful, will qualify for the same planting grants.

Unplantable Areas

These are included in the Plan only where it is more convenient to manage them along with the woodlands than in any other way. Examples are small lakes or ponds and patches of bare rock.

Chapter 16

SAFETY IN FORESTRY: A LEGAL SUMMARY

In 1970, the Government convened a Committee under the chairmanship of Lord Robens to look into the situation within industry generally regarding health and safety at work; to advise on the effectiveness of existing safety legislation; and to attempt to qualify the reasons why people have accidents.

The report of the Robens Committee was published in 1972 and amongst its conclusions were:
—apathy is a major cause of accidents;
—management is not sufficiently involved in accident prevention and the control of safety performance;
—there is too much law in some situations and seemingly none at all in other, not dissimilar, situations.

THE 1974 ACT

In the last point, Robens was clearly alluding to the mass of detailed regulations applying to employed persons but which could be neatly side-stepped by self-employed doing identical work. The Robens Report was generally accepted by all political parties, and so became the basic framework for the Health and Safety at Work etc. Act of 1974. The 1974 Act covered, for the first time, several million employed persons (e.g. in schools and hospitals) who had previously been unprotected by safety legislation. The Act also covered the self-employed and, through the provisions of its general duties, made it an offence to endanger the health or safety of the general public who may be affected by work practices, such as hazardous felling alongside a picnic site or public car park. Leaflets on aspects of the legislation are listed in the Bibliography.

Duties of Employer

The 1974 Act lays duties on an employer to:
—provide and maintain plant and systems of work that are, so far as is reasonably practicable, safe and without risks to health;
—make arrangements for ensuring, so far as reasonably practicable, safety and absence of risks to health in connection with the use, handling, storage and transport of articles and substances;
—provide such information, instruction, training and supervision as is necessary to ensure, so far as reasonably practicable, the health and safety at work of his employees;
—maintain any place of work in his control in a condition, so far as reasonably practicable, that is safe and without risks to health;
—provide and maintain a working environment which is, so far as reasonably practicable, safe and without risks to health;

—provide and maintain a written statement of safety policy, identifying the organisation and arrangements for the time being in force for carrying out that policy. (NB. Employers with less than five employees are exempted from preparing a written safety policy statement.)

In addition to the specific duties described above, employers have a general all-embracing duty to ensure, so far as reasonably practicable, the health, safety and welfare at work of all their employees.

Duties of Employee

The employee, too, has been given legally enforceable duties:
—to take reasonable care for the health and safety of himself and other persons who may be affected by his acts or omissions at work;
—to co-operate with his employer so far as is necessary to perform any duty or comply with any requirement imposed by current legislation;
—not to interfere with or misuse anything provided in the interests of health, safety or welfare at work.

Official Bodies

Two bodies have been set up to operate under the 1974 Act. The first of these, the Health and Safety Commission, is reponsible for providing assistance and encouragement to those persons engaged in furthering the objectives of the Act; for carrying out research and publishing research findings; for providing an information and advisory service to employers, manufacturers etc.; and for submitting regulations to the Secretary of State and approving 'Codes of Practice' upon which the Act confers a special legal status. The Commission is also responsible for carrying out consultative procedures with industry and other interested parties on matters of significant interest in the health and safety field.

The Health and Safety Executive is the Commission's operational arm. Put simply, the executive is responsible for carrying out the Commission's advisory function and for policing the Act. In connection with the latter function, inspectors have been given wide powers to issue 'improvement' and 'prohibition' notices, and to institute legal proceedings against offenders.

THE 1956 AGRICULTURE ACT

The preceding paragraphs are merely a brief summary of the 1974 Act, and it would be prudent to mention here that the legal provisions contained in The

Agriculture (Safety, Health and Welfare Provisions) Act, 1956, remain in force until repealed and re-enacted under the Health and Safety at Work Act. The Agriculture Act has been the major piece of Forest Safety legislation, until the present time, and the various regulations contained therein, including such items as first aid, ladders, power take-offs, circular saws and field machinery, are still to be observed.

TRADE UNIONS

The Trade Unions have an important function in the quest for a safer and healthier work place. This is recognised by the legal provision of the right of trade unions to appoint work place safety representatives, and to be represented on safety committees established by an employer. Succinctly stated, a safety representative is the go-between on all safety and health matters between the people he represents and the employer.

FORESTRY SAFETY COUNCIL

In recognition of the far-reaching implications of the new legal framework for health and safety matters, the Forestry Commission decided to set up the Forestry Safety Council in 1974. The Council's terms of reference are:

1. To promote safety in forestry by every means, including the encouragement of cooperation and consultation at all levels within the industry.
2. To make representations to the Safety Authority on the special problems of forestry and be consulted by them on proposed legislation, regulations, and other relevant matters.
3. To sponsor the production and maintenance of codes of safe working practice.
4. To co-ordinate publicity and the collection of statistics on health and safety matters and to encourage research into health and safety.
5. To liaise with the Forestry Training Council and other appropriate bodies on education and training in safety.
6. To review and report progress annually to the Minister of Agriculture, Fisheries and Food and the Secretary of State for Scotland, through the Forestry Commissioners who will submit the report to the Home Grown Timber Advisory Committee for comment.

The constitution of the Council provides for the membership of interested parties covering a very wide spectrum of the industry. Such bodies as the Merchants' and Growers' organisations are represented, together with the Trade Unions, the Forestry Training Council and the Forestry Commission.

REGULATIONS AND CODES OF PRACTICE

Regulations on specific subjects may be made under the 1974 Act, and forestry practitioners should be on the alert for these as and when they are published. Codes of Practice may also be issued giving detailed advice on carrying out the requirements laid down in the new Regulations.

SAFETY METHODS AND EQUIPMENT

Guidance on safe working methods and on personal safety equipment in forestry is given in the various Forest Industry Safety Guides designed and published by the Forestry Safety Council. Details of these will be published in the Forestry Commission's Catalogue of Publications.

BIBLIOGRAPHY: SAFETY IN FORESTRY

The Agriculture (Safety, Health and Welfare Provisions) Act, 1956. HMSO
The Health and Safety at Work etc. Act, 1974. HMSO.
Report of the Committee on Safety and Health at Work, 1970–72. (The Robens Report). Cmnd. 5034. HMSO.
Health and Safety Commission free leaflets on the 1974 Act:

HSC 1.   Some legal aspects and how they will affect you.
HSC 2.   The Act outlined.
HSC 3.   Advice to employers.
HSC 4.   Advice to the self-employed.
HSC 5.   Advice to employees.
HSC 6.   Guidance notes on employers' policy.
HSC 7.   Statements for health and safety at work.
HSC 8.   Safety Committees.
              Regulations, approved Codes of Practice and guidance literature obtainable from the Health and Safety Executive, 1 Chepstow Place, London W2 4TF

Appendix
LIST OF ADDRESSES

Main Offices of the Forestry Commission

Headquarters:
The Forestry Commission
231 Corstorphine Road
Edinburgh EH12 7AT
(Telephone: 031 334 0303)

Research Stations

The Forestry Commission
Forest Research Station
Alice Holt Lodge
Wrecclesham
Farnham
Surrey GU10 4LH
(telephone: 042 04 2255)

The Forestry Commission
Northern Research Station
Bush Estate
Roslin
Midlothian EH25 9SY
(Telephone: 031 445 2176)

Conservancy Offices

England | **Description of Area Covered**

NORTH WEST
Dee Hills Park
Chester CH3 5AT
Tel: 0244 24006

The counties of Cumbria, Lancashire, Derbyshire, Nottinghamshire, Cheshire, Salop, Staffordshire, West Midlands, Warwickshire, Hereford and Worcester—that part north of road A44 and west of road B4361, Leicestershire—except the District of Rutland; Merseyside, Greater Manchester.

NORTH EAST
1A Grosvenor Terrace
York YO3 7BD
Tel: 0904 20221

The counties of Northumberland, Tyne and Wear, Durham. Cleveland, North Yorkshire, West Yorkshire, South Yorkshire, Humberside—except the Districts of Glandford, Scunthorpe, Grimsby and Cleethorpes.

EAST
Block D
Government Buildings
Brooklands Avenue
Cambridge CB2 2DY
Tel: 0223 58911

The counties of Lincolnshire, Bedfordshire, Norfolk, Suffolk, Essex, Hertfordshire, Buckinghamshire, Northamptonshire, Cambridgeshire, Oxfordshire, Leicestershire—the District of Rutland, Humberside—the Districts of Glandford, Scunthorpe, Grimsby and Cleethorpes, Greater London—that part north of the river Thames.

NEW FOREST and SOUTH EAST
The Queen's House
Lyndhurst
Hants SO4 7NH
Tel: 042 128 2801

The counties of Hampshire, Isle of Wight, Berkshire, Greater London—that part south of the river Thames, Surrey, Kent, East Sussex, West Sussex, Dorset—that part east of a line from a point on the Dorset/Hampshire boundary at Bokerly Junction south-westwards along the road A354 as far as Blandford Forum then south-eastwards along the road A350 as far as Poole.

SOUTH WEST and DEAN FOREST
Flowers Hill
Brislington
Bristol BS4 5JY
Tel: 0272 713471

The counties of Cornwall, Devon, Somerset, Avon, Gloucestershire, Wiltshire, Dorset—except that part east of a line from a point on the Dorset/Hampshire boundary at Bokerly Junction south-westwards along the road A354 as far as Blandford Forum then south-eastwards along the road A350 as far as Poole, Hereford and Worcester except that part north of road A44 and west of road B4361.

Scotland	**Description of Area Covered**

NORTH
>   21 Church Street
>   Inverness IV1 1EL
>   Tel: 0463 32811

The whole of the Western Isles Authority area, Shetland Isles Authority area and Orkney Isles Authority area.
The whole of the Highland Region area with the exception of that portion of Lochaber District east of Loch Linnhe and south of Loch Leven, the River Leven, the Blackwater Reservoir and the Blackwater, to where the Highland Region boundary reaches the river at Lochan A'chlaidheimh. Strathclyde Region—The Isles of Mull, Iona, Coll and Tiree only.

SOUTH
>   Greystone Park
>   55/57Moffat Road
>   Dumfries DG1 1NP
>   Tel: 0387 2425

The regions of Lothian, Borders, and Dumfries and Galloway, and the three southernmost Districts of Strathclyde—Lanark, Cumnock, and Doon Valley, and Kyle and Carrick.

EAST
>   6 Queen's Gate
>   Aberdeen AB9 2NQ
>   Tel: 0224 33361

The regions of Grampian, Tayside and Fife.

WEST
>   Portcullis House
>   21 India Street
>   Glasgow G2 4PL
>   Tel: 041 248 3931

That portion of the Highland Region Lochaber District, east of Loch Linnhe and south of Loch Leven, the River Leven, the Blackwater Reservoir and the Black Water, to where the Highland Region boundary reaches the river at Lochan A'chlaidheimh.
Central region—all.
Strathclyde Region—all except the Isles of Mull, Iona, Coll, and Tiree and the Districts of Lanark, Cumnock and Doon Valley, and Kyle and Carrick.

Wales	**Description of Area Covered**

NORTH
>   Victoria House
>   Victoria Terrace
>   Aberystwyth SY23 2DA
>   Tel: 0970 2367

The counties of Gwynedd and Clwyd. The Montgomery and Radnor Districts of the county of Powys. The Ceredigion District of the county of Dyfed except the following Communities: Cardigan, Verwig, Llangoedmor, Aberporth, Llandygwydd, Brongwyn, Bettws Evan, Penbryn, Troedyraur, Llandyfriog, Llangynllo, Orllwyn, Teifi, Llandyssul, Llanddewi Brefi, Caron-is-Clawdd and Caron-Uwch-Clawdd.

SOUTH
>   Churchill House
>   Churchill Way
>   Cardiff CF1 4TU
>   Tel: 0222 40661

The counties of West Glamorgan, Mid Glamorgan, South Glamorgan and Gwent. The South Pembrokeshire, Preseli, Carmarthen, Llanelli and Dinefwr Districts and the Communities of Cardigan, Verwig, Llangoedmor, Aberporth, Llandygwydd, Brongwyn, Bettws Evan, Penbryn, Troedyraur, Llandyfriog, Llangynllo, Orllwyn, Teifi, Llandyssul, Llanddewi Brefi, Caron-is-Clawdd and Caron-Uwch-Clawdd in Ceredigion District, in the county of Dyfed. The Brecknock District in the County of Powys.

Other Useful Addresses

Royal Forestry Society of England, Wales and Northern Ireland, 102 High Street, Tring, Hertfordshire HP23 4AN (0442 82 2028).

Royal Scottish Forestry Society, 26 Rutland Square, Edinburgh EH1 2BT (031 229 8202).

Royal Institution of Chartered Surveyors, 12 Great George Street, Parliament Square, London SW1P 3AD (01 839 5600)

Timber Growers' Organisation Ltd., c/o National Agricultural Centre, Kenilworth, Warwickshire CV8 2LG (0203 21559).

Scottish Woodland Owners Association Ltd., 6 Chester Street, Edinburgh EH3 7RD (031-226 3475).

Institute of Foresters of Great Britain, 6 Rutland Square, Edinburgh EH1 2AU (031 229 4010).

Association of Professional Foresters of Great Britain, Brokerswood House, Brokerswood, Westbury, Wiltshire BA13 4EH (0373 822238).

Arboricultural Association, incorporating The Association of British Tree Surgeons and Arborists, Brokerswood House, Brokerswood, Westbury, Wiltshire, BA13 4EH (0373 822238)

Institute of Landscape Architects, 12 Carlton House Terrace, London SW1Y 5AH (01 839 4044).

Countryside Commission, John Dower House, Crescent Place, Cheltenham GL50 3RA (0242 21381).

Countryside Commission, Committee for Wales, 8 Broad Street, Newtown, Powys (0686 6337)

Countryside Commission for Scotland, Battleby, Redgorton, Perth PH1 3EW (073 827921)

Nature Conservancy Council, 19 Belgrave Square, London SW1X 8PY (01 235 3241)

Printed in England for Her Majesty's Stationery Office
by Staples Printers Kettering Limited at The George Press, Kettering Northamptonshire

Dd. 586028 K.64 9/78